To Annie & Eddy,

In the search for a more broad-based discourse to development in general and to HIV & AIDS, in particular.

Real pleasure meeting you!

Scholastica
RRPC for SA
13 Aug 2005

Turning a *CRISIS* into an **Opportunity**

Strategies for Scaling Up the National Response to the HIV/AIDS Pandemic in Lesotho

Turning a *CRISIS* into an **Opportunity**

Strategies for Scaling Up the National Response to the HIV/AIDS Pandemic in Lesotho

EDITED BY

Scholastica Sylvan Kimaryo • *Joseph O. Okpaku, Sr.*
Anne Githuku-Shongwe • *Joseph Feeney*

Foreword by **Prime Minister Pakalitha Mosisili**

A Publication of the Partnership of the **Government of Lesotho** and the **Expanded Theme Group on HIV/AIDS, Lesotho**

Third Press Publishers
New Rochelle, New York USA

Library of Congress Control Number: 2003098220
ISBN: Cloth Edition:0-89388-236-4
Paperback Edition:0-89388-237-2

The Government of the Kingdom of Lesotho—through its Cabinet Decision of 21 October 2003—adopted this document as an official working/reference document in its national response to the HIV/AIDS pandemic, in partnership with the Expanded Theme Group on HIV/AIDS, Lesotho, several of whom are UNAIDS Co-Sponsors. Hence the joint Government of Lesotho and UNAIDS logos on the cover page. Although the collaborating institutions endorse the main message of this publication, it does not necessarily reflect the official views of the individual institutions or of their boards of directors or affiliated institutions. The views expressed in documents by named authors are solely the responsibility of those authors.

The Expanded Theme Group on HIV/AIDS, Lesotho
c/o United Nations Development Programme (UNDP)
3rd Floor, United Nations House
P.O. Box 301
Maseru, 100
Mountain Kingdom of Lesotho
Tel: +266 22 313 790 / Fax: +266 22 310 042
E-mail: fo.lso@undp.org / registry.ls@undp.org

Third Press Publishers
222 Forest Avenue
New Rochelle, New York, 10804, USA
Tel: +1 914 632 2355 / Fax: +1 914 632 2320
Email: publications@thirdpress.com

Book Production by Third Press Publishers
Interior Design and Typesetting by Desktop Miracles Stowe, Vermont
Index and Copy-editing by Josephine Ofili, Third Press

ACKNOWLEDGEMENTS

Since my appointment as Government Secretary just over two years ago, I have dedicated myself to scaling up the fight against the HIV/AIDS pandemic in this country. My key goal has been to build on the extraordinary leadership of His Majesty the King and the Right Honourable the Prime Minister, both of whom have left no stone unturned in finding ways to defeat this pandemic since the late 1990s. We know there is no blueprint—no model for a national strategy to fight against HIV/AIDS; but our success will not only enable us to defeat the pandemic, but it may also help to pave the way for other countries which are now at a stage of infection similar to what we had a decade ago. With an infection rate in Lesotho of over 30% of the adult population, we have no choice but to succeed, and, in the process, we should manage to also turn this crisis into an opportunity for significant development in our country.

The consistent leadership of the Prime Minister, Mr. Pakalitha Mosisili, has been and continues to be crucial in mobilising Government and its people, as well as the international community, to take the HIV/AIDS crisis as the opportunity for "thinking out of the box" as we look for new and more effective solutions. From the start, the Prime Minister has been absolutely clear that this is a problem that can and will be addressed by Basotho. He has, accordingly, sought to ensure that the international community is mobilised to share in the efforts to find durable solutions to this crisis.

In a country with a literacy rate of over 85%, with an open and democratic society—one which is the largest exporter in Sub-Saharan Africa of textiles to the US market and one which has led the region in the fight against corruption, we simply do not buy the mantra that "Lesotho has no implementation capacity" as has often been said by some in the international community and, yes, even at times by ourselves. If the Independent Electoral Commission could deliver world-class General Elections in May, 2002, working with the same Government and people of Lesotho—including some 17,500 volunteers, how could it continue to be said that Basotho have no capacity? It must be that the problem lies in the way we perceive development challenges—like HIV/AIDS—and the kind of solutions which we devise for addressing them. This is why so many of us are so excited about this "Scaling Up" document as it has engaged a very pragmatic and thus creative approach to addressing the pandemic. Hence also my advice to all of you who manage to obtain copies of this book is to make the time to judge for yourselves—at the very least by thoroughly reviewing it.

Let me also hasten to add that we do know that we need broad-based partnerships in order to succeed in fighting this pandemic. Happily, I am delighted to hereby acknowledge the tremendous support and solidarity of the international community in walking the extra mile on this exciting journey of innovation and discovery with us. Led by the Expanded UN Theme Group on HIV/AIDS—chaired by the UN Resident Coordinator and UNDP Resident Representative, Mrs. Scholastica Sylvan Kimaryo, and co-chaired by the US Ambassador, Mr. Robert Loftis, we have seen an outstanding example of how the international community can work in partnership with National governments in the search for viable solutions to pressing development challenges. This consistent concern for the well-being of our people and the collaboration thus far extended to us is most highly appreciated. For, indeed, development cooperation is not just about the size of the cheque book—important as this always is—but also about the depth and quality of the partnership. In this context, I would like take this opportunity to pay tribute to donors and other Governments who have been with us on this journey: Ireland, the United Kingdom, Germany, France, the United States, China, Sweden, Denmark, Canada, Norway, Japan, South Africa and India.

Further, let me also highly commend the UN System, especially the nine UNAIDS co-sponsors—through the UN Resident Coordinator, Mrs. Scholastica Kimaryo who, upon her appointment as chair of the UN Expanded Theme Group in January, 2002, began to seek urgent support from within and outside the UN System in search of answers to the question: *How can we help Lesotho to find and put its best foot forward in response to HIV/AIDS?* Mrs. Kimaryo consulted with the

Government, in particular with my office and that of the Executive Director of LAPCA, to begin a dialogue on the first steps to take to support Lesotho's efforts.

Needless to say, the writing up of this book comprises work undertaken by technical advisors from several UNAIDS co-sponsoring agencies, based on the outcomes of various national consultative workshops, seminars, a variety of meetings with Cabinet Ministers, Principal Secretaries and various Government Officials, business leaders, civil society organisations, as well as bringing on board, knowledge and positive experiences from other countries. I would, therefore, like to hereby recognise the role played by the Pretoria-based UNDP Africa Project on HIV/AIDS and Development, for the lead role it has played in helping us take the fight against HIV/AIDS beyond the bio-medical programme interventions into systems thinking, transformation for increased capacity utilisation, as well as addressing HIV/AIDS as a governance challenge. In this regard, Ms. Anne Githuku-Shongwe deserves special mention for having stayed the course. Others from UNDP include Ms. Barbara Barungi, Dr. Gabriel Rugalema, Ms. Mandisa Mashologu and Mr. Joseph Feeney; Mr. Dan Odallo of UNAIDS, Mr. J. Forde of UNICEF, Dr. Owen of WHO, as well as two renowned development consultants, Ms. Mirjiam Van Donk and Dr. Joseph Okpaku Sr. Special recognition goes to Mrs. Scholastica Kimaryo who rolled up her sleeves to apply her knowledge and experience as a development policy expert of long standing, to lead a daunting process that ultimately resulted in the compilation of this forward-looking strategic document.

Because so many people from all sectors of society and all walks of life have been involved in the development of this book, it is simply impossible to mention them all here. Suffice it to say that for me as Government Secretary, and for my fellow senior public servants, we recognise your contribution and hereby ask you to continue with us as we re-dedicate ourselves to leading the scaling up of the public sector response to the pandemic. Many of the people involved are listed in the appendices of this book and there are many more that have been on this journey of discovery: for those not mentioned, please stay with us. However, I would like to hereby acknowledge particularly those people living openly with HIV and AIDS; the church groups which live their faith and show compassion and care for those who are living with the disease; the community groups who often—with little recognition—support neighbours and friends who are affected and infected. I would also like to acknowledge the contribution of our traditional leadership around the country. With some 2,700 chiefs, we know they have a unique role to play in the fight against the pandemic. They have already taken giant steps in this direction, as evidenced by the work of the Senate as well as the National Assembly. This is a journey towards an HIV/AIDS Competent Society which, by definition, must involve all Basotho and all our partners. We must together change the way we do business, take up the challenge and succeed.

In looking back at the breath-taking efforts to date, one cannot help but realise that it is not often that a group of people can engage in a process as challenging as this one and have such a concrete response so early in the process. The swift action by Government is a credit to the commitment and relentless efforts of the leadership and members of the Expanded UN Theme Group on HIV/AIDS, the individual institutions which comprise it, senior officials and staff, and others who have devoted so much effort to this ground-breaking initiative.

For its part, Government, under the eminent leadership of the Prime Minister, the Rt. Hon. Pakalitha Mosisili, has fully taken up the challenge. For us in the Lesotho Civil Service, especially for all of us Principal Secretaries, Deputy Principal Secretaries and Directors, we have already undertaken to rise to the challenge by leading the public sector response. We stand ready—all of us in the public service— to engage with equal courage in the fight for our own future. When this Scaling Up process began, we could not even dream of what direction it would take us. It has since advanced to the point of becoming a concrete reality that has captured the imagination of the nation.

In the final analysis, we are convinced that the journey that we have embarked on to "Turn the Crisis of HIV/AIDS into an Opportunity" is unstoppable. Indeed, the process of Scaling-Up the fight against HIV/AIDS has already begun in earnest. The collective wisdom and possibilities that are contained in this reference manual bear witness to the fact that Lesotho has already taken some bold first steps toward this exciting and compelling journey. I pledge to continue to lead the public service in scaling up the national response to this pandemic and will do my utmost to achieve an HIV/AIDS Competent Society. Let all of you join us in this endeavour.

Mr. Tlohang Sekhamane
GOVERNMENT SECRETARY
KINGDOM OF LESOTHO

Decision of the Cabinet of Ministers on the Adoption of the Scaling Up Document as a Lesotho Government Working Document

In late October 2003, the government announced a number of key decisions which will put Lesotho at the centre of the fight against the pandemic in southern Africa. At a meeting of the cabinet of Ministers on 21 October, 2003, it was decided that government would adopt this book as an official working document to guide the national response to the pandemic. The cabinet also decided to establish a new broad-based **National AIDS Commission**, and to core stream the fight against HIV/AIDS into all government activities and programmes. Details of the government decision are as follows:

1. Cabinet has adopted the document on *Strategies for Scaling Up the Fight against HIV/AIDS* as an official working/reference document on HIV/AIDS.

2. A National AIDS Commission (NAC) will be established to coordinate and support the scaling up of innovative efforts that involve multiple players/actors at various levels. The structure of the NAC will be as follows:

   - The Commission will be chaired by an eminent and respected individual who will be nominated by the Prime Minister. There will be five other Commissioners who will represent the following constituencies: People Living with HIV/AIDS; Faith-Based Organisations; Women; the Private Sector and Youth. These Commissioners will be elected from their respective constituencies and will be full-time employees of the Commission.

   - The Lesotho Aids Programme Coordinating Authority (LAPCA) will act as the Secretariat to the National AIDS Commission and will function and serve as the technical arm of the Commission.

3. The Government will, with immediate effect, draft enabling legislation for the establishment of the National AIDS Commission.

4. All government sectors and programmes will core stream the fight against the pandemic at all levels and each sector will develop the capacity to ensure that this takes place as a matter of urgency.

CONTENTS

AIDS	Acquired Immuno-Deficiency Syndrome
AGOA	African Growth and Opportunities Act
ARV	Anti-retroviral
CBO	Community Based Organisations
CEDAW	Convention on the Elimination of all forms of Discrimination Against Women
CRC	Committee on the Rights of the Child
DCI	Development Cooperation Ireland
DfID	Department for International Development
FAO	Food and Agriculture Organisation
GDP	Gross Domestic Product
GFATM	Global Fund to Fight AIDS, Tuberculosis and Malaria
GIPA	Greater Involvement of People living with HIV/AIDS
HBC	Home-Based Care
HIV	Human Immuno-deficiency Virus
ICT	Information and Communications Technologies
IEC	Information, Education and Communication
LAPCA	Lesotho AIDS Programme Coordinating Authority
MDGs	Millennium Development Goals
MMP	Mixed Member Proportional representation system of the General Elections
MTCT	Mother-To-Child Transmission
MTEF	Medium-Term Expenditure Framework
NAC	National Aids Commission
NASP	National AIDS Strategic Plan
NEPAD	New Partnership for Africa's Development
NGO	Non-Governmental Organisation
NUL	National University of Lesotho
ORID	Other Related Infectious Diseases
OVC	Orphans and Vulnerable Children

PLWHA	People Living With HIV/AIDS
PMTCT	Prevention of Mother-To-Child Transmission
PTCT	Parent-To-Child Transmission
PRSP	Poverty Reduction Strategy Paper
SADC	Southern African Development Community
SMME	Small, Micro and Medium Enterprise
SMS	Short Messaging System
STI	Sexually Transmitted Infection
TB	Tuberculosis
UN	United Nations
UNAIDS	United Nations Programme on HIV/AIDS
UNDP	United Nations Development Programme
UNGASS	United Nations General Assembly Special Session
UVT	Universal Voluntary Testing
VCT	Voluntary Counselling and Testing
WFP	World Food Programme

A New Resolve to fight the HIV/AIDS Pandemic

Since the year 2000, there has been increasing global concern over the seemingly relentless scourge of HIV/AIDS, resulting in the intensification of national and international efforts in search of more effective strategies for tackling the pandemic. The United Nations Millennium Development Goals (MDGs), for instance, prioritise HIV/AIDS as one of the major health and development challenges for Africa in general, and for the Southern Africa Development Community (SADC), in particular. However, long before the Millennium Declaration, SADC Heads of State and Government had already declared HIV/AIDS a national as well as a regional disaster. This led to the development and implementation of a multi-sectoral strategic framework for HIV/AIDS in the Region. Since then, the issue of HIV/AIDS has remained a top priority on the agenda of SADC. In early July 2003, Lesotho was privileged to host the SADC Extra-Ordinary Summit on HIV/AIDS, resulting in the *Maseru Declaration on the Fight Against HIV/AIDS in the SADC Region.* Amongst other undertakings, the Heads of State and Government reaffirmed their commitment to combat the pandemic in all its manifestations and as a matter of urgency through multi-sectoral, strategic interventions as contained in SADC's new (2003-2007) HIV/AIDS Strategic Framework and Plan of Action.

At the Second Ordinary Session of the African Union (AU) in Maputo in July, 2003, African Heads of State and Government unanimously reaffirmed, in the *Maputo Declaration on Malaria, HIV/AIDS, Tuberculosis, and Other Related Infectious Diseases*, the commitments enshrined in the *Abuja Declaration and Plan of Action on Rolling Back Malaria* (April 2000) and in the *Abuja Declaration and Framework Plan of Action on HIV/AIDS, Tuberculosis and Other Related Infectious Diseases* (April 2001), resolving to intensify and consolidate their efforts for their implementation. They declared:

> In addition, we, the AU Heads of State and Government, urge the international community to honour their pledges by disbursing the funds needed to fully execute the programmes for the prevention, care, support and treatment of HIV/AIDS, TB, Malaria and ORID[1], especially through the Global Fund, the World Bank Multi-Country AIDS Programmes and other initiatives, including removing conditionalities associated with debt relief and others that contribute to constraining health sector spending.

The Maputo Declaration also urged "the Global Fund and recipients of its funding[2] to work together to develop simpler and expeditious mechanisms to ensure that these large additional financial flows are quickly and easily available to institutions in Africa that can utilise them effectively in the fight against the diseases. We further urge the Global Fund, the UNAIDS family and the recipient countries to work together to ensure the realisation of our common objectives."

The African Union Heads of State and Government further expressed their "determination to ensure that all opportunities for scaling up treatment for HIV/AIDS are pursued energetically and creatively, and in this connection, seek diverse and effective partnerships with international donors, civil society, the business sector and people living with HIV/AIDS, in order to extend effective care, support and treatment to the maximum number of people, particularly women, orphaned children and others made vulnerable by HIV/AIDS, in conformity with the principles of equal access and gender equity."

They committed themselves "to promote partnerships with the private sector and relevant specialised agencies of the United Nations System, pharmaceutical companies and other partners in order to increase local and regional capacity for the production and distribution of affordable generic pharmaceuticals for the management of HIV/AIDS, TB, Malaria and ORID—the diseases with the highest impact on Africa's socio-economic development."

They resolved to continue to support the implementation of the Plan of Action for the AU Decade for African Traditional Medicine (2000–2010), especially research in the area of treatment for HIV/AIDS, TB, Malaria and ORID.

Finally, they also requested "the AU Commission on HIV/AIDS, in collaboration with UNAIDS and its joint UN Co-Sponsoring Agencies, the Economic Commission for Africa and other partners, to coordinate and intensify efforts among Member States, monitor implementation of this Declaration and report regularly to our Assembly."

"We believe," the AU Heads of State and Government concluded in the Declaration, "that Malaria, HIV/AIDS, TB and ORID can, must and will be defeated!"[3]

I want to state categorically that we Basotho, the Government and the people alike, acting in unison and driven by a common commitment and shared sense of the utmost urgency, are irrevocably and indefatigably determined to fight the scourge of HIV/AIDS, whatever it takes, however long it takes. That commitment goes also for our battle against Malaria, Tuberculosis and Other Related Infectious Diseases. **They can, must and will be defeated.** What is at stake, is the very future of the Basotho. Accordingly, we must fight to preserve one's destiny. What is called for, is for each and every one of us—individually and collectively—to **act decisively.**

His Majesty King Letsie III has long declared HIV/AIDS a national disaster. A National AIDS Strategic Plan—which was drawn up in September 2000—has since been overtaken by other events. It must urgently be reviewed to reflect current realities and new commitments for action. Likewise, the structure of the Lesotho AIDS Programme Coordinating Authority (LAPCA), which was set up under my Office with the express objective of facilitating implementation of the National AIDS Strategic Plan as well as coordinating an appropriate national response, must also be urgently reviewed and suitably strengthened.

In addition, when the Government decided to allocate 2% of the annual budget of each and every sectoral Ministry to fighting the HIV/AIDS pandemic, the prevalence rate was estimated at around 9%. Today, we know that the national average is 31%, with possibly much higher rates in Maseru and other "hot spots". Today alone, seventy people will die from AIDS. That is one person every 20 minutes. We have to act NOW if we are to avert potential annihilation of our nation. With immediate effect, we must make sure that all major policies—beginning with the 2020 Vision, the Poverty Reduction Strategy Paper, the Millennium Development Goals Report, the goals and objectives of the Medium-Term Development Plan as well as the annual plans and budgets of every Government Ministry—will be completely reviewed and restructured to take into account these new realities regarding the HIV/AIDS pandemic and to prioritise action to fight this scourge.

In order to facilitate our work in this regard, I had challenged the resident members of the international community—during the first visit of the UN Secretary-General Kofi Annan's Special Envoy on the HIV/AIDS Pandemic in Africa, Mr. Stephen Lewis—to come up with good advice on the best strategies for scaling up the national response to this crisis. The outcome of those joint efforts are presented here in this comprehensive reference manual, *Turning a Crisis into an Opportunity: Strategies for Scaling Up the National Response to the HIV/AIDS Pandemic in Lesotho.* I am very pleased to commend this work to you as the foundation of our battle plan against HIV/AIDS. I personally consider this a groundbreaking, seminal piece of work on which we should build our national struggle against this scourge. I am truly grateful to the Expanded Theme Group on HIV/AIDS in Lesotho, under the joint leadership of Mrs. Scholastica Kimaryo, the UNDP Resident Representative and Coordinator of the UN System, and His Excellency, the Ambassador of the United States of America to Lesotho, Mr. Robert Loftis, for having accepted my challenge to them, as partners in this fight, and for having acquitted themselves admirably.

Last but by no means least, let me remind all of us that we are a nation of resilient and resourceful people. It is a well-known fact that the Basotho Nation has never been defeated in any conventional warfare. We are also known to have defeated many past adversities and natural calamities from the very beginning of the founding of our nation under the valiant and wise leadership of His Majesty King Moshoeshoe I. This is why I am personally convinced that by working together as a nation and in partnership with all people of goodwill, we cannot but emerge triumphant over this HIV/AIDS pandemic. We are determined to use this crisis as the opportunity that forces us to ultimately catapult this nation from the shackles of poverty and under-development into a prosperous and peaceful nation. This is the beginning of our struggle to turn a crisis, which threatens our very survival as a people, into an opportunity to build a future worthy of our heritage. **It is a task** that must be done. It can be done. Let all of us, individually and collectively, play our part.

Khotso, Pula, Nala!

Pakalitha Mosisili
PRIME MINISTER

NOTES

1. Other Related Infectious Diseases.
2. Includes Lesotho.
3. Maputo Declaration on Malaria, HIV/AIDS, Tuberculosis, and Other Infectious Diseases, Maputo, Mozambique, 10-12 July, 2003.

United Nations Theme Groups on HIV/AIDS have been in existence for many years in most, if not all, host countries. The membership is usually comprised of Heads of United Nations Agencies representing the family of UN agencies that are co-sponsors of the UN Programme on HIV/AIDS, commonly known as the United Nations Programme on HIV/AIDS (UNAIDS). In Lesotho, all the resident UN agencies and the donors have come together as the international partnership on HIV/AIDS, commonly referred to as the Expanded Theme Group on HIV/AIDS, with a Chairperson and Co-Chairperson nominated on a two-year rotational basis by the Executive Director of UNAIDS, Mr. Peter Piot. So, both of us—who coincidentally arrived in Lesotho on the same day to take up our new assignments almost two years ago—have very much enjoyed serving as Chairperson and Co-Chairperson of the Theme Group on HIV/AIDS. Our goal for the tenure has been to work closely with the Government and people of Lesotho in search of viable strategies for scaling up the national response to the HIV/AIDS crisis in this country.

Our resolve to search for, compile and present a set of doable strategies for beating the pandemic was strengthened when The Right Honourable Prime Minister, H.E. Mr. Pakalitha Mosisili, challenged us to take the HIV/AIDS crisis as the opportunity for "thinking out of the box" as we look for new and more effective solutions. In particular, he was emphatic in arguing that he no longer believed the common assertion that "Lesotho has a low implementation capacity". In his view, if the Independent Electoral Commission could deliver world-class General Elections in May 2002, working with the same Government and people of Lesotho—including some 17,500 volunteers—how could it continue to be said that Basotho have no capacity? It was on this basis that he challenged us to come up with a synthesis of home-grown strategies informed by international best practices that would not only succeed in scaling up the national response to the pandemic, but would also catapult the Basotho Nation well into a prosperous and peaceful future.

And so the members and leadership of the HIV/AIDS Theme Group set off with great enthusiasm in pursuit of this ambitious but hugely desirable dream. The result has been the compilation of an equally ambitious reference manual titled: *Turning A Crisis Into An Opportunity: Strategies for Scaling Up the National Response to the HIV/AIDS Pandemic in Lesotho.* Whereas the text alludes to the magnitude and complexity of the problem, it also argues that HIV and AIDS are not automatic death sentences. Those infected can and do live longer if they know their status early, have access to adequate food and nutrition, get treated for opportunistic infections and with anti-retrovirals (ARVs), as the situation warrants, change their life-styles and receive family and community support. This manual also argues that this is only possible if the Government and people of Lesotho strive to create what is known as an HIV/AIDS-Competent Society.

Turning A Crisis Into An Opportunity makes specific recommendations on *how* to create an HIV/AIDS-competent society as well as *what* national, district and local mechanisms would make that possible. Of particular interest are the chapters with specific *ideas* on what each and every Government Ministry can do immediately to make a discernible difference, even as they work on more comprehensive sectoral strategies, plans and budgets. We should hasten to hereby add that this manual should be seen as a living document, new editions of which should be compiled and published as new insights and best practices become manifest. Concurrently, there are many different information, communication and social mobilisation products that need to be compiled, published and widely distributed. These would include, for example: a pocket-size, fact booklet in *Sesotho*, which will enable Parliamentarians, Traditional Chiefs and other leaders to pass on correct messages as they go around the country and thus raise the awareness of all Basotho; and the development of appropriate teaching and learning materials for all levels of formal and non-formal education.

The extensive process of dialogue, debate and consultation leading to the compilation of this manual has been based on the principle of partnership, as stipulated in the outcomes of two milestone global Summits: the September 2000 *United Nations Millennium Summit Declaration*, which prioritised HIV/AIDS as one of the major challenges for health and development, and the June 2001 *UN General Assembly Special Session's Declaration and Commitment on HIV/AIDS,* both of which constitute the strongest common mandate to date, and form a basis for political accountability for national governments as well as for international development cooperation. It is in this vein, therefore, that we have worked very closely with many officials and institutions of government, the private sector as well as civil society.

At the overall coordination level, our core Government partners have been the Government Secretary, Mr. T. Sekhamane, the Chief Executive Officer of LAPCA, Dr. M. Moteetee and her staff, the Minister of Finance and Development Planning, the Honourable Tim Thahane and his senior officials, the Minister of Health and Social Welfare, Dr. Phooko and his senior officials as well as the Minister of Foreign Affairs, the Honourable Ken Tsekoa and his staff. In facilitating and participating in various consultative meetings by virtue of their respective coordination mandates, they play a role, which has and will continue to be vital to the success of this initiative.

Similarly, many people from all walks of life were engaged in various meetings, workshops and seminars, giving of their time, knowledge and expertise. They included various Government Ministers, their Principal Secretaries and other senior officials, as well as representatives of civil society from all levels—national, district and community—enabling us to learn a great deal from their views and experiences. In these consultations, we have paid particular attention to the voices of women, the youth and the valiant people living openly with HIV/AIDS. In compiling this manual on *Strategies for Scaling Up the National Response to the HIV/AIDS Pandemic in Lesotho*, therefore, every effort has been made to ensure that all views, concerns and experiences have been given due consideration, and appropriate action taken to reflect the growing consensus among Basotho on what should be done better or differently, and how it should be done.

In this process of joint exploration and learning, we have been hugely impressed by the valiant efforts of the Honourable Deputy Prime Minister and Minister of Education, Dr. L. Lehohla, and his staff. His is the only Government Ministry that has undertaken a study on the impact of the pandemic on the Education Sector, thus placing his Ministry in the best position to re-cast its plans and budgets. This is a critical pre-requisite for getting into the scaling up mode. Furthermore, the Ministry is streets ahead in creating HIV/AIDS competence in the workplace, through extensive skills training, with about 7,000 teachers already trained, out of a targeted 10,000. These are definitely commendable examples of homegrown best practices.

Several other Ministries we consulted with are engaged in various levels of inspirational work. They include Agriculture and Food Security, Home Affairs, Labour, as well as Trade and Industry. In addition, the Office of the First Lady deserves special commendation for its work with the spouses of Parliamentarians and tra-ditional chiefs across the country. We have also come to appreciate a great deal more, the complexity of the challenges facing both the Lesotho AIDS Programme Coordinating Authority (LAPCA) and the Ministry of Health in delivering on their mandate, resulting in a growing recognition of the need to better understand and thus re-define their roles. The reasons for this include the following:

- First, although the health sector plays a very important role in treating the dif-ferent opportunistic infections that result from HIV infection as well as ulti-mately treating the various manifestations of full-blown AIDS, this in and of itself should *not* place the primary responsibility for fighting the pandemic on the shoulders of the health sector;

- Secondly, it has now become very clear that part of LAPCA's fabled inability to be more effective has to do with the fact that it has two conflicting roles: a strategic, policy, advocacy and networking role, on the one hand and, on the other hand, an operational role that engages it in actual implementation of HIV/AIDS-related activities, many of which should be implemented by the Ministry of Health. Thus, the very act of LAPCA engaging in project implementation has given many people—including some Government Ministries, different NGOs and other organs of civil society the impression that they, in turn, no longer have to do anything about HIV/AIDS because LAPCA now exists. The result is the unrealistic and ever-growing demand for LAPCA to deliver on operational-type activities having to do with HIV/AIDS.

  Furthermore, LAPCA is but a small unit in a Government Ministry. Given the way any government bureaucracy works, it is impossible for a unit of itself to leverage the kind of clout required to take to task another unit in the same ministry, let alone all the ministries of Government. The fact is that in order for the Government and people of Lesotho to succeed in effectively coming to grips with a development challenge as complex as the HIV/AIDS pandemic, it will require the forging of partnerships from *all* key stakeholders in society. It is not possible for this to be done by one Government Unit, no matter how creative and energetic the Chief Executive Officer of LAPCA may be.

- Thirdly, there is also a need for a re-definition of the roles and responsibilities of all other key stakeholders (such as each and every government ministry, vari-ous stakeholders in civil society as well as the private sector) in shouldering the responsibility for creating an HIV/AIDS-competent society and coming to grips with the pandemic.

Very strong partnerships have also been forged with both Houses of Parliament, through the Honourable President of the Senate, Mr. T. Lejaha, the Speaker of the National Assembly, Madam Motsamai, and the Leader of the House and Honourable Deputy Prime Minister, Dr. L. Lehohla. Through their tireless leadership, we have witnessed the establishment of two Select Committees on HIV/AIDS: one of the Senate and the other of the National Assembly. We have also witnessed the enthusiasm and energy with which Honourable Members of both Committees have set off to get themselves HIV/AIDS competent, especially through skills-training workshops on HIV/AIDS. We have been inspired by how quickly these Parliamentarians have gone forth to spread the good news that for the majority of Basotho who are not yet infected, HIV/AIDS can be avoided and, for those who are already infected, it can be managed and controlled. In addition, the Senate has taken several key decisions and actions in the recent past, which convince us that Lesotho has a very high potential for success in leading the SADC and other African countries in the fight against the pandemic. Some highlights of these are:

- The Senate decision to ensure that as soon as Parliament resumed at the end of August 2003, all Members of the Senate—led by the Senate President—would undergo voluntary testing, with the objective of leading by example. Although this is yet to take place, there are ongoing discussions aimed at expanding the testing to include members of both the Senate and the National Assembly.
- The decision that all Principal Chiefs would ensure that all traditional leaders (including traditional healers, owners, "principals" and "teachers" of "Initiation Schools") under their jurisdiction throughout the country will become HIV/AIDS competent before the end of the year (2003).
- The immediate implementation, by several Principal Chiefs, of the decision to go out and teach all chiefs under their jurisdiction about HIV/AIDS and what they, as Chiefs, can do about it, together with educating people about the pandemic and encouraging them to test and take better care of themselves.

These activities by Senators and Principal Chiefs, led by the President of the Senate, have been widely publicised by the media in Lesotho. If the Senators and Principal Chiefs do sustain this level of commitment and action, it could constitute the single most important catalytic contribution to the attainment of HIV/AIDS competence in the country, not least because of the central role that culture and traditions play in the lives of Basotho.

Naturally, the leadership and members of the Theme Group have worked tirelessly—from the conceptual stage of this initiative to the production of the final draft of this manual—to make sure that the ideas contained herein will not only constitute "value added" to the efforts of the Lesotho Government and people, but also that the implementation of even some of these ideas would pave the way for increased collaboration and higher absorption of existing and future funding. This is very important, because up until now, the Government has, on the one hand, felt that this country is not receiving enough resources to enable it to effectively tackle the pandemic whereas, on the other hand, the donors and other members of the international community have felt that it will be difficult to make the case for additional resources for Lesotho unless it can be demonstrated that it is possible for the country to absorb such additional funds. This was, in fact, the basis of the conversation between The Right Honourable Prime Minister, and the UN Special Envoy on HIV/AIDS in Africa, Mr. Stephen Lewis, last year, when the Honourable Pakalitha Mosisili challenged the international community to join hands with his Government and people in coming to grips with the pandemic.

So, as we submit this reference manual to the Government and people of Lesotho, we do so with a certain sense of satisfaction. And although we are aware of the fact that a great deal more work still needs to be done, we take comfort in the knowledge that a journey of a thousand miles starts with the first step. We are convinced that all of us, the Government and the people of Lesotho in consort with the international development and donor community, working indefatigably, will win the scaled up national response to the HIV/AIDS pandemic. Such a compelling undertaking is the very essence of global partnership. Such is our common vision for Lesotho. Such, as well, is our social commitment.

Scholastica Kimaryo (Mrs.)
UNDP RESIDENT REPRESENTATIVE,
UN RESIDENT COORDINATOR AND CHAIRPERSON,
EXPANDED THEME GROUP ON HIV/AIDS

Robert Loftis (Mr.)
AMBASSADOR
EMBASSY OF THE UNITED STATES OF AMERICA
AND CO-CHAIRPERSON, EXPANDED THEME GROUP
ON HIV/AIDS

Why Strive for an HIV/AIDS-Competent Society?

When the first AIDS case was reported in the world some 20 years or so ago, it was viewed as a disease only affecting a few people in some population groups, such as the gay community, substance abusers and commercial sex workers. When the first AIDS case was diagnosed in Lesotho in 1986, it was seen as a disease of *Makwerekwere*, simply because the patient was a foreigner. This mindset has hugely delayed the formulation of appropriate national and international responses to the pandemic worldwide.

HIV stands for the "Human Immuno-deficiency Virus" and AIDS denotes "Acquired Immuno-Deficiency Syndrome". HIV is a retrovirus that infects cells of the immune system and destroys or impairs their function. Infection by HIV results in the progressive depletion of the immune system, leading to "immune deficiency", which means that the immune system can no longer fulfil its role of fighting off infection and cancers. This leaves the body open to attack from what are known as "opportunistic infections", because they take advantage of a weakened immune system.

The first cases of unusual immune system failure were identified among gay men in the United States in 1981, and in the following year, Acquired Immuno-Deficiency Syndrome (AIDS) was first defined. In the course of 1982, three modes of transmission (blood transfusion, sexual intercourse and mother-to-child transmission) were described. In 1983/84, the Human Immuno-deficiency Virus, or HIV, was isolated and identified as the source of what was then a newly recognised disease.

Like other viruses, HIV has diversified. We now know that there are two types of HIV: HIV-1 and HIV-2. Both are transmitted by sexual contact, through blood transfusion, and from mother to child, and they appear to cause clinically indistinguishable AIDS (although HIV-2 seems to be less transmittable and less pathogenic in terms of the fact that the period between initial infection and illness is longer).

Thankfully, there is now a growing national, regional and global political commitment to scaling up the response to the pandemic, largely as a result of advocacy by individuals and communities whose lives have been variously touched by the pandemic. However, as the UNAIDS states in its *2002 Report on the Global HIV/AIDS Epidemic,* "this new political resolve is not universal. An unacceptable number of governments and civil society institutions are still in a state of denial about the HIV/AIDS epidemic, and are failing to act to prevent its further spread or alleviate its impact… By failing to act, governments and civil society are turning their backs on the possibility of success against AIDS."[1]

The good news for the Basotho Nation, as clearly stated by The Right Honourable Prime Minister, Mr. Pakalitha Mosisili, in the *Foreword* to this manual, is that the Heads of State and Governments of the African Union (AU), the Southern African Development Community (SADC) and Lesotho itself, have just recently (July 2003) renewed their individual and collective commitment to fight the pandemic. This is most commendable.

The Challenge and Opportunity

The primary challenge, therefore, is to figure out how best to translate these firm commitments into appropriate individual and national actions. From what we know, there are two sets of life-saving and complementary actions that must be taken in order to defeat the pandemic:

- To make sure that those who are not yet infected and who happen to be the majority of the population (about 69% of Basotho) take the necessary preventive measures so that they do *not* become infected; and

- To make sure that those who are already infected can live long and good quality lives through treatment, care and support.

Once any Government and its people can manage to do this, they will have scored tremendous success in breaking the back of the pandemic. How does one do this? By making sure that each and every Mosotho—child, adult, male, female—is HIV/AIDS competent.

What is HIV/AIDS Competence?

What exactly is HIV/AIDS competence? HIV/AIDS competence means a society whose citizens are knowledgeable about what HIV is, what AIDS is, how one gets it, what one should do to avoid getting it, how one knows whether or not one has it and what one should do if one or a loved one already has it. Above all, one needs to know that although there is not yet a cure for HIV/AIDS, being HIV-positive is NOT an automatic death sentence; it can be managed through appropriate treatment, food and nutrition, care and support.

UNAIDS describes HIV/AIDS Competence as *"a society in which all people accept that HIV/AIDS is affecting their lives and their work. They deal with HIV/AIDS in their lives by assessing accurately the factors that may put them or their communities at risk and hamper the quality of the lives of people affected by HIV/AIDS. Through local partnerships, they mobilise the means and generate the knowledge to act to reduce those risks and improve their quality of life."*[2]

An HIV/AIDS-Competent Society

An HIV/AIDS-Competent Society requires that each and every citizen should:
- Know what HIV is and how it evolves to become AIDS;
- Know how it can be prevented;
- Know how it can be managed through testing, treatment and care;
- Know what to do if a loved one is infected;
- Know that HIV/AIDS is not an automatic death sentence;
- Know how one can live a long and productive life, if one looks after oneself.

In other words, striving for and achieving an HIV/AIDS-competent society is of critical importance to the success of any national, district, community and household response to the pandemic. It includes children who must be informed about these issues, in a nurturing way and to the level of their comprehension. This is all the more important especially considering that children, generally, and young girls, in particular, are at greater risk, mainly through sexual violence and other forms of child abuse.

Why Strive for HIV/AIDS Competence?

For a country like Lesotho, with a high national infection rate of over 30%, it is logistically and financially both impossible and unaffordable to target only those who are infected, with either information for awareness-raising or with such services as treatment, care and support. On the other hand, we know from the experiences of the mid-1980s to the early 1990s, during the campaign for universal child immunisation[3], that it is infinitely more practical—and one is likely to get good value for money—if one focuses national efforts for community mobilisation and service delivery on reaching at least 90 per cent of the population. That way, one not only creates *demand* for the services on hand, such as voluntary counselling, testing, treatment, care and support, but the demand is also most likely to be self-sustaining as more and more people who were once visibly weakened by AIDS begin to improve and start to live longer and better lives. They will undoubtedly serve as living testimony that not only does the pandemic exist, but also that if people come forward, it will be beneficial to them.

How Does a Country Attain HIV/AIDS Competence?

How does a country make sure its citizens are HIV/AIDS competent? Simply, by each and every major stakeholder and its institutions—the Government, civil society (the Church, traditional leaders, traditional healers, people living positively with HIV/AIDS, women's and youth organisations, and more), the business sector, the media—committing to striving for an HIV/AIDS-competent society as their priority agenda for action. As a next practical step, it means that with immediate effect, every effort must be made by all key stakeholders to develop, publish and ensure wide dissemination of appropriate learning and teaching materials, especially in Sesotho, containing the information required for different target groups, such as Senators and other

Parliamentarians, Cabinet Ministers, Principal Secretaries, other senior officials and all public workers.

It means that the Senate, the National Assembly and each and every Government Ministry have to immediately draw up and implement a plan for the leadership and workers at their places of work, thereby equipping themselves with the knowledge and skills to make the people they serve HIV/AIDS competent. Likewise, the Church, traditional leaders, other organs of civil society, the media as well as business have to immediately draw up and implement appropriate teaching and learning programmes in order to ensure that their leaders and workers become HIV/AIDS competent as a matter of urgency. The leaders will then be able to go out and ensure that all citizens—worshipers, consumers, farmers, herd boys, the youth, women, teachers and their pupils/students, those using health facilities, ordinary villagers and urban dwellers going about their business, subjects, and society-at-large—will be given the required knowledge and skills to become HIV/AIDS competent.

What is the Role of the Individual?

At the individual level, an HIV/AIDS-competent society also means that every Mosotho should know what his or her rights and responsibilities are, and act accordingly. This means that every individual is not only able to lay claims on society to have his/her rights respected in the context of this emergency, but also accepts that he/she has a duty to contribute to the fight against HIV/AIDS and the devastation and tragedy it causes. What these duties entail depends on the social position of each individual and the nature of their relationships. Parents have a duty to protect and support children, whilst children have a duty to respect their parents and be mindful of other children. Doctors and health workers have a duty to provide quality care to patients, regardless of their health status or the cause of their ill health, and to treat all patients with respect, whilst patients have a duty to adhere to the treatment offered. Civil servants have a duty to provide government services to all Basotho in a way that respects their dignity and promotes their human rights, whilst users of these services have a duty to utilise them without damaging them and, where possible, contribute to the upkeep of these services. Leaders have a duty to lead their constituents to become HIV/AIDS Competent, whilst constituents have the duty to learn and become HIV/AIDS Competent.

What are the Chances for Success in Lesotho?

The most exciting thing about Lesotho is that there is a very high potential for success, due to the extensive delivery capacity in this country. On the Government side, the planned local government elections should go a long way not only in decentralising political power but also in devolving responsibility for the delivery of basic services, especially health services, to local authorities. This will be very important in ensuring extensive access to essential drugs for treating opportunistic and other diseases, as well as ARVs for treating HIV/AIDS patients. In addition, the extensive network of traditional leaders, from Principal Chiefs all the way down to the village elders, traditional healers, and owners and "principals" of initiation schools, is a fantastic resource in fighting the pandemic.

Understandably, there may be those who may be skeptical about the extensive engagement of the institutions of traditional governance due to their past partisan history. But this is true of all Basotho institutions. So, as we all strive for Lesotho's transformation on the principles of democratic pluralism, we must ensure that every Mosotho is afforded the chance to put his or her best foot forward in the struggle for a peaceful and prosperous nation. At any rate, the HIV/AIDS pandemic knows no politics, no race, no gender, no social class, and no national or international boundaries. So, if any nation is to triumph over this crisis, it will only manage to do so on the basis of a united front. In other words, this may well be the societal crisis that may very well help Basotho to transcend the past as they join hands beyond partisan lines to defeat this new common enemy.

Present circumstances bode well. Since the Sixth Parliament was sworn-in in June 2002, we have witnessed close and harmonious working relations between the 10 political parties in Parliament. On the specific matter of tackling the HIV/AIDS pandemic, we have witnessed very focused and concerted efforts, already leading to significant achievements.

- The establishment of a Senate Committee on HIV/AIDS.
- The establishment of a National Assembly on HIV/AIDS.
- Skills training for HIV/AIDS competence for Members of both Committees.
- The Senate Committee on HIV/AIDS already working relentlessly through the Principal Chiefs to make Basotho HIV/AIDS competent by organising meetings and seminars for all Chiefs working under them, at times including traditional

healers and leaders of initiation schools. Many of the meetings we have been privileged to witness have been organised through the District Secretaries and addressed by the President or Vice President of the Senate, the Principal Chief for the area as well as the Parliamentarian for the Constituency. A strong foundation has been laid for this *modus operandi* to become the standard.

• The recent two-day National Seminar for Traditional Healers on the Culture of Initiation and how initiation schools can play an active role in the national response to the pandemic was inspirational. Imagine ALL the Initiation Schools in this country becoming a centre of excellence for promoting HIV/AIDS competence. Not only does this exponentially expand the country's institutionalised capacity for attaining HIV/AIDS competence in a relatively short span of time, but it is also self-sustaining. Every Mosotho who goes through an initiation school will then receive this knowledge as part and parcel of his or her life skills for the right of passage from childhood to adulthood. This augurs very well for Lesotho, as it will have a life-long positive impact on the society.

The other very important reason why Lesotho is poised for great success in this campaign for an HIV/AIDS-competent society is the existence of an extensive and very well-established network of the Church and its related institutions. Since the early days of the founding of the Basotho people, when the Church was invited to Lesotho by its Founder and Leader, King Mosheoshoe I, it has played a substantive role in shaping the destiny of this country. This was also evident in the critical role it played in the political negotiations leading to the very successful 2002 General Elections.

By the same token, the Church can and must play a key role in the struggle for an HIV/AIDS-competent society. Throughout the country, it can use its pulpits, health and educational establishments to educate people on the pandemic. Equally importantly, the Church can go a long way in extending services like voluntary testing, counselling, treatment, care and support to communities throughout the length and breadth of this country. Naturally, there are those who may be uncomfortable with this notion on moral grounds, or even with the fact that some Churches do not condone the use of condoms. But everything considered, the positive role of the Church far outweighs these kinds of considerations. At any rate, there are those who also believe that it is very important to educate children and adults alike that abstinence and mutual faithfulness is, indeed, a viable option.

Furthermore, there is the fact that Lesotho is **one people**, with one official language and predominantly one religion. Basotho are also proud people who have never been defeated in any conventional war and who pride themselves in having survived many past calamities. In other words, Basotho do not believe in defeat. When Basotho put their mind to something, it will happen, especially when backed up by the requisite organisational and financial resources.

On the other hand, the business sectors as well as the media in this country are relatively small by any standards. However, they can play a very important complementary role. First, they have the important role of making sure that their leaders and workers are HIV/AIDS competent. Secondly, they have the responsibility to ensure that those infected by the virus not only get access to the requisite preventive and curative services but that they are not discriminated against and/or lose their employment. Furthermore, it is about forging partnerships in the interest of synergy and improved effectiveness: partnerships with the Government, with the Church, traditional leaders, people living positively with HIV/AIDS, other organs of civil society and, ultimately, partnerships with communities. The scope is simply infinite and the potential benefits for all concerned, enormous.

How Will Lesotho Pay For All This?

Where will the financial resources come from? First, there is the need to re-focus resources to address the HIV/AIDS pandemic as the *core* challenge—and opportunity—for saving the Basotho people from potential extinction. In truth, with more than 30% of Basotho already infected and increasing, combined with the impact of the current food crisis (with two thirds of the population in need of food supplementation), and also taking into consideration the impact of structural poverty, it is a certainty that most of the 35% currently infected could be dead within the next 5–10 years *unless drastic action* is taken by each and every institution in society.

We also know from international experience that, of the 40 million people who are infected globally, a full 25 million (or roughly 60%) are workers. It can be assumed that the proportion of workers to those infected in Lesotho is similar, if not higher. With this kind of picture, what are the implications for this country's production and reproduction, be it of goods and services, or of the population? What point is a *Vision 2020* or a three-year, rolling *PRSP, a sectoral Ministry/other*

Government Budget, or business plan for any private sector institution, if it does not take full cognisance of the impact of the pandemic on the Basotho Nation? What stronger case should one make to convince policy makers and planners that today, smart money is that which is invested in fighting the pandemic?

In addition, there is in Lesotho today, some allocation of external financial resources specifically focused on HIV/AIDS projects and programmes, most of which are geared towards implementation by certain Government Ministries and NGOs. However, there is an urgent need to see how future plans can be drawn up with a view to factoring in implementation by institutions such as the Church, traditional leaders, and civil society, thus exponentially expanding programme planning, delivery/outreach and thus financial absorptive capacity. There are numerous possibilities for public/private sector/community collaboration, including expanding possibilities for micro savings and credit schemes, more affordable life assurance schemes especially for resource poor communities, promotion of agri-business production cooperatives, among other creative investment and saving schemes. This would broaden the options that poor people will have for obtaining better care for their own health, nutrition and general well-being. As The Right Honourable Prime Minster, Mr. Pakalitha Mosisili, said in his challenge to the Expanded Theme Group on HIV/AIDS, we must think creatively, "out-of-the-box". This is only a start. We are sure that there are many creative initiatives out there in different parts of Lesotho that are already operating on this basis. The challenge now is to identify them, learn from their successes, and then see how we can take such initiatives to scale.

Structure of this Manual

The way we interpret and understand HIV/AIDS influences our choice for programmatic interventions. Therefore, this report begins by providing conceptual starting points for a comprehensive understanding of the HIV/AIDS epidemic.

Chapter 1 sets the national historic context, which serves as a backdrop to the heritage which we seek to preserve, and the will of the people to win.

Chapter 2 presents the substance of the presentation by the UN Resident Coordinator and Chairperson of the Expanded Theme Group on HIV/AIDS to the pivotal August 2003 meeting of the Prime Minister, the Cabinet and Principal Secretaries and members of the Expanded Theme Group on strategies for scaling up the national response to the HIV/AIDS pandemic in Lesotho and the discussions that followed. It provides a comprehensive overview of the main thrust of this critical exercise.

Chapter 3 reflects on the various shifts in the global understanding of HIV/AIDS over time. It concludes by advocating a comprehensive approach that addresses four core domains of action:

   I. Prevention;
  II. Treatment and care;
 III. Mitigation of current and anticipated impacts;
  IV. Addressing systemic development factors, which collectively constitute a context of risk, vulnerability and reduced capability to cope with HIV/AIDS.

Chapter 4 provides a situation and response analysis of HIV/AIDS in Lesotho. It builds on the conceptual framework of *Chapter 3* by relating the analysis to the four domains of action (prevention, treatment and care, impact mitigation, and addressing systemic development factors).

Chapter 5 discusses the mobilisation of all sectors of society in striving for an HIV/AIDS-competent society, as a core operational strategy for success. It draws on successful lessons from Uganda and Senegal, which could inspire Lesotho to follow suit.

Chapter 6 presents the critical enabling capacities of Information and Communications Technologies (ICT) for Development, and how they can be deployed strategically in the fight against the HIV/AIDS pandemic. It addresses the creative use of ICT to provide meaningful and gainful employment for those infected with the disease and are homebound.

Chapter 7, Culture, the Message and the Messenger, examines the role of culture in the communication of critical social messages. Introducing the novel concept of a "Cultural Immune System" (CIS), by which cultures and societies instinctively resist invasion by alien cultural norms, it advocates, in addressing the limited success of such interventions as condom promotion programmes, a process by which the HIV/AIDS message can be isolated from any embedded "alien" cultural biases, and how subsequently the message can be infused into the indigenous traditional methods of communicating critical social messages in order to achieve maximum acceptance and buy-in. The important potential role of the Initiation Schools in the Lesotho culture in this regard, is discussed.

Chapter 8 examines the personal and institutional transformation that would be required as pre-requisites for a successful response to the HIV/AIDS pandemic.

Chapter 9 examines the key role of government in the national response to the pandemic, indicating that it must lead the fight against HIV/AIDS thought, ensuring that all institutions of state, including the parliament, the cabinet, and the ministries, are involved at all levels.

Chapter 10 provides clear examples where civil society can scale up its response to the pandemic through the mobilisation of all stakeholders to support the attainment of an HIV/AIDS-Competent Society.

Chapter 11 presents options for the private sector and stresses its important role in the scaled up response to the pandemic. The chapter also challenges the private sector to play a more dynamic role in the fight against HIV/AIDS.

Chapter 12 reviews the role of international partners in supporting the move towards an HIV/AIDS-Competent society.

Chapter 13 provides an analysis of the situation of orphans and vulnerable children, or "children rearing children", which is perhaps the starkest evidence of the impact of the pandemic on society. It provides a number of options for addressing the plight of these children.

Chapter 14 presents the key national mechanisms required to mobilise the whole of Basotho society towards an HIV/AIDS-Competent Society and clarifies the roles and responsibilities of the different structures and organisations.

Chapter 15 examines ways to finance the scaled up response to the pandemic and makes a number of concrete recommendations for consideration by all stakeholders.

Chapter 16, the Conclusion, puts the entire initiative and effort in perspective and within the context of the overall development challenge to Lesotho and Africa as a whole. It concludes that in order to meet the challenge of the HIV/AIDS pandemic head-on, and to win no matter the obstacles, the government and people of Lesotho, as indeed Africa and all of us, must find the courage to take ownership of the challenge, and commit and combine the best of our genius and resources, to fight to win.

An HIV/AIDS-Competent Society is not a pipe dream; it is within our reach. It is hoped that the conceptual and pragmatic road map presented in this manual will help bring about an HIV/AIDS-Competent Society.

NOTES *for Introduction*

1 Report on the Global HIV/AIDS Epidemic 2002, UNAIDS, Geneva, Switzerland, 2002.

2. Ibid.

3. In this case, vaccines, cold chain equipments, needles, syringes, amongst others.

Lesotho: A Heritage of Will

From the dawn of its creation, the land now known as Lesotho, the "Mountain Kingdom in the Sky", has cultivated a strong culture and heritage to overcome the most daunting challenges with a true sense of pride and a will to survive. This heritage of will is enshrined in the historical founding of the nation to come together in search of peace and prosperity, the preservation of independence against war, the apartheid era and political turmoil, and the strong role of the extended family, religion, and chieftainship, remaining the only constitutional monarchy in sub-Sahara Africa today.

The Lesotho of today is no far different. Facing yet again many development challenges, the Kingdom of Lesotho is striving to survive as an independent and sovereign nation in our increasing globalised world, and taking all opportunities to ensure that its voice and actions are heard for the overall well-being of the people.

Lesotho is a small mountainous country covering over 30,000 square miles, with the unique feature that it is landlocked and completely surrounded by another country—the Republic of South Africa. For this reason, the history and socio-economic development of the country has been intricately linked to that of its neighbour.

Lesotho, with an estimated population of 2.2 million, is a constitutional monarchy which, through its internationally-hailed national elections in 2002 resulting in its most representative Parliament since its independence in 1966, now has a solid foundation to further its development agenda for the people of the country.

External relations are dominated by its economic and geographic dependence on it neighbour, with income earnings from migrant mine workers accounting for a large share of the Gross National Product, and over 85% of imports originating in South Africa. It is further estimated that over 250,000 Lesotho nationals are normally resident in South Africa, and their numbers have tended to grow as job opportunities in the new South Africa have increased, creating an opportunity to support the ever important extended family in its rugged and boundless terrain.

Lesotho's scenic beauty lies in hidden wonders amongst its many natural waterfalls that form spectacular frozen stalactites in the winter months. The country boasts of the highest single-drop waterfall in Southern Africa—the Malentsunyane Falls—and the highest road pass and highest peak in Southern Africa—Thabana-Ntlenyane, with the entire country rising over 1000 metres above sea level. Spectacular valleys, the snow-capped Maluti (mountain) range, and unique flora and fauna with evening skies cluttered with an abundance of stars, can please even the most reluctant dreamer. The people of Lesotho are a nation of travellers and horsemen, as for many years this was the best means of transportation to reach the most remote corners of its mountainous paradise.

Since the 1980s, the economic boom in Lesotho has been attributed to the infrastructural developments of the Lesotho Highlands Water Project, a massive water transfer project to the neighbouring South Africa, creating an opportunity to generate its own electricity and develop its rural infrastructure and an eco-tourist industry as a unique add-on destination to Southern Africa. The Katse Dam wall and the Malibamatso Bridge are striking pieces of modern engineering having won international awards for their architectural and engineering design. Taking advantage of its geographical location, the country benefits from receipts of revenues from the Southern African Customs Union, which include Swaziland, Botswana, Namibia, and South Africa, and the growing export-oriented textile and manufacturing sector, due to favourable trading international agreements. This economic growth put Lesotho well above the average for low and middle income countries. However, things have since changed dramatically for the worse, compounded by the 1998 political violence that resulted in the burning down of significant portions of the capital city,

Maseru, and of two other cities, a decline in SACU revenues, inflation, and more, now making Lesotho number 137 in the 2003 Human Development Report. In 2002, it emerged as a major exporter of apparel to the United States, creating over 10,000 jobs for many young women from the rural hinterlands, to even surpass the traditional major Government employer, with over 45,000 jobs at present.

The country's colourful and at times trying history is testament to the resilience of its people—the Basotho. The official languages, Sesotho and English, are spoken and understood even in the most remote corners of its mountain ranges.

In moments of crisis, the Basotho have always banded together to find solace and solutions in order to be able once again to celebrate their heritage in peace and unity. This is exemplified in the annual Morija Arts and Cultural Festival first held in 1999 after the political turmoil of 1998, in which Basotho sought to come together and promote traditional culture and arts and play a positive role in bringing the nation closer to transcend the divisions of the past. Morija is one of Lesotho's most important historical and cultural sites, known as the Selibeng sa Thuto—the Well-Sping of Learning, where the first French Protestant missionaries settled in 1833 to house the oldest church in the country. The town also houses the Morija Museum and Archives, well known for supporting research and preserving valuable records and documents of Lesotho's history.

Origins of a Nation

The earliest known inhabitants of Lesotho, who date back to at least the 10th century A.D., were the Late Stone San hunters and gatherers, who traversed the rugged mountainous terrain, leaving a rich legacy of rock art and paintings in caves throughout the country. By the 16th Century, other Bantu-speaking people and ethnic groups had occupied the land as cattle-owners, adapting themselves to the extreme and harsh climatic conditions of the mountains.

Moshoeshoe the Great

The people of Lesotho, the Basotho, identify their origins and strength from the vision of one man—Moshoeshoe I, who built the nation on the principles of leadership, family, loyalty, diplomacy and, when necessary, war[1]. The nation endured wars with the Afrikaner settlers and the British, forging partnerships to introduce Christianity and education, and making Moshoeshoe one of the greatest strategists for his people.

Moshoeshoe the Great, a commoner, described as "merely the senior son of a village headman"[2], gathered various ethnic and autonomous Sesotho-speaking tribes scattered by the rise of the Zulu in 1816–1830 and established a stronghold as King and leader in 1823, first in what is now known as Butha Buthe, then further inland to Thaba Bosiu or "Mountain of the Night". This is an historical landmark housing the Royal Cemetery and the remains of Moshoeshoe's homestead.

Building alliances and farming the land as successful grain farmers, the Basotho, under the leadership of Moshoeshoe, were able to enjoy good years of peace and prosperity, trading with neighbouring peoples to consolidate their wealth, with their population reaching over 80,000 in the 1850s.[3] In the ensuing years, through war with the Afrikaners and the British, much land was lost, and Moshoeshoe placed the nation under the protection of the British in 1865. Moshoeshoe died in 1871 having left a legacy of pride in his people, best stated in one of his many quoted sayings, "Peace is the mother of nations".

Living the Apartheid Era

Being landlocked and completely surrounded by South Africa, Lesotho's history and socio-economic development have been intricately linked to that of its neighbour. The apartheid years of South Africa have had a profound impact on the country, which was governed by the Cape Colony in 1871, and fortunate to have been returned to British control as it would have formed part of the Union of South Africa. Lesotho has survived as a labour reservoir for the mining industry, creating an opportunity for young men to support their families even in the most remote highlands through miner's remittances. The country also supported the education and well-being of many of South Africa's leading freedom fighters and refugees, who now play a prominent role in the new South Africa. The closing of the borders in 1983, when Lesotho denounced South African apartheid, is a telling tale of its vulnerability to its neighbour. As is true to Lesotho's history, this challenge too has passed, and the country now has the opportunity to draw on the wealth and power of South Africa while still retaining its independence as a sovereign nation.

Deepening Democracy and Political Stability

Since independence in 1966, Lesotho has endured a number of trials in civil unrest in its political arena. The first Prime Minister, Chief Leabua Jonathan, was overthrown in 1986 by a military coup. The country was under military rule until 1993, first under Major General Justin M. Lekhanya (1986-1991), and after him, under Major General Elias Ramaema, who spearheaded democratic elections in March 1993. The election was won by the Basotho Congress Party whose leader, the late Ntsu Mokhehle, became Prime Minister. There were challenging times between 1994 and 1998, including skirmishes between rebel army troops, the dissolution of Parliament by King Letsie III, and the breakup of the Basotho Congress Party to form the Lesotho Congress for Democracy under the leadership of Ntsu Mokhehle. National elections were held in 1998, resulting in one of the darkest times for Lesotho as the people contested the victory of the Lesotho Congress for Democracy. Through international support and national dedication to peace and democracy, world-class general elections were held in May 2002, based on the Mixed Member Proportional Representation Model. This resulted in 10 parties getting into Parliament, with the Lesotho Congress for Democracy—under the leadership of Prime Minister Pakalitha Mosisili—as the Majority Party. With the most representative Parliament since its independence, Lesotho has now entered a new dawn in its history, with infinite possibilities for deepening democracy as well as accelerating efforts to develop the country.

Forging Partnerships for Development

Lesotho enjoys many regional and international agreements through the Southern African Customs Union, the Southern African Development Community, the New Partnership for African Development, the African Union, the African Growth and Opportunities Act, the World Trade Organisation and the United Nations.

Strengthening the Role of Women in a Patriarchal Society

With the traditional high dependence on predominantly male migrant labour, women, accounting for more than 60% of the national population, have played an important role in the Basotho society. The Basotho society, however, is still very patriarchal, with the man as the head of the family and the sole decision maker, based on the customary and common laws enshrined in the Constitution. Notwithstanding this challenge, women in Lesotho, enjoy higher rates of educational attainment and literacy, and dominate the running of rural small land holdings, which provide subsistence agriculture to the majority of the population. Women also account for 62% or almost two-thirds of the professional and technical positions in the formal sector, and continue to strive to break the barrier to hold higher administrative and managerial posts in Government and the private sector.

Instinct for Survival

Basotho have in the past always triumphed against diverse challenges to their survival, and triumphed where others might not have done as well. This time, the challenge is bigger than any they have ever faced. The challenge of the HIV/AIDS pandemic is the mother of all challenges. But it is a veritable truth that such challenges bring out the best in a people. The same fortitude, resilience and will that have seen Basotho through in the past now can—MUST—hold them in good stead, when they most need them. With the total commitment of all its people, and of its partners and friends, Lesotho will win this fight too, long and hard as the struggle will be, drawing strength from its Heritage of Will.

NOTES *for Chapter 1*

1. Stephen Gill. *A Short History of Lesotho*, 1993.
2. L. Thompson, *Survival in Two Worlds: Moshoeshoe of Lesotho*, 1975.
3. Martin M. Lelimo, *The Question of Lesotho's Conquered Territory: It's Time for an Answer*, 1998.

2

Turning A Crisis into an Opportunity—An Overview

On Thursday, August 21, 2003, The Right Honourable Prime Minister, Mr. Paka-litha Mosisili, for the express purpose of achieving consensus-building as well as facilitating accountable decision-making, convened an unprecedented joint meeting of his Cabinet, Principal Secretaries and other senior government officials, and the Expanded Theme Group on HIV/AIDS, to receive a briefing by the United Nations Resident Coordinator and Chairperson of the Expanded Theme Group on HIV/AIDS, Mrs. Scholastica Kimaryo, on progress being made with respect to formulat-ing creative ideas to facilitate the *Strategies for Scaling Up the National Response to the HIV/AIDS Pandemic in Lesotho* and emerging recommendations for action. Present at the meeting were all Heads of UN Agencies represented in Lesotho (UNICEF, UNDP, WFP, WHO, FAO, UNFPA), other senior technical staff from the UN Resi-dent Coordination Office and from the Pretoria-based UNDP Africa Regional Proj-ect on HIV/AIDS. What follows is, in essence, the substance of what was presented and discussed at that meeting, which is basically an overview of what is contained in this manual itself. It is a compilation of the results of an extensive consultative process. A list of the officials present at the meeting is appended as *Appendix 2.*

Situation Assessment

One cannot escape the fact that the HIV/AIDS pandemic in Lesotho has reached crisis proportions. Currently, at least one in three Basotho adults are infected with HIV/AIDS. This translates into approximately 350,000 people now living with the pandemic and about 70 people dying each day of AIDS-related illnesses. The Government is very concerned that despite various efforts thus far to curtail the spread of HIV, infection rates continue to rise. As early as the year 2000, His Majesty King Letsie III declared HIV/AIDS a national disaster and has since continued to use every opportunity to exhort all citizens and partners of goodwill to do everything in their power to help control and manage the pandemic. A National AIDS Strategic Plan (NASP) was drawn up, and a Lesotho AIDS Programme Coordinating Authority (LAPCA) set up to oversee implementation of the national strategy, with 2% budget allocation from every Government Ministry set aside to address pressing HIV/AIDS priorities in the respective sectors.

Despite all these efforts, it is now becoming increasingly clear that for Lesotho, and indeed for several other countries in the SADC Region with high HIV/AIDS prevalence rates, the combination of chronic poverty, structural food insecurity (heightened by last year's adverse weather conditions that resulted in some 700,000 people needing food assistance) and HIV/AIDS will lead to even greater loss for the country and its people. Furthermore, it is estimated that of those infected by HIV/AIDS, at least 60% are part of the workforce: they are farmers, engineers, teachers, nurses and other public servants. But they are also husbands and wives, sons and daughters, parents, custodians of society's norms and values, role models and valuable members of their communities. Thus, it is such a tragedy for so many of them to be dying off in such huge numbers, not least because they are simply irreplaceable, as much in human terms as in terms of economic and social reproduction. Already, one in ten children between 0-14 years old has lost one or both parents due to HIV/AIDS and the total number of orphans, estimated at present to be over seventy thousand, is expected to rise significantly.

Impact on Socio-Economic Development

Because HIV/AIDS erodes Lesotho's greatest asset, its people, and thus threatens its very survival as a nation, it is the single most important development challenge facing the country. One of the most frightening indicators of the effect of HIV/AIDS on Lesotho is the rapid decline in life expectancy. Before the onset of HIV/AIDS, average life expectancy was expected to increase to 60 years in 2003. Now, it is estimated to be only 40 years by 2005. As The Right Honourable Prime Minister said in July 2003, at the official opening of the SADC Extra-Ordinary Summit on HIV/AIDS hosted by the Lesotho Government in Maseru, a person who became 15 years old in 2000 has a 74% chance of becoming HIV-positive before reaching the age of 50. This is a sobering statistic.

The pandemic also has significant implications for the prospect of economic growth. A recent World Bank report estimates that HIV/AIDS will reduce Gross Domestic Product in Lesotho by almost a third by the year 2015. With HIV/AIDS deepening poverty, eroding public sector capacity to deliver public services and undermining people's quality of life, the outlook for human development is also rather negative. Despite various efforts, Lesotho's prospects for realising the Millennium Development Goals (MDGs) are diminishing rapidly. Hence the concern and commitment by the Government and people of Lesotho as well as international partners to search for ways of scaling up the fight against the pandemic.

There is Hope

Against such a backdrop, it is easy to feel overwhelmed by the scale of the problem, the suffering associated with HIV/AIDS and the fact that HIV continues to spread. However, experience elsewhere, perhaps most notably in Uganda, categorically demonstrates that it is possible to turn the pandemic around. Infection rates can be curtailed. Those who are already infected can be helped to live longer and better quality lives. Some of the negative implications of the pandemic can be prevented, if certain decisions and actions are taken immediately. Other negative impacts can be minimised, if the right support mechanisms are put in place and existing structures made more responsive, flexible and accountable.

Other countries have demonstrated the efficacy of hope in such a seemingly hopeless situation. In Uganda, for example, the HIV prevalence rate fell from 21% in 1991 to less than 10% in 1998, and stands at about 6% today. Senegal and Thailand also seem to have curtailed the spread of HIV/AIDS in their countries. In Senegal, the national HIV prevalence rate has consistently remained below 1% since 1990, through a combination of actions, including the legalisation of prostitution, coupled with the provision of health care (including use of condoms) to sex workers and their clients. Thailand introduced a 100% condom use programme among sex workers and their clients, which helped to halve the national HIV prevalence rate from about 4% to less than 2%. One can draw valuable lessons from these stories of hope.

Turning The Crisis Into An Opportunity: Some Catalytic Actions

With an infection rate of more than one third of the adult population and rising, compounded by the current food crisis and structural poverty, it is very likely that without drastic intervention, most of those in Lesotho currently living with the disease will die between the next five to ten years while many more will have been infected. This could potentially threaten the very survival of the Nation unless urgent and innovative steps are taken to combat this scourge. Most of us who engaged in the consultative process that gave birth to this manual do strongly believe that Lesotho can take certain steps not only to prevent possible annihilation but also to turn the crisis into an historic opportunity to catapult itself from the shackles of poverty and under-development to prosperity. This can be achieved through taking the following decisions and actions:

- Make every Mosotho HIV/AIDS Competent.
- Stop the pandemic from spreading to those not yet infected.
- Help those already infected to live longer and better quality lives.
- Ensure that every key stakeholder—hereinafter also referred to as "duty bearer"—take immediate steps to *core stream* HIV/AIDS into all their policies, for example—Vision 2020, PRSP, MDGs, sector and other policies, plans, budgets and actions/implementation plans. These duty bearers include the Government (the Executive, the Judiciary, the Civil Service), Civil Society (the Church, traditional leaders, healers and Initiation School Owners and Principals, as well as people living with HIV/AIDS), folk and conventional Mass Media Channels as well as the private sector.
- Accelerate transformational change in society, with particular focus on the Civil Service, without whose commitment it will be impossible to deliver on the *Strategies for Scaling Up the National Response to the HIV/AIDS Pandemic in Lesotho*,

by building on the gains made through the political process leading to the May 25, 2002 world-class General Elections, which ushered in a new dawn for democratic pluralism in the country since its independence some 36 years ago.

- Make a commitment to e-governance as a core strategy not only for enabling Government to deliver on its development commitments in spite of the rapidly depleting number of civil servants and other producers, but also as a classic opportunity for attaining competitive edge in a highly globalised, electronic world.
- Strengthen existing development management and oversight arrangements and mechanisms in order to underpin the setting of clear targets for the achievement of the *Scaling Up Agenda*, under-scoring the need for more effective implementation, monitoring, oversight, as well as individual and institutional accountability.

Mobilising for an HIV/AIDS-Competent Society: The Roles of Various Key Duty Bearers

Lesotho has a wealth of organisational capabilities, experiences and insights that can be harnessed to rapidly achieve an HIV/AIDS-Competent Society. The *secret* lies in each duty bearer recognising that effectively fighting the pandemic requires that each and every one of them take responsibility for taking *action*—within the context of their respective policy and operational mandates—to address the four domains of the national response to the pandemic. These are Prevention; Treatment, Care and Support; Impact Mitigation; and addressing relevant Systemic Development Factors, such as food insecurity, structural poverty and inequality, in order to reduce risk and vulnerability to HIV infection, thereby also strengthening the coping capabilities of individuals, households and communities. While action by the Government is very important, in and of itself, it will not be sufficient to break the back of the pandemic. Below are highlights of what each duty bearer could do, with immediate effect.

Parliament

Parliament has the responsibility to first and foremost ensure that all of its Honourable Members are HIV/AIDS competent; that is, that they know what HIV is, how one contracts it, how it progresses to become AIDS, how people can prevent themselves and others from contracting it, as well as what to do if one gets infected. Only by becoming HIV/AIDS competent can Members of Parliament be able to take better care of themselves as well as help other citizens to become HIV/AIDS competent. In addition, Parliament has both the authority and the responsibility to pass appropriate legislation to mitigate the impact of the pandemic. In this regard, it behoves Parliament to commence to use an HIV/AIDS competency *lens* to review and pass legislation, policies and budgets, as well as to exercise its oversight role in ensuring their due implementation.

Furthermore, Parliament should publicly adopt the Greater Involvement of People living with HIV/AIDS (GIPA) Principle as a cornerstone of all national programmes. Parliament is also ideally placed to lead the advocacy for comprehensive HIV/AIDS workplace policies and programmes, be it in the public or private sector, as well as within civil society. In order to be a credible advocate, Parliament should adopt an HIV/AIDS Workplace Policy and Programme for all Parliamentarians and Parliamentary staff. In this regard, both Houses of Parliament deserve recognition for leading the national fight against the pandemic by establishing, early in 2003, two Select Committees on HIV/AIDS: one for the Senate and the other for the National Assembly. Both Committees are already very active in striving for HIV/AIDS competence of their Members as well as embarking on a campaign to make Traditional Chiefs and their subjects HIV/AIDS competent. This is a huge step in the right direction.

Traditional Leaders, Healers and Initiation School Leaders

Traditional Leaders, Healers and Initiation School Leaders have a high potential to play a catalytic role in making every Mosotho HIV/AIDS competent. This is because Basotho have very strong cultural traditions, some of which can be put into excellent use for the control and management of the pandemic. In addition, traditional leaders are spread out among the people throughout the country and usually live among them. They know the needs of their people, their "language," and are thus best placed not only to play an effective awareness-raising role towards HIV/AIDS competence, but to also offer their people counselling on the need to go for testing, treatment, care and support. Of great importance is the traditional institution for the initiation of young people (especially boys) from childhood to adulthood. This involves teachings about the essence of a Mosotho man: how to be a responsible man, husband, father, son, son-in-law and citizen.

In particular, it is about sexuality and responsible manhood. It is for this reason that the Initiation School is the best institution through which to promote the principles of an HIV/AIDS-competent society, in general, and the prevention of HIV/AIDS, in particular. Certainly, one of the objectives of responsible manhood is procreation for posterity. Hence the pressing need to make sure that young initiates are taught **why** they should protect their "seed" from the HIV virus and **how**, for example, by immediately introducing the practice of "one man, one blade" for circumcision, to practice the "**a,b,c**"—**a**bstain, **b**e faithful, **c**ondomise/use a "shield"—to protect one's self and one's partner from infection. In many ways, once a young man learns these basic facts from Initiation School and, therefore, realises that unless he protects himself from HIV-infection, his name, clan and nation will end with him, he should have sufficient motivation to comply, if only for the sake of self-preservation.

People Living With HIV/AIDS

People Living With HIV/AIDS (PLWHA) must be involved in all efforts to scale up the national response to the diseases, as a matter of basic principle. They have a right—and a duty—to participate in making informed decisions about their well-being, including decisions on how to live longer and better-quality lives. People living positively and openly with HIV/AIDS are also the greatest asset in the national fight against the pandemic as they make the best ambassadors to help make the point that being infected does not have to be an automatic death sentence. They and their civil society organisations and networks have a key role to play in all aspects of the national response, from awareness raising and prevention, to treatment, care and support, as well as in impact mitigation. Their views and experiences are critical in ensuring that other duty bearers address the needs of those infected and affected population groups in a sensitive and effective manner.

The Church

The Church in Lesotho comprises an extensive network of national, district and local level institutions and infrastructure, which include church buildings, schools and health facilities. Its widespread social, economic and spatial infrastructure and the network of influential people associated with it—pastors, priests, lay leaders and workers, teachers, health workers as well as the faithful/followers—are indispensable in the fight against HIV/AIDS, using tools ranging from awareness-raising through the pulpits and other public fora, to counselling, treatment, care and support to the infected and affected individuals, households and communities. The Church is already playing a pivotal role in providing Home-Based Care (HBC) as well as counselling, but it can definitely do far more to take on the fight against the pandemic as a core responsibility and accountability.

Naturally, whereas it may be expected that the Church may take the moral approach to its fight against HIV/AIDS, it would be most helpful if it did not stand in the way of those who take a different, more secular approach to the pandemic. In addition, it could forge the kind of partnership with the Government, which would make it possible for certain funding to be challenged through it, based on its Strategic Plan to fight HIV/AIDS, as long as procedures for disbursements and accounting for allocated funds are agreed upon. This kind of partnership could exponentially increase the country's capacity for outreach throughout the length and breadth of this country.

The Business Sector

Today, the Business Sector in Lesotho employs more people than the public sector, especially on account of the 45,000 workers or so employed by the African Growth and Opportunities Act (AGOA)-focused garment manufacturers, as compared to about 35,000 public sector employees. Already, it is known that as much as 70% of the garment workers—most them young women—are already suffering from sexually transmitted infections, itself a high risk factor contributing to HIV infection. Yet, few private sector employers have any HIV/AIDS workplace programmes for their workers and some are known to be letting go of their sick employees. There is, therefore, a great deal that the business sector must do in order to place the fight against HIV/AIDS at the core of its commitments and work in this country. The compelling reason to do so is self-evident in the fact that a weakened and declining work force threatens the very survival of business.

Business Coalition on HIV/AIDS

Under the circumstances, it would seem prudent to establish a *Business Coalition on HIV/AIDS*, which would play a key role as an advocate in the business community to ensure that companies adopt HIV/AIDS Workplace Policies and Programmes, including awareness raising for prevention as well as provision of treatment, care and support for infected employees. The Coalition and its members would also have to adopt the Principle of Greater Involvement of People Living With HIV/AIDS as well as commit themselves to other principles like non-discrimination in the workplace on the basis of HIV status. Above all, the Business Coalition on HIV/AIDS could take the lead in spearheading the forging of creative private/public partnerships—from the national to community levels—that could transform the process of fighting the pandemic into a win-win outcome for all duty bearers involved.

Folk and Conventional Mass Media

Folk and Conventional Mass Media have a key role to play in creating deeper aware-ness about HIV/AIDS. Music (traditional, modern and choral), dance, arts, poetry, painting, debating clubs, radio, television, and newspapers are all effective chan-nels for mass communication on HIV/AIDS. They can and should address the issue of stigma and discrimination associated with infected and affected people. These channels are also ideally placed to develop different messages for different target audiences and to reach the youth, in particular, with appropriate messages. In addi-tion, folk and conventional mass media institutions should develop an HIV/AIDS Workplace Policy and Programme—as should other employers—to ensure the pro-tection of the rights of infected/affected employees, as well as contribute to a culture of respect within the organisation.

Youth

The young people of Lesotho constitute by far the largest group most at risk of con-tracting HIV/AIDS. They also constitute the core of the nation's productive capacity and its future. Engaging the Basotho youth, not only as targets and recipients of HIV/AIDS public enlightenment efforts, but also to help drive the process as key players in the campaign, promises a critical impact on the potential success of the fight against HIV/AIDS. Creative adoption of their own means of peer group communications, such as mobile SMS (Short Messaging System) and radio, should be exploited to its maximum possibilities.

Other Key Duty Bearers

Other key duty bearers, like NGOs, community-based organisations, women's and youth groups, are already involved in various activities and aspects of HIV prevention, treatment and care, and/or impact mitigation. The challenge is to ensure that these small-scale interventions do not remain isolated islands of excellence, but are linked into the national response to bring about an HIV/AIDS-Competent Society.

The Individual

Every individual has a right and a responsibility to know their rights and responsibilities in the fight against HIV/AIDS and to exercise them. Whereas leaders have a duty to ensure that those who are placed under their jurisdiction are HIV/AIDS competent, each of us has a duty and a responsibility to become individually HIV/AIDS competent. Whereas health workers have a duty to extend good quality care to patients (including those who are immuno-compromised), every patient has a duty to seek medical care and to adhere to the protocols of treatment and care. Whereas public and private sector workers have a duty to deliver services in an efficient, affective and courteous manner, every service user/consumer has a duty to utilise these services in a proper manner.

Core Streaming HIV/AIDS into Every Sector

In many countries of the world, conventional responses to the HIV/AIDS pandemic have been incremental and piece-meal, as an "add on" to a sector's core mandate. Perhaps this approach has worked in countries where public sector systems function relatively well through, for example, decentralised systems of service delivery such as in Uganda, thereby making it possible to handle the additional challenges of addressing HIV/AIDS by merely adding on some modest resources. This welfare approach to responding to the pandemic has also been designed on the assumption that HIV/AIDS is a static problem with short-term implications and can, therefore, be addressed by tinkering with the problem at the edges, for example, through poster promotions of condom use intended to result in behaviour change.

However, for countries such as Lesotho whose infection rate has already surpassed the 30% mark, the expected impacts on development as a result of increasing illness and death are likely to be so far-reaching as to affect the entire system of governance and society. Hence the critical need for the national response to be systemic rather than fragmented and additional. A systems approach means

seeing beyond what appears to be isolated and independent incidents to seeing patterns of influence and the underlying structures. Once we understand the real foundations for the situations we experience, we are in a much better position to respond in enlightened fashion.

We are able to act responsibly and interact with the structures in ways, which will enhance or improve the situation without creating new and different problems elsewhere. An effective response by Government and other institutions such as Parliament and the Private Sector and Civil Society, therefore, will require a comprehensive understanding of the underlying vulnerabilities to HIV in relation to development, as well as an understanding of the impact of AIDS on the entire society, and its corresponding implications. A systems approach would accordingly require an examination of how best to mobilise the entire society to respond in a way that enhances the broader situation of development while addressing HIV and AIDS. [1]

The concept of *core streaming* is, therefore, a systems approach and is crucial in moving towards the achievement of an HIV/AIDS-competent society—a process in which Government has a critical role to play. In essence, what is needed is the *core streaming* of HIV/AIDS into all government policies, plans and programmes; in other words, putting HIV/AIDS at the centre of all plans and activities aimed at facilitating development. HIV/AIDS needs to be at the centre of Vision 2020, the Poverty Reduction Strategy Paper (PRSP) and all sector plans and budgets. It also needs to be a core element of plans and strategies to meet the Millennium Development Goals (MDGs), including those that are concerned with public sector reform.

Core streaming starts by taking account of the two main pathways through which HIV/AIDS affects sectors: morbidity (illness) and mortality (death). In turn, morbidity and mortality will affect *demand*, by increasing the quantity, quality and complexity of services required, and *supply*, by reducing the number and quality of service providers. The overall effect is a fundamental change in service delivery priorities, income and expenditure, and overall productivity and effectiveness of a particular sector.

Systemic Impact on the Agricultural Sector

Let us take the case of Agriculture. HIV/AIDS increases the demand for food assistance, as an increasing number of people and households affected by HIV/AIDS will be unable to provide for themselves. This became particularly apparent during the food crisis in 2002. Also, people living with HIV/AIDS have specific nutrition needs to ensure that they do not fall ill or succumb to certain infections. At the same time, supply will be negatively affected, because households affected by HIV/AIDS are likely to see their agricultural output reduced due to ill-health and death. Furthermore, AIDS-related illnesses and death among agriculture extension workers will reduce the availability and quality of agricultural services. In the end, there will be fewer extension workers, who will be faced with more demand for services and support. The reduced capacity of the Agricultural sector, combined with the increased demand for services, negatively affects the productivity and effectiveness of the sector. Ultimately, the United Nations Millennium Development Goals of halving the proportion of underweight under-five-year olds by 2015 will be thwarted.

Systemic Impact on the Health Sector

Another example comes from Health. Undoubtedly, HIV/AIDS is increasing demand on the sector for adequate health care. HIV/AIDS is associated with a significant increase in tuberculosis and other opportunistic infections. This leads to an increase in bed occupancy, up to the point that many hospitals are unable to cope with the increasing demand. At the same time, the quality of care required changes substantially, as there is an increasing complexity in the manifestation of AIDS-related illnesses. This growing demand in terms of both the quantity and quality of health care for AIDS-related illnesses is likely to negatively affect the provision of treatment for other diseases or injuries. Already, there is evidence of the crowding out of other conditions. As in other sectors, health staff will also be affected, leading to a loss of qualified nurses, doctors and other personnel. Again, the combined effect of increasing demand and reduced supply will reduce the effectiveness and productivity of the sector as a whole. Amongst others, these trends will undermine the prospect of reducing maternal mortality by three-quarters by the year 2015, as articulated in one of the MDGs.

Systemic Impact on the Education Sector

Similarly, HIV/AIDS affects both demand for and supply of Education (*see Table 1*). In this case, demand for education may actually decrease, as an increasing number of children and orphans can no longer afford to pay school fees or "lose" productive time by attending school. Yet, the educational needs of children, particularly of vulnerable children and orphans, are likely to change. They are likely to require more support and attention from teachers and may need special classes or flexible school hours. With a significant number of teachers and education officials infected with HIV, the quantity and quality of services provided will be negatively affected. Not only does this mean that the sector may not be able to deliver on its existing mandate, it also means that it is unlikely to be able to respond to the increasing demand. As a result, it is unlikely that the MDG of achieving universal primary education by the year 2007 will be realised. Moreover, it also raises questions about the human development of youth who have finished school, and about their future work prospects.

Over the years, it has become increasingly clear in Lesotho that notwithstanding the genuine concern at the highest level for the need to urgently address the pandemic across the entire society, beginning with the public sector, there has not been significant success in tackling the pandemic. In addition to the basic stage of nominal or passive response, there are four stages of proactive intervention, which are now recognised as crucial if a sector is to seriously core stream the fight against HIV/AIDS.

- *Stage Zero:* Here, all a ministry has done is to put condoms in toilets, along with a number of public information posters.
- *Stage One:* In this stage, the sector has an HIV/AIDS plan with the following key elements—sector workers' AIDS risk analysis, evidence-based communication for behaviour change, condom promotion, focal point person designated, and financial resources made available.

- *Stage Two*: Stage Two involves all of Stage One, with the addition of an AIDS sector impact analysis conducted, policies, strategies and action plans developed and activities to mitigate the impact of HIV/AIDS implemented.
- *Stage Three:* The third stage involves moving towards a deeper engagement in the implementation of a comprehensive strategy, including establishing an evaluation framework and actions to evaluate all new and existing activities in the context of their impact on the spread of the virus.
- *Stage Four*: A sector is deemed to have reached Stage Four when it has all of the elements of the first three stages, along with evidence of incorporating lessons learnt in sector policies, strategies and actions.

Table 1.	Impact of HIV/AIDS on Supply and Demand in Education	
	Impact of HIV and AIDS on Education	**HIV Competent Education System**
SUPPLY	• Increased absenteeism of civil servants within the Ministry of Education. • Increased absenteeism of teachers and lecturers. • Increased death of civil servants between 25-49 yrs. • Increased death of teachers and lecturers, 25-49 yrs. • Reduced productivity of staff members who are well. • Reduced coverage of teaching and related activities. • Increased teacher/student ratio. • Reduced quality of education.	• Treatment and care of teachers and civil servants to prolong life. • Interim recruitment of retired teachers. • Shortened teacher training. • New HIV Competence curriculum. • Review of labour intensive approaches to teaching. • Extensive use of technology to maximise teaching with reduced capacity. • Review of roles and responsibilities in the sector to reflect new realities. • Prioritise HIV prevention and wellness in the sector.
DEMAND	• Dramatic increase in Orphans and Vulnerable Children (OVC). • OVC likely to drop out depending on resources. • OVC require additional support from school for parental support, and basic needs. • OVC require additional skills to cope with new challenges, e.g. as heads of households. • Increased absenteeism of learners. • Loss of learners due to AIDS.	• OVC policy offering free education, food, clothing and books. • School and community parenting support to OVC. • Review of school system to ensure maximum support to OVC. • Change curriculum to ensure HIV competence. • Treatment and Care for learners. • Aggressive prevention campaigns in schools involving communities.

Note: "Supply" refers to the labour or human resource capacity of the education sector, both within the civil service and in schools, to deliver on its core mandate. "Demand" refers to the pattern and size of the core mandate or services of the education system.

Local Government as an Agent of Change

The strengthening of systems of local governance—once the local government elections have taken place and the functions of basic service delivery decentralised—will have a pivotal contribution to make in enhancing the effectiveness of the fight against HIV/AIDS. As the structure that represents government at the local level, it is the ideal vehicle to facilitate community mobilisation, district planning and the delivery of social services in communities. In addition, it will be responsible for financial management (including revenue generation and collection), the formulation of by-laws and local level legislation, as well as law enforcement.

It is for this reason that in establishing Local Government, due attention needs to be given to how HIV/AIDS changes the patterns in demand for local services and reduces household incomes, and thereby the ability of the people to pay for services and to contribute to local taxes. HIV/AIDS will also change the demographic profile of communities, with a disproportionate number of children, youth and the elderly. This means, amongst others, that the demand for services will change. The ability of Local Government to fulfill its responsibilities will be negatively affected by HIV/AIDS-related illness and death among officials and counsellors, resulting in an increasing proportion of citizens being the elderly, orphans and other vulnerable children. As a result, the capacity of Local Government institutions to facilitate local development and deliver community-level services may be significantly reduced. HIV/AIDS can also result in the ineffective representation of the community at the national level. All of these impacts will have to be monitored and appropriate corrective measures put in place to mitigate the situation.

Need for Transformational Change

Lesotho is a Mountain Kingdom completely surrounded by the Republic of South Africa. It was founded in the 19th Century by King Moshoeshoe I, who offered patronage to several warring groups and galvanised them into the Basotho Nation. During the many years of *apartheid* rule in South Africa, Basotho endured many socio-economic hardships as they fought to retain their nationhood. They experienced many forms of divide and rule—including from their colonial masters—resulting into a fractured and divided people. Many Basotho also lost their lives and also had limited access to further education and other productive opportunities, as a result of their support for the struggle against the inhumane system of apartheid. Since it gained independence on 4 October 1966, some 36 years ago, the country has experienced much political strife and civil unrest, that is, until the milestone elections held on May 25, 2002. That election, which was based on mixed member proportional representation, resulted in a dramatically more peaceful outcome and marked the dawn of a new era of democratic pluralism with ten political parties represented in the Sixth Parliament.

Since the protracted political negotiations leading from the hotly contested 1998 General Elections to the May 2002 world-class General Elections, Basotho politicians have managed to forge closer working relations based on democratic rules of engagement. Today, the Multi-Party Parliamentary System of governance is working relatively well and an inclusive system of Parliamentary Select Committees is slowly but surely under way. A number of workshops and seminars have been held to explore ways of ensuring a smooth transition from the confrontational, Westminster style to the more consensus-oriented Parliamentary System, which was the outcome of the Mixed Member Proportional (MMP) representation system of the General Elections. An important lesson from Lesotho's experience with the May 2002 General Elections and the relative calm that has so far prevailed in the country's Sixth Parliament is that it was only after the leaders of all the political parties and their followers were committed to a *win-win* approach to the elections that the MMP was finally agreed upon, ultimately paving the way for peaceful and lawful elections.

Stephen Covey, the author of *The Seven Habits of Highly Effective People,*[2] who has for years been running transformational leadership courses, defines win-win as a frame of mind and heart that constantly seeks mutual benefit in all human interactions. Win-win means that agreements or solutions are mutually beneficial and mutually satisfying. With a win-win solution, all parties feel good about the decision and feel committed to the action plan. Win-win sees life as a cooperative, not a competitive arena. Most people tend to think in terms of dichotomies: strong or weak, hardball or softball, win or lose. But that kind of thinking, argues Covey, is fundamentally flawed, because it is based on power and position rather than on principle. Win-win is based on the paradigm that there is plenty for everybody, that one person's success is not achieved at the expense or exclusion of the success of others. In essence, this was the political process that culminated in the MMP. This, in many respects, places the Members representing the 10 Parties in Lesotho's Sixth

Parliament (most, if not all, of whom were actively engaged in the political negotiations that followed the 1998 General Elections debacle) streets ahead of the transformation process in Lesotho. The outcome of this process has also put Lesotho and its people, way ahead of many countries in the world, in terms of the conduct of transparent, peaceful and lawful elections.

However, a similar transformation has not yet fully taken place in the civil service, which has to implement Government's overall development agenda, most significantly an accelerated HIV/AIDS programme. Over the years, many factors have contributed to inefficiencies in the civil service, resulting in low delivery over time and thus the creation of the "lack of capacity" myth. One of the problems may be that the issue of capacity is so often seen from the perspective of capacity building rather than capacity utilisation. Capacity building approaches organisational development from the perspective that something is wrong and solutions are to be found from outside. Development practitioners, both from within and outside the country, tend to take comfort in what they can provide rather than what is required. This often results in their providing what is tangible and quantifiable, because this suits conventional development paradigms.

Within government structures, civil servants have learned to ask for capacity building initiatives from their external partners because the paradigm demands this. The challenge (and indeed the opportunity for Lesotho, especially, as it accelerates programme delivery to combat the pandemic) is to understand the different and new environment within which one is operating world-wide and, by extension, within Lesotho. It is an environment of globalisation where one sees a considerable shift in thinking and in the way institutions work—shifts from financial to intellectual resources, from the elite to the masses, from boundaries to no boundaries, and from highly preserved knowledge to the speedy obsolescence of knowledge.

In a country with a literacy rate of over 80%, including a substantial literacy rate in the English language, one with a hunger for education going back to the 19th Century, where girls have received education to the same or greater extent than boys, one has to learn that institutions that focus on skills-training, especially in a country where there is a considerable reservoir of skills, completely miss the point about capacity utilisation. Instead, one needs to look at structures and institutions and the people within them. Often, the issue of capacity building is approached from the perspective of change, with approaches that do not bring change but are dressed up in the language of change. In the end, they contribute to strengthening the *status quo*. Transformational change, on the other hand, must start with clear political commitment at the top and be implemented with change champions in all institutions that lead the process.

In a resource-limited environment like Lesotho, one needs to seek new solutions through drawing on ideas that point to new ways to address problems and reduce the time between the generation of ideas and their implementation. It is clear that ideas can only be nurtured in an environment that focuses on the person and encourages new thinking and risk-taking; one that is open to change, including structural change. In essence, the focus must be on the person within the institution, changing the way he or she relates to the institution and changing his or her role in relation to clients (in this case, the Basotho themselves). It is also clear that the focus needs to be on the total person, with an emotional investment in relationships. One needs to move towards not managing people but helping people to better manage themselves. Within the public service and elsewhere in Lesotho, one has learnt that people are mobile assets that walk out the gate every evening and, with access to the market in South Africa, not infrequently go across the border. It is particularly important that efforts are made to keep this asset—human resources—motivated and at home to serve the goals of the nation.

Key to working with a people-centred approach is the development of competencies. Experience indicates that enhanced performance can be best achieved and maintained if one focuses not only on the knowledge and skills required for the job, but also on behaviour and attributes. The combination of knowledge, skill, behaviour and attributes determines whether or not one handles situations appropriately and professionally, as much in the workplace as at a personal level. Of greater importance, these determine whether one is able to move towards achieving goals and objectives laid out by the institution one belongs to, and whether one can bridge that delivery gap, which we all know exists within the public service and other sectors. A competency framework must, therefore, be at the centre of the management framework so that one can move from a focus on skills and gaining knowledge to building competencies and seeking to develop centres of excellence, beginning with the public service.

Transformational change is about centres of excellence. It is about building a situation where people are able to understand their role not just as health workers or teachers or accountants or engineers from the professional sense, but also from the point of view of their contribution to achieving broader, societal/organisational objectives by starting with themselves. Aiming for a centre of excellence is a decision that can only be made by the Basotho and their Government, driven by the clear knowledge that the capacity with which to achieve this is within the country. The centre of excellence is not about improving the skills and knowledge of personnel; rather, it is a commitment to the development of a new institutional culture of teamwork, sharing and learning, communication, relationship building, and a commitment to the core values of the new political dispensation of democratic pluralism, where people, generally, and civil servants, in particular, are judged not by their political affiliations but by their delivery of results, based on established goals and objectives as set out in respective strategic plans.

What are the implications of this? One key implication is the need to develop abilities, such as:

- The ability to find the right questions to enable the organisation to take the first step forward towards change;
- The ability to manage tensions that arise from ambiguity and uncertainty;
- The ability to observe and listen;
- The ability to use metaphor and imagination;
- The ability to reflect on one's own interventions;
- The ability to conceptualise and thus analyse; and
- The ability to overcome cynicism.

Of greatest importance is the ability to believe in oneself. If one thinks it can be done, it will be done. If one thinks the tasks at hand are impossible, they will be impossible, not least because that person will not take any steps to make sure they are actually done. With a lack of belief in oneself comes the growth of cynicism, one of the most corrosive influences on any institution and one that undermines the very structure and motivation of the people that make up the institution.

Implications for the Public Service

In order to bridge the delivery gaps that are so obvious from the manner in which the HIV/AIDS crisis has been addressed, there is need to take a good hard look at the way the public service is managed. Turning the HIV/AIDS crisis into an opportunity demands a total new look at the way the public service operates in this country.

We must start by debunking the liberal use of the term, *We Have No Capacity*, and adopting in its place, a *Can-Do* approach to dealing with problems. The PRSP and Vision 2020 represent key opportunities for the public service to determine how it will change the way it does business. These, combined with the commitment to fight HIV/AIDS, represent a commitment by Government to a new society. This can be implemented in an environment where there is commitment to transformation, and where there is commitment to developing accountability on a personal and institutional level. The required competencies for such transformational change can be learned. There are a number of courses developed on the basis of this need; institutions can be commissioned to work with counterparts in Lesotho, such as the National University of Lesotho (NUL) and the Lesotho Institute for Public Administration and Management, to develop a new kind of training for the public service. This would represent a very important first step.

In short, it is clear that there is an urgent need to improve public sector performance to adequately respond to the HIV/AIDS pandemic. Almost paradoxically, recognition of the impact of HIV/AIDS on the public service and the nation as a whole is a prerequisite for improved public sector performance. Thus, it needs to be recognised that HIV/AIDS leads to a loss of employees, skills and organisational memory in the public sector, which will result in poor delivery of services. These internal aspects of the impact of HIV/AIDS on the organisation also require the adoption of an HIV/AIDS Workplace Programme for the entire civil service that will protect the rights of employees infected and affected by HIV/AIDS. At the same time, the public sector requires new competencies to respond to the developmental challenges associated with HIV/AIDS. For example, it will have to approach issues like poverty, food security and HIV/AIDS in a holistic and integrated manner, rather than the fragmented approach that has characterised past development interventions. Such a new approach requires not only specific analytical competencies, but also technical competencies to operationalise such insights.

In developing interventions aimed at improving public sector performance, one needs to be mindful of past lessons from traditional public sector reform, in Lesotho and elsewhere. These have not been successful enough in creating the robust yet flexible and capable public sector institutions required to address the challenges of development. For one, there is a need to consider how existing capacity can be utilised most effectively, instead of focusing almost exclusively on capacity building. Secondly, there must be a commitment to institutional transformation, which includes a fundamental change in the way personnel relate to the public service, and to de-politicising the public service. Finally, there is also the need to shift to a demand-driven model of change through community empowerment, which is made even more acute by the changing scope and patterns of demand due to HIV/AIDS.

Strengthening Management and Oversight Mechanisms

It is clear that the fight against the HIV/AIDS pandemic is everyone's business. To avoid duplication and to ensure that the interventions of various stakeholders support and complement those of others, a coordinating mechanism is needed. For this reason, it is proposed that a National HIV/AIDS Commission be established, with LAPCA as its Secretariat.

Until now, LAPCA has played a vital role in the fight against HIV/AIDS and it will no doubt continue to do so. Yet, in and of itself, it is not a sufficiently appropriate structure to coordinate the collective efforts in bringing about an HIV/AIDS-Competent Society. When LAPCA was established, the national HIV prevalence rate was around 25%. Today, hardly four years later, the rate has jumped by at least another 5% and is still climbing. At the time, LAPCA was set up as a unit in the Prime Minister's Office, with the intention of establishing a National AIDS Commission, with LAPCA as its Secretariat. Somewhere along the line, this decision seems to have fallen in-between the cracks. However, the level of coordination required now demands both political clout and an institutional mandate that far outstrips LAPCA's current mandate and scope. In the past, there has also been a tendency to shift programmatic responsibilities for HIV/AIDS to LAPCA, which has not only exceeded LAPCA's capacity, but has also inadvertently led to the marginalisation of HIV/AIDS in the work of other sectors and duty bearers. Hence the need to strengthen LAPCA, including the establishment of a National AIDS Commission with wide representation from key stakeholders in society.

Given the appropriate levels of authority, capacity and resources, the proposed National HIV/AIDS Commission will be an essential asset to propel the national response into an acceleration mode. Without this, it will take this country many years to make a dent on the impact of the pandemic. This is time that the country can ill afford since, as stated earlier in this manual, most of those already infected will have died within the next five to ten years, unless radical action is taken. Once in place, the National AIDS Commission would have to urgently prioritise its pressing commitments by revising the National AIDS Strategic Plan to include a comprehensive Social Mobilisation Strategy for an HIV/AIDS-Competent Society as an integral part, and drawing up an Annual Business Plan for implementing the National AIDS Strategic Plan.

In administrative terms, it may not be necessary for the Commission to have district or local-level offices. This is simply because, as alluded to above and in far more detail later, the operational responsibility to strive for (and attain) an HIV/AIDS-competent society rests primarily with the different duty bearers under their regular mechanisms for development planning and implementation at all levels (*see Figure 1*). At the national level, there will be the Commission, Parliament and its Select Committees, Cabinet Committee, Committee of Principal Secretaries, the Business Coalition and International Partners, all of whom have their own existing channels for planning and implementation, as well as oversight from national to district and community levels.

Similarly, the Business Sector and different organs of civil society have well-defined structures for accountability, which should be followed and/or strengthened, as the case may be, in the process of core streaming HIV/AIDS into all national endeavours. It is very important not to create separate mechanisms for implementing the National AIDS Strategic Plan, because to do so would be contrary to the principles of core streaming and would, without a doubt, result in the inadvertent marginalisation of HIV/AIDS from the overall national development agenda. As long as the "systems thinking" principles of core streaming are understood and observed, all that the AIDS Commission would have to do is to keep its finger on the pulse of what is happening (or not happening) with regard to the National AIDS Strategic Plan, what corrective action should be taken and by whom.

As a semi-autonomous body, the Commission would have unfettered access to the highest level of Government, Civil Society and the Business Sector in its quest for ensuring that every duty bearer pulls its weight behind the National AIDS Strategic Plan. The National AIDS Commission would also do its work best if, as was done with the crafting of the mandate and structure of the Independent Electoral Commission, it would have similar structure and freedom to liaise directly with donors and other international partners for the purposes of advocacy and resource mobilisation. Suffice it to say here that it would be necessary for a small team of people to be tasked with the responsibility to define in more detail the structure of the proposed Commission as well as how to transform LAPCA into the Commission's Secretariat.

Relationships Between Different Structures For HIV/AIDS Programme Acceleration

National AIDS Commission, Cabinet Committee, Parliament & Senate Committee, Committee of PS's, Business Coalition, International Partners

HIV/AIDS at the core of development planning and sector mandates

Structures interface with national levels

Village development committee

Orphan & care

organs

Behaviour change

National Volunteer Service

Churches, volunteers & traditional organizations

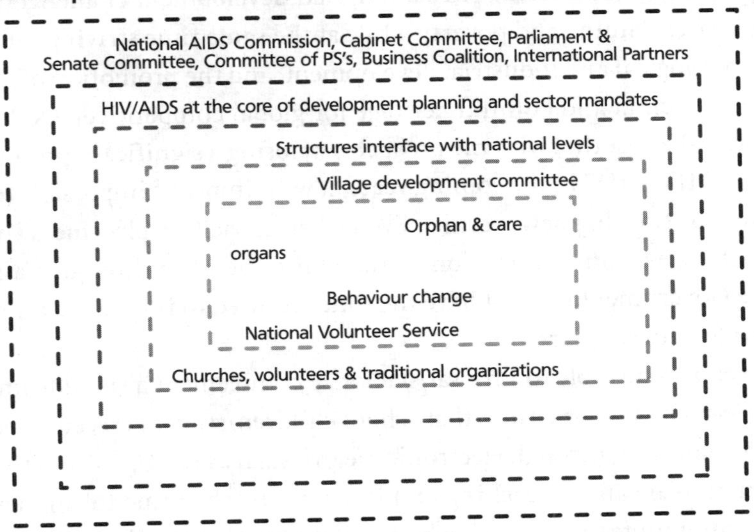

Figure 1. Diagrammatic Representation Of Relationships Between Different Structures For HIV/AIDS Programme Acceleration At National, District, Community And Household Levels.

Information and Communications Technologies as Dynamic Tools for Lesotho's Accelerated Development

It is now a well-known fact that the information revolution has not only changed the world, as we know it, but also its future potential. Information and Communications Technologies (ICTs), with their major technological leaps, have affected the lives and lifestyles of people across the globe, as well as the way in which institutions and organisations do business. In their wake, jobs have been created, businesses expanded, and life for many people has improved. However, not all outcomes of the spread of information technologies have been positive. A majority of the world's population, especially those who live in poverty, have been largely bypassed by this revolution. Least developed nations, especially their rural societies, and in particular, in Africa, are in danger of falling further behind in this Information Age. The gap between them and the rest of the world has expanded precisely as a result of the facilitating capacity of these technologies for those who have access to them.

And yet, ICTs offer a remarkable opportunity and set of tools for achieving substantive progress in addressing Africa's myriad development challenges, including fighting diseases, famine and poverty while at the same time striving for socio-economic, technological and industrial development, and the promotion of Africa's vast material, intellectual and cultural heritage for global competitiveness. In addition, for a country like Lesotho, with the prospects of losing a significant proportion of its workforce to HIV/AIDS in the coming years, it will simply be impossible to expect to replace them by training new recruits. Even when capacity replacement (of teachers, nurses, doctors, and other extension workers) is to be done through training more people, the Government will not have the time required to train a doctor or teacher/lecturer for four to six years.

However, it is possible to very satisfactorily complement a small team of nurses through tele-medicine, or ensure that school children/students receive good quality standard of education through electronic means, such as radio, TV and the Internet, as an alternative means of teaching and learning. By the same token, new recruits for the teaching profession can also be trained largely through distance education while they work to help supervise students as they learn electronically. This can be supplementary, or coupled with face-to-face teacher training courses during school holidays. As the UN Secretary-General, Mr. Kofi Annan, said in his address at the Opening of the Third Meeting of the United Nations Information and Communications Technologies Task Force: ".... *There is a vast potential for investment growth in the developing countries. Information and communication technologies (ICT) can help us turn this potential into concrete opportunities that will help the poor work their way out of poverty while, at the same time, benefiting the world community as a whole.*"[3]

In short, Lesotho can turn this HIV/AIDS crisis into an opportunity for development and prosperity. However, this will only be possible if it is fully recognised that 'business as usual' is no longer an option for this country, with its high infection rates, which are still rising. What is required are extraordinary measures at all levels, from the Government right down to ordinary people, communities and organisations, and including the country's external donors and other partners. The external donors and development partners are fully committed to this major task, and stand ready, with their sleeves rolled up, to get to work. As the Prime Minister says in his Foreword, it can be done. All that is needed is for each and every one of us to play his or her part!

NOTES *for Chapter 2*

1. Joseph O'Connor and Ian McDermott, *The Art of Systems Thinking.* New York: Thorsons Publisers, 1997.
2. Stephen R. Covey, *The Seven Habits of Highly Effective People: Powerful Lessons in Personal Change.* New York: Free Press, 1989.
3. UN Secretary-General, Mr. Kofi Annan's address at the Opening of the Third Meeting of the United Nations Information and Communications Technologies Task Force, September 30, 2002, New York.

Understanding the Linkages between HIV/AIDS and Development

Our understanding of HIV/AIDS continues to develop and deepen as the epidemic endures. Because this understanding informs our actions and the types of interventions we think are appropriate to prevent the further spread of HIV and deal with the impacts of HIV/AIDS, it is important to continuously reflect on this. This chapter outlines the progression in global thinking on HIV/AIDS over the past two decades. The following stages of the progression of HIV/AIDS have been fairly well established:

- Discovery of the Human Immuno-deficiency Virus (HIV), resulting in biomedical interventions;
- Concern with individual behaviour as a core factor in the spread of HIV/AIDS, leading to an emphasis on behavioural interventions and the promotion of the use of condoms;
- Attention to treatment and care in response to HIV/AIDS-related illnesses;
- Focus on a limited set of impact mitigation measures to cope with the immediate consequences of AIDS-related adult mortality (that is, orphan care);

- Recognition of the need for a much wider set of impact mitigation measures to respond to local level and future impacts;
- Appreciation of determinants in the broader socio-economic and political environment that constitute a context of risk, vulnerability and reduced capabilities; and
- Realisation that HIV/AIDS holds the potential of reproducing and reinforcing the determinants of risk, vulnerability and reduced capability, thereby perpetuating a vicious cycle.

Although recognition of the need for a trans-sectoral response to HIV/AIDS is becoming increasingly accepted wisdom, national responses to the pandemic still tend to slip back into programmatic interventions that are largely biomedical, health sector and behavioural (and thus psycho-social) in nature, with minimal impact mitigation. The challenge facing countries like Lesotho is, firstly, to shift and deepen the conceptual understanding underpinning the national response to a more comprehensive understanding and, secondly, to reflect this conceptual shift in HIV/AIDS-related programmes and interventions.

Discovery of a New Virus

When the Human Immuno-deficiency Virus (HIV) was first discovered, it was perceived as a disease and thus a public health problem. The initial response was, therefore, concerned with the virus, how it was transmitted and how it progressed in the human body to become full-blown Acquired Immuno Deficiency Syndrome (AIDS). As a consequence, the main concern was with developing biomedical interventions that could halt the spread of the virus as well as hopefully provide a cure for those already infected (*see Figure 2*). Although the limitations of the biomedical framework to understand and respond to the HIV/AIDS epidemic are becoming obvious, biomedical interventions remain an important element in the response to HIV/AIDS, such as the importance of blood safety, the treatment of opportunistic and other related infectious diseases, the appropriate treatment of sexually transmitted infections (STIs) and the anti-retroviral treatment for people infected with the virus, particularly during pregnancy and childbirth to prevent Mother-To-Child Transmission (MTCT).[1] The continuing global search for a cure or at least a vaccine also falls within the realm of biomedical interventions.

Figure 2. Biomedical Framework of HIV/AIDS

Shifting the Focus to the Immediate Causes of HIV Infection

Over time, as the limitations of a biomedical response to the HIV/AIDS pandemic became increasingly clear, the international response to HIV/AIDS expanded to include a focus on individual behaviour as a core risk factor for becoming infected with HIV (*see Figure 3*). The majority of HIV/AIDS programmes and interventions today seek to somehow address this, typically by emphasising responsible behaviour and/or informed choice. In sub-Saharan Africa, this usually centres on sexual behaviour related to the number of concurrent sexual partners, sexual mixing patterns, sexual practices and unprotected sex. A secondary focus is on breastfeeding as a means of transmitting the virus from mother to infant.[2] As a result of the conceptual shift, the nature of HIV/AIDS interventions has expanded to include interventions aimed at changing individual behaviour through communication and awareness-raising activities, promotion and marketing of the use of condoms, voluntary counselling and testing (VCT) and the promotion of breast milk substitutes.

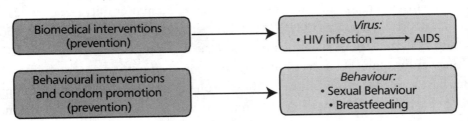

Figure 3. Shifting the Focus to Individual Behaviour

Expanding the Response to Address Treatment and Care

As the HIV/AIDS epidemic progressed, the first noticeable impact was the increasing demand for appropriate treatment and care for those suffering from opportunistic diseases and other AIDS-related illnesses. This reality necessitated a shift from the paradigm, which suggested that in the absence of a cure, prevention was the only appropriate response and that those infected were essentially on a rapid pathway to inevitable death. Thus, a health response became an increasingly important element of efforts to cope with the immediate impacts of the epidemic (*see Figure 4*).

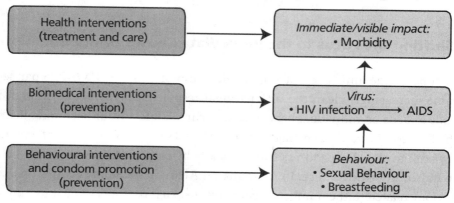

Figure 4. Expanding the Response to Include Treatment and Care

Incorporating Impact Mitigation Measures

A second visible impact of the HIV/AIDS epidemic was the increasing level of mortality, especially adult mortality and, to a lesser extent, infant mortality (*see Figure 5*). As a result, national responses to HIV/AIDS further expanded to include interventions seeking to address the devastating impacts of the disproportionate number of deaths among young adults between 15-49 years old. More often than not, such interventions have tended to focus on the plight of orphans and the need to provide appropriate care and support for these children, possibly because this is one of the most visible and tragic impacts of increased adult mortality. In addition to the concern with orphans, some attention has also been given to income-generating projects for affected households.

Figure 5 represents what currently tends to constitute the mainstay of national responses to HIV/AIDS. However, HIV/AIDS-related morbidity and mortality have far-reaching, devastating impacts beyond the health sector, beyond the need for appropriate treatment and care for people living with HIV/AIDS and beyond the need for targeted support for orphans. There is another layer of impacts, which currently remains largely hidden from the perspective of governments. These impacts are hidden, either because they make themselves felt at a localised level (individual, household or community), or because they only manifest themselves much later in the progression of the disease.

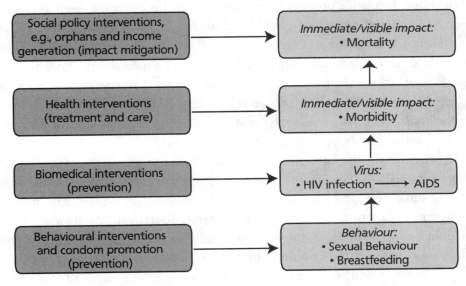

Figure 5. Incorporating Immediate Impact Mitigation Measures

Expanding Impact Mitigation to the Local Level and Other Impacts

Figure 6 summarises the key impacts at the local level and in the medium to longer-term. The list is by no means exhaustive. The fact of the matter is that we still do not fully comprehend what the long-term implications of HIV/AIDS may be. Nor, it should be stressed, are all these impacts unavoidable. With the right mindset, and through appropriate interventions, some of these impacts can be prevented, or at least mitigated.

Impacts on Household and Community Levels

Individuals and households affected by HIV/AIDS tend to experience deeper impoverishment, in large part due to the loss of labour and thus loss of income caused by the inherent bouts of ill health and the ultimate death of a productive member (or of members) of the household. In poor households, income and assets tend to be diverted towards medical care for those infected with HIV/AIDS, particularly if they are considered valuable productive members of the household, as well as towards funerals. As a result, fewer and fewer household resources are available for food and other essentials, including education-related costs (such as school fees, uniforms and books), leading to a decline in nutritional status and an increase in school drop-out rates, especially by girls. Indications from the current food crisis across Southern Africa suggest that HIV/AIDS leads to an erosion of common coping mechanisms of poor households, which seriously undermines their capacity to deal with (and recover from) any additional shocks and emergencies.

In other words, the rapid increase in the number of people infected with, and dying from, HIV/AIDS is having a correspondingly negative impact on the social and economic development of affected households, communities and nations. Furthermore, due to the absence of appropriate social safety nets and afford-able public support systems, the burden of care for the sick and dying and their dependants usually falls on women, children, the elderly and whatever community social support networks that may exist. Children may be compelled to drop out from school to contribute to household income and/or look after a sick parent or siblings—with serious implications for future development prospects of these children.

The greatest impact of HIV/AIDS on households is usually as a result of the death of both parents, when the responsibility for caring for and raising children falls on the young shoulders of older siblings. This situation of children rearing children is bound to have profound and unimaginable negative effects on the fabric of society. Governments and communities have to continue to find ways to deal with the plight of orphans and other vulnerable children (including protection from rejection, stigma and discrimination), not only because children have a right to care, love and support, but also in the interest of the promotion of a semblance of normality in affected communities.

Impact on Demographic and Societal Structure

In Lesotho, as in many SADC countries, HIV/AIDS, made worse by the current food crisis as well as chronic poverty, is rapidly changing the demographic profile of the worst affected countries, resulting in more dependants (children and the elderly) altering the gender ratio, whereby men will increasingly outnumber women. At the same time, the loss of productive adults and parents means, amongst others, the loss of support networks for children and the elderly, loss of role models, loss of the labour supply, with a corresponding adverse impact on economic development as well as social reproduction. In other words, HIV/AIDS is now accelerating the reversal of the major socio-economic gains made in the recent past, such as in health, education, agriculture, and trade and industry, to name but a few.

Whilst the demand for a variety of public services will increase, public sector capacity will be eroded from within, as public sector employees themselves are infected and affected by HIV/AIDS. Increased absenteeism and levels of attrition result in reduced performance and productivity. This, in turn, will negatively impact on the quantity and quality of services across all sectors. As governmental and societal systems are eroded and pushed to the breaking point, the prospect

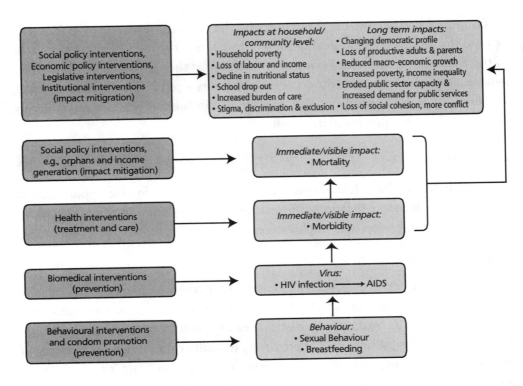

Figure 6. Widening the Response to Address Hidden Impacts

of social strife and conflict is likely to increase, jeopardising good governance and social cohesion.

As mentioned earlier, it is both necessary and possible to prevent some of the key impacts at household and community levels as well as to lessen the socio-economic and political burdens associated with these impacts. Effective impact mitigation requires a broad range of interventions in the domains of social and economic policy and legislative and other institutional arrangements, in addition to efforts to promote prevention, treatment and care. Likewise, comprehensive impact mitigation measures targeting households and communities can lessen the devastating, long-term impacts on society.

Understanding the Underlying and Structural Context of HIV/AIDS

So far, a case has been made for expanding the national response to HIV/AIDS beyond the biomedical and health domain to address the developmental impacts of the epidemic. It is, therefore, important to look at the context in which we live, behave, act and engage with others, as this presents a possible context of risk and vulnerability to HIV infection. This context also influences people's capability to cope with the consequences of infection.

Underlying Factors

Underlying factors include access to basic services and productive opportunities, including health care, education, information and knowledge, housing, water and sanitation, social services and employment.

Access to Health Services

Lack of adequate health care, such as treatment for common diseases and sexually transmitted infections, enhances the risk of contracting HIV. At the same time, lack of essential drugs to treat opportunistic diseases, insufficient number of hospital beds and medical personnel, lack of proximity to health care services and the cost of medical care, all conspire to make appropriate treatment and care for people living with HIV/AIDS inaccessible.

Access to Information and Knowledge

Where basic education, knowledge and information are not easily and equitably accessible, those without access will not be able to act on vital information that could protect their health and lives. This is not to say that information and knowledge in and of themselves are sufficient to enable people (both men and women) to make correct decisions concerning their behaviour and the behaviour of others, particularly in sexual matters. Power relations, especially between men and women, are also significant.

Power Relations and Gender-based Violence

Even when they have the necessary information and knowledge, women, and especially young girls, often lack the power to determine when and with whom to have sex, let alone to insist that their sexual partner use a condom. Rape, sexual abuse and violence against children and women are the most aggressive expressions of male power and the powerlessness of women and children. In other instances, women and girls engage in sexual encounters in exchange for money, food, protection or other favours (even relative trivia, such as lipstick and other cosmetics), significantly increasing their risk to HIV infection.

Access to Housing and Other Basic Services

Lack of adequate housing, basic services and infrastructure may also facilitate the spread of HIV/AIDS. For example, overcrowding can engender frustration and anger, which may be expressed through (sexual) violence directed at women and children. Also, inadequate housing does not offer the protection and security required against outside intruders, leaving women and children vulnerable to rape and abuse. For young girls, the availability of protected boarding houses in close proximity to school does not only reduce the risk of rape, but can also influence decisions they make regarding sex in exchange of income for housing or a boarding room. Similarly, women seeking employment in urban centres are often faced with choices that may place them at higher risk of HIV infection when seeking cheap accommodation. At the same time, overcrowded and inadequate housing and the lack of basic services and infrastructure significantly hamper the ability of individuals and households to cope with the consequences of HIV infection, such as illness, stigma and rejection, and death.

Sustainable Livelihoods, Food Security and Employment

Unemployment, lack of income-generating opportunities and food insecurity may force women and children to engage in unprotected sex to support themselves and their families. At the same time, lack of food security and low nutritional status have a debilitating effect on the immune system's ability to cope with infections, making people living with HIV/AIDS more vulnerable to opportunistic diseases and accelerating death. Lack of household income and assets also make it more difficult to pay for appropriate treatment and care, the dietary requirements of those infected with HIV and, ultimately, funeral costs.

Social Networks

The relative importance of these underlying factors also depends on the extent to which people and households can draw on social networks at the household and community level to provide support and care, and to help mitigate the impacts of HIV/AIDS.

Migration, Mobility, Displacement and Urbanisation

The rapid spread and prevalence of HIV/AIDS in southern Africa have puzzled many people. Nine out of the 10 most seriously affected countries are SADC members, including Lesotho. International experience shows that over time, it has become increasingly clear that migration, mobility, displacement and urbanisation are very important factors facilitating the spread of HIV. For example, labour migrants like miners tend to show disproportionately higher rates of HIV infection than the rest of the population. The epidemic also tends to follow major transportation routes within and across countries. Major urban centres also show a higher HIV infection rate compared to smaller towns and rural areas, unless where these are connected to transportation routes or major construction of development projects such as roads, mines and dams, to name a few.

In addition, people displaced by conflict, war, natural disasters (such as migrants and refugees) or any range of major development projects resulting in the creation of internally displaced people, are often plunged into poverty, powerlessness and social instability, all of which contribute to the spread of the virus. It is, therefore, important to recognise the vulnerability of these population groups to HIV infection, which largely stems from *conditions* beyond their control. In the case of migrants, for example, a main contributing factor to their vulnerability to HIV infection is the lack of provision, by policy makers and planners, of adequate housing and other community amenities for migrant workers to be accompanied by their partners and families. Single-sex hostels at mines, army and police barracks, as well as at major construction sites, are a classic example.

The practice, by many Governments, of posting employees, like teachers and health workers, to remote areas without making adequate provision for their families to join them also increases the likelihood of multiple sexual partners, thereby facilitating the spread of the pandemic. Also vulnerable to unprotected sex with multiple partners (and thus to higher risk of HIV infection) are communities living around army and police barracks, as well as industrial construction sites. Furthermore, the fast rate of urbanisation in most African countries, combined with a lack of government capacity and resources to meet emergent demands, is a major cause leading to a serious backlog in basic service provisions. This places an inordinate burden on individuals, households and communities to cope with HIV/AIDS and its devastating consequences.

As *Figure 7* indicates, addressing the underlying factors that contribute to an environment of risk and vulnerability requires a wide range of interventions by all sectoral ministries, in the spheres of social and economic policy, employment creation, provision of social safety nets, legislation and other protection measures.

Structural Factors

The root causes of systemic development factors underpinning the socio-economic vulnerabilities outlined above can be positively or negatively impacted upon by a country's social and economic policies regarding how the national resource base is exploited, utilised and distributed. These are, in turn, influenced by the cultural, political, religious and legal policies and systems.

Macroeconomic Policy

Macroeconomic policy exerts a significant influence on the extent to which public services are made available and affordable to various population groups. Most African governments have adopted macroeconomic frameworks that significantly

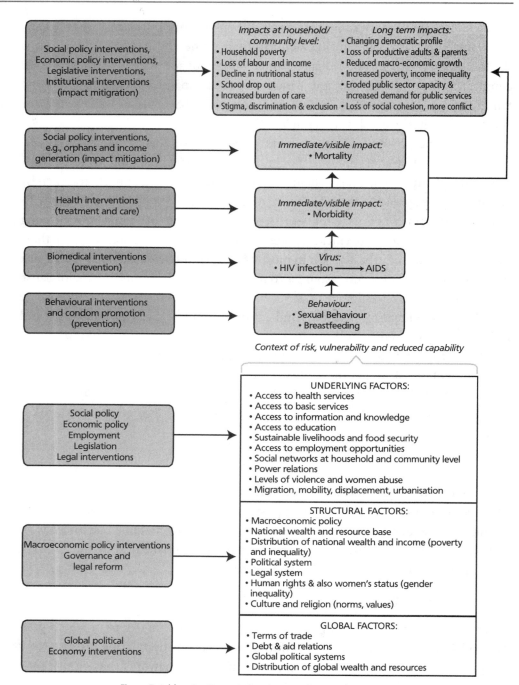

Figure 7. Addressing Systemic Development Factors That Constitute
A Context of Risk, Vulnerability and Reduced Capability to HIV/AIDS

reduce the level of public resources made available to provide services such as health, education, housing, water and sanitation, on the false assumption that all users can afford to pay for them, largely through the private sector, which is presumed to be more efficient. However, available evidence from several of these countries reveals that charging user fees for basic health and education services has led to the exclusion of the poor majority.

National Resource Base and Wealth Distribution

National wealth and the resource base of countries and states—as well as their social and economic policies—are important factors in influencing the levels of resource availability for investment in public services and infrastructure. In addition to the impact of globalisation (discussed below), in sub-Saharan Africa (where the highest rates of HIV/AIDS infection worldwide are found), poor social and economic policies as well as poor fiscal management and corruption are important contributing factors to the poverty of states and their people. Furthermore, the Gross Domestic Product (GDP) of countries with high HIV/AIDS infection rates is being significantly reduced, leaving most if not all of them, especially Lesotho with its people, to face difficult budgetary constraints and choices as their diminishing resources have to be fundamentally re-focused to address the HIV/AIDS pandemic.

Human Rights

The provision and protection of the rights of all of a country's people is a fundamental pre-requisite, as stipulated in various international conventions and UN declarations. In addition, special protection measures for the most vulnerable, especially those infected and affected by HIV/AIDS, can be a matter of life and death. In other words, safeguarding these rights can greatly contribute to the reduction of the many risk factors that lead to infection, as well as help those who are already infected to cope more easily with the various impacts of the pandemic. It was for this reason that Heads of State and Government attending the June 2001 UN General Assembly Special Summit on HIV/AIDS resolved that by the year 2003, they would enact, strengthen or enforce, as appropriate, legislation, regulations and other measures to eliminate all forms of discrimination against, and to ensure the full enjoyment of all human rights and fundamental freedoms by, people living with HIV/AIDS and members of vulnerable groups.[3]

Importance of Politics and Democracy

Lesotho's landmark General Elections in May 2002 ushered in a new dawn for democratic change. It is very important to nurture this democratic transition because it is now a well-known fact that developing and structuring a democratic system is, indeed, an essential component of the development process. As argued by Nobel Prize Laureate, Amartya Sen in his book *Development as Freedom* (1999), the significance of democracy lies in three distinct values: (a) its intrinsic importance, (b) its instrumental contributions, and (c) its constructive role in the creation of values and norms. No evaluation of the democratic form of governance can be complete without considering each, he continues. It can, therefore, be argued that no effort should be spared in helping the country to build democratic institutions—beyond mechanical devices for development—but rather it should be based on the evolution of new values, priorities like HIV/AIDS, as well as using every available opportunity to promote participation. It is a well-known fact that public debate and dialogue—including the identification of needs as well as solutions to societal challenges like the HIV/AIDS pandemic—permitted by political freedoms and civil rights, can play a major part in the formation of a country's democratic values. Not only is the force of public discussion one of the correlates of democracy, with extensive reach, but its cultivation can also make democracy itself function better.[4]

Culture and Religion

Culture and Religion form the basis on which social and ethical norms, values and practices are founded. These, in turn, regulate how people interact with each other, what type of behaviour is condoned and encouraged for men, women and children of different ages, who is entrusted with power and authority, and more. In many societies across the world, these tend to be a lesser social stigma for men who have sexual liaisons prior to and during marriage. However, such behaviour is frowned upon when practised by women, and is looked upon as prostitution. Similarly, social relations are based on power relations and, more often than not, with some significant exceptions in matrilineal societies, power is vested in men. As such, cultural norms and practices can serve to facilitate the spread of HIV. Furthermore, culture and religion do greatly influence the coping capabilities of people infected and affected by HIV/AIDS, either by entrenching the stigma and rejection associated with HIV/AIDS, or by promoting a culture of care and support. In order for a country to successfully address the HIV/AIDS challenge, therefore, it is of crucial importance for all institutions of religion and culture to engage in this struggle as key stakeholders, in partnership with government, business, people living with HIV/AIDS and civil society in general, if lasting success is to be achieved. In the case of Lesotho, the Church and Traditional Leaders are the two most powerful institutions of culture and religion. They possess far-reaching networks that can and must be effectively put to good use in this life-and-death fight against the scourge of HIV/AIDS.

Global Factors

Another set of development factors relates to the global political economy. Factors such as terms of trade, external debt and aid relations, the distribution of global wealth and resources, and global political systems are important in this regard. As the *2002 UNAIDS Report on the Global HIV/AIDS Epidemic* observes:

> Despite the widely recognised benefits of globalisation, more than a billion of the world's 6 billion people still cannot fulfill their basic needs for food, water, sanitation, health care, housing and education. Worldwide, an estimated 1.1 billion people are malnourished. An estimated 1.2 billion people live on less than US$1 a day. In more than 30 of the poorest national economies (most of them in sub-Saharan Africa), real per capita incomes have been declining since the early 1980s. At the same time, pressure on States to provide basic services and infrastructure has not eased. The HIV/AIDS epidemic, along with other diseases, conflicts and droughts, is worsening matters further ...
>
> But the global response to AIDS shows that the negative effects of globalisation need not be *'Facts of life'*. Greater access to high-income countries' markets, debt relief and more development aid will go a long way towards enabling countries to reduce poverty. High-income countries spent more than US$300 billion in 2001 on agricultural subsidies—roughly equivalent to the combined gross domestic product of all of sub-Saharan Africa. It is clear that AIDS represents a long and devastating tale of exclusion for millions of people, with or without HIV infection.[5]

Recognising the Vicious Cycle of HIV/AIDS

There are numerous ways in which HIV/AIDS holds the potential to aggravate and fundamentally alter the determinants of the epidemic, as indicated in *Figure 8*. As highlighted earlier, HIV/AIDS aggravates poverty by pushing more people into poverty and deepening the impoverishment of poor households through loss of household income, as well as increasing medical spending and funeral costs. Likewise, inequality is likely to become further entrenched, for example, where poor households are compelled to sell off assets, such as land and livestock, which are bought by wealthier and unaffected households. Because HIV/AIDS undermines national productivity, the prospect of increasing or maintaining national economic growth rates is also under threat, thereby eroding the national resource base of a country.

HIV/AIDS also has the potential to variously aggravate existing social fault lines and inequalities, including inequalities between men and women. Due to the increased burden of care on women and girls to look after people suffering from AIDS-related illnesses, gender inequality is likely to be further entrenched. Combined with the higher levels of vulnerability of women to become infected with HIV and the tendency to regard women as a potential 'risk group' responsible for the spread of the epidemic, results in a situation in which the cycle of vulnerability, risk and reduced capability disproportionately affects women (*see Box: Gender and HIV/ AIDS: Towards an Integrated Response*).

Furthermore, HIV/AIDS-related stigma and discrimination also undermine the prospect of entrenching a human rights culture. In the absence of an environment in which human rights are respected, vulnerability and risk to HIV infection is enhanced and capabilities to cope with the consequences of infection are undermined. This serves to perpetuate the cycle of risk, vulnerability and reduced capability.

Similarly, HIV/AIDS is likely to aggravate some of the underlying factors that contribute to an environment of risk, vulnerability and reduced capability to cope with the consequences of the pandemic. Through increased levels and depth of poverty and inequality, access to basic services like health, education, housing, water and sanitation, is likely to become even more inequitable. Access to employment and other income-generating opportunities will also be jeopardised, particularly for those households affected by HIV/AIDS.

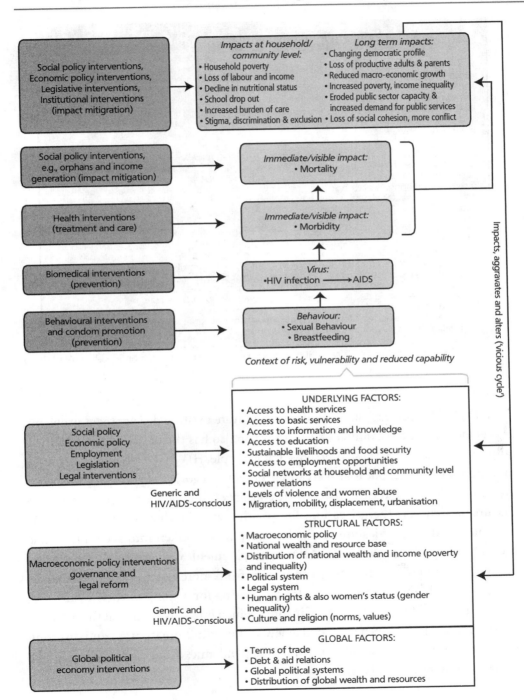

Figure 8. Recognising the Vicious Cycle of HIV/AIDS

Gender and HIV/AIDS: Towards an Integrated Response

In a recent publication, the UNDP Regional Project on HIV and Development in sub-Saharan Africa emphasises the importance of using 'gender spectacles' to better understand the nature and manifestation of the HIV/AIDS epidemic and to ensure that prevention efforts do not, unwittingly, serve to entrench gender inequality. The publication notes that unless gender inequality is addressed as an integral component of poverty reduction, poverty reduction strategies are likely to reinforce the disempowerment of women, with the potential of fuelling the HIV/AIDS epidemic.

An effective response to HIV/AIDS will address the gender imbalances that drive and characterise the HIV/AIDS epidemic. This requires an array of social, economic and political interventions to entrench the rights of women and to ensure that women have equal access to resources and opportunities in society. It also means addressing those cultural values, beliefs and practices that facilitate the spread of HIV and that place undue responsibility for care of people living with HIV/AIDS on women.

Clearly, HIV/AIDS affects both men and women, therefore both women and men need to be part of the solution. Women are not just helpless victims of the epidemic, nor are men simply the aggressors. Both are valuable resources in the fight against HIV/AIDS and need to be empowered to protect themselves (and their loved ones) against HIV infection. Women need information, skills, access to services and technologies, access to economic resources and a voice in decision-making processes. Men need to become partners in HIV prevention, which means that they should be encouraged to adopt healthier sexual behaviour and to respect the rights of women, particularly to prevent gender-based violence. One good example of this is a programme called 'Stepping Stones', which uses peer groups to help people translate information about prevention into behaviour change.

Sources: Commonwealth Secretariat (2002); UNDP Regional Project on HIV and Development in Sub-Saharan Africa (2002).

HIV/AIDS does not only magnify or aggravate existing development problems, as is evident from the examples given above, it also has the potential to fundamentally alter the nature of these problems. For example, HIV/AIDS does not only result in more poor people, but it also creates different categories of poor people, such as orphans, widows and the elderly, who are consequently experiencing poverty in ways that are particular to their situation. The peculiar ways in which HIV/AIDS can render household economies unsustainable must also be taken into account, such as access by people living with HIV/AIDS to employment opportunities. Efforts must be stepped up to ensure that they can benefit from more flexible working arrangements that will enable them to continue working for as long as their health will permit. This will provide security of income, which is largely lacking at the moment. Furthermore, HIV/AIDS has created a new social evil: stigmatisation and discrimination of people infected and affected by the pandemic. More vigilance is required in fighting these social ills.

Mention has already been made of the corroding effect of HIV/AIDS on the financial and human resource base and capabilities of affected governments, as a significant number of public sector employees are infected with, and affected by, HIV/AIDS. Examples include the need to cope with significant financial expenditure due to HIV/AIDS-related illness, absenteeism, low productivity, and death of employees, as well as the erosion of government's resources as a result of affected households failing to pay for services. This, in turn, fuels the dynamics of the vicious cycle, by denying the public sector the capacity to deliver on its core mandate—to address systemic development factors that perpetuate an environment of risk, vulnerability and reduced capability in the context of HIV/AIDS.

From a Vicious to a Virtuous Cycle

Figure 9 illustrates the vicious cycle of HIV/AIDS. It shows how HIV infection leads to ill-health and death, which in turn lead to a range of social, economic, political and institutional impacts at household, community and society levels. It also shows how determinants in the environment influence vulnerability to HIV infection and the capability to cope with infection and HIV/AIDS-related illnesses. Moreover, it shows how these environmental factors determine susceptibility to the impacts of HIV/AIDS and the capability to cope with the immediate and future consequences of the epidemic.

The challenge—and thus the opportunity—is how to break the vicious cycle of HIV/AIDS and to ensure that the epidemic does not reproduce and entrench similar determinants of risk, vulnerability and reduced capability. This can only be realised if the complexity of HIV/AIDS, as presented in schematic form in *Figure 8,* is recognised and if multi-faceted interventions that go beyond the current mainstay of HIV/AIDS responses (prevention, treatment and care, and impact mitigation measures) are formulated.

Figure 10 translates the vicious cycle depicted in *Figure 9* into four domains of action—prevention, treatment and care, impact mitigation and systemic development factors—which are generally recognised as key components of the enhanced response to HIV/AIDS. In the centre, we find the broad area of intervention concerned with addressing systemic development factors. In other words, these are the various underlying, structural and global factors discussed earlier that collectively enhance the vulnerability of certain groups of people to HIV infection and that

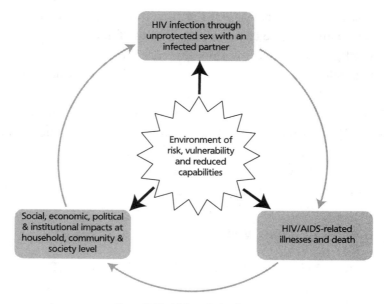

Figure 9. The Vicious Cycle of HIV/AIDS

undermine the capability of certain groups, communities, organisations and sectors to deal with the immediate and long-term consequences of HIV/AIDS. This domain of addressing systemic development factors is essentially concerned with the range of interventions in the sphere of policy, planning, legislation and institutional arrangements that bring about an enabling environment for development. To an extent, this domain of action refers to the variety of interventions that governments already embark upon to address development concerns, such as poverty, gender inequality, the realisation of human rights and the satisfaction of basic needs through public service provision, social inclusion and sustainable economic development. At the same time, HIV/AIDS adds a sense of urgency to address these systemic development factors in a more comprehensive manner in order to minimise the risk of further spreading HIV and to strengthen the coping capabilities of households, communities and organisations.

Furthermore, interventions in this domain are crucial to ensure that HIV/AIDS does not reproduce or entrench the systemic development challenges, thereby perpetuating the vicious cycle. For example, a comprehensive poverty reduction programme would also benefit those households and affected individuals (e.g. orphans and widows) that have become poor, or poorer, due to HIV/AIDS. This could be a crucial safety net that enables these individuals not to engage in unsafe sexual practices as a means of securing their immediate needs. The importance of this was seen in Lesotho in 2002, when the country experienced a major food shortage as a result of drought and unseasonal frost during key planting times, resulting in some 700,000 people needing food assistance. There is now general agreement that the problem was made more severe as a result of the impact of HIV/AIDS, causing a crisis of vulnerability at the community and household levels.

As *Figure 10* further depicts, only when mutually supportive development interventions in all four domains are jointly formulated and implemented will the vicious cycle become transformed into a virtuous cycle.

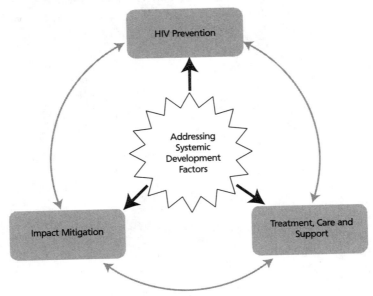

Figure 10. Breaking the Vicious Cycle of HIV/AIDS: Four Domains of the National Response

NOTES *for Chapter 3*

1. It may be more appropriate to use the term Parent-To-Child Transmission (PTCT) to highlight the joint parental responsibility for preventing the spread of HIV and, by implication, the need to protect both parents from contracting HIV. Although from a biomedical perspective, it is correct to refer to MTCT, this notion holds the danger of shifting responsibility and blame on mothers for passing HIV onto their babies. It also ignores the reality of how women have become infected themselves.

2. In some countries, especially in high-income countries, Eastern Europe and Central Asia, needle-sharing between intravenous drug users is also an area of concern for programmatic intervention.

3. UN General Assembly Special Session (UNGASS) on HIV/AIDS Declaration of Commitment. Goals set to be achieved by 2003 and 2005, June 2001 (paragraph 58).

4. Amartya Sen, *Development as Freedom*. Oxford University Press, 1999.

5. UNAIDS Report on the Global HIV/AIDS Epidemic 2002, UNAIDS, Geneva, Switzerland, 2002.

HIV/AIDS in Lesotho:
A Situation Analysis

HIV/AIDS is one of the most pressing development challenges facing Lesotho. The dynamics of the epidemic in Lesotho are similar to the dynamics of HIV/AIDS in the region: HIV is mainly transmitted through heterosexual sex; certain social groups are more at risk of becoming infected with HIV; systemic development factors facilitate the spread of HIV; and the impacts of HIV/AIDS occur at various levels and at various time scales. Building on the conceptual model presented in the previous chapter, this chapter starts by presenting a situational analysis of the HIV/AIDS epidemic in this country. The latter part focuses on the national response to the pandemic and the critical gaps needing to be addressed in order to achieve an HIV/AIDS-Competent Society.

Situation Analysis[1]

The first AIDS case was reported in Lesotho in 1986. Since then, adult prevalence of HIV has risen from around four percent in 1993 to 25 percent in 1999, and to

31 percent in 2002 (*see Figure 11*). This makes Lesotho the country with the fourth highest HIV prevalence rate in the world—and the poorest of the four countries; the first three being Botswana, Swaziland and South Africa. However, in the year 2000, even before the pandemic had reached these alarming rates, the Lesotho Government declared HIV/AIDS a national disaster, drew up and launched a National AIDS Strategic Plan (NASP), and established a Lesotho AIDS Programme Coordinating Authority (LAPCA) to oversee implementation of NASP. The current goal is to cut the prevalence of HIV from 31 percent of the population in 2002 to 25 percent in 2007. However, given the rapidly increasing sero[2] conversion rates, it may be necessary to set a more ambitious target.

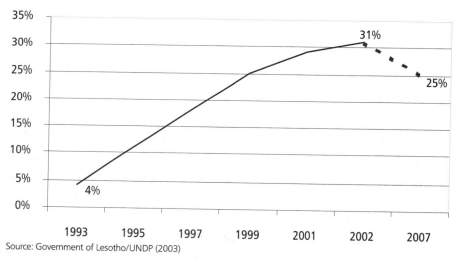

HIV Prevalence among 15-49 year olds, 1993-2002

Source: Government of Lesotho/UNDP (2003)

Figure 11. HIV Prevalence among 15-49 year olds, 1993-2002.

Social Groups at Risk

Certain population groups are at a disproportionately higher risk of being infected with the virus. These include children, girls, women, youth, migrants and people already infected with sexually transmitted infections (STIs). Statistics also suggest that HIV/AIDS is concentrated in urban areas, although the prevalence rate is very high across the country.

Women: UNAIDS estimates that by the end of 2002, at least 180,000 of the estimated 330,000 adults living with HIV/AIDS were women, from a total population of 2.2 million. This is 55 percent of the total number of adults infected with HIV. Similarly, 55 percent of the nearly 4,000 new cases reported in 2001 were women. Young women between the ages of 15-29 years old are particularly affected, as they constitute almost 75 percent of all reported AIDS cases in this age group.

Young Adults: The majority of Basotho infected with HIV are between 15-49 years old. It is estimated that one out of three Basotho in this age group is living with HIV/AIDS. By June 1999, over 80 percent of AIDS deaths came from this age group.

Infants, Children and Youth: According to UNAIDS, about 27,000 Basotho children between 0-14 years old were living with HIV/AIDS in 2002. Nearly 10 percent of all new HIV/AIDS cases in 2001 were among children less than four years of age, who had contracted the virus through mother-to-child transmission (MTCT). Despite these alarming statistics, reported AIDS cases and new infections among those aged 5 to 14 years old are very low (*see Figure 12*). These children were born at a time when the risk of MTCT was relatively low, and are unlikely to have yet become sexually active. As such, they constitute a "window of hope" for an AIDS-free generation in Lesotho, especially if they can be reached with information on how they can protect themselves from being infected. It is now well known that reaching young people holds the promise for preventing the spread of the pandemic.

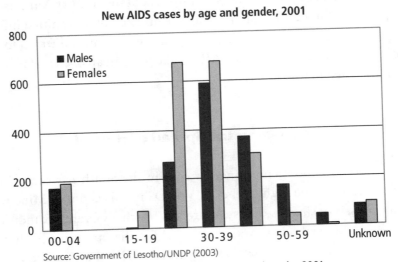

New AIDS cases by age and gender, 2001

Source: Government of Lesotho/UNDP (2003)

Figure 12. New AIDS cases by age and gender, 2001

Migrants: Although there is no reliable data to establish the HIV prevalence rate among Basotho migrant workers, it is widely believed that HIV/AIDS prevalence rates among miners and other migrants are disproportionately higher than with other, not-so-mobile population groups. Many migrant workers find jobs in the mines of South Africa, where for many years the only available housing were single-sex hostels, away from their families. Without the security and support of family life, many of the migrant workers tend to engage in high-risk sexual activities.

STI Patients: International experience shows that a person already suffering from a sexually transmitted infection (STI) is much more susceptible to contracting HIV. In Maseru, HIV prevalence among STI patients increased from one percent in 1989 to 11 percent in 1993, after which it rose sharply to 39 percent in 1996 and to 65 percent in 2000. Other regions reveal a similar pattern.

Urban Residents: According to ante-natal surveys, HIV/AIDS is disproportionately concentrated in urban areas. In the district of Maseru, HIV prevalence increased from 5.5 percent in 1991 to 42 percent in 2000, whereas in the district of Quthing, the comparable figures are 0.7 percent and 23 percent. However, all areas have a prevalence rate close to or greater than 20 percent, which shows that the pandemic has clearly taken root throughout the country.

It would, therefore, appear that whereas certain groups in society are disproportionately at higher risk of becoming infected with HIV, the scale of the pandemic in Lesotho is such that it has become endemic throughout the country. Various factors, such as high levels of migration, high prevalence of sexually transmitted infections, deepening structural poverty and traditional practices making it difficult to discuss matters of sexuality (and thus the HIV/AIDS pandemic) in an open and frank manner, have contributed to this situation.

Factors Fuelling the Spread of HIV/AIDS

The tradition for Basotho men taking up work in the South African mines is a critical explanation for the high level of HIV/AIDS in this country. Mine workers are typically housed in single-sex hostels, around which a vibrant sex industry has established itself. Men who live away from their families are more likely to have multiple sexual partners. Once they have contracted HIV, they are likely to infect their sexual partners upon return to their families and communities. More recently, an increasing number of female migrants are seeking work in the newly developed urban industries. It is estimated that the garment manufacturers in Lesotho employ almost 50,000 workers, most of whom are young women, many of whom come from all over the country and are considered a potential high-risk group. Available data shows that some 70 percent of these workers were already suffering from sexually transmitted infections—another high risk factor—by the end of 2002. It can, therefore, be assumed that the HIV/AIDS prevalence rates among these workers are likely to be higher than the national average. This is a matter of serious concern.

Persistent and deepening levels of poverty also constitute another key risk factor contributing to higher vulnerability to HIV infection. As is well known, the vast majority of Basotho live in deepening structural poverty, with recurring food crises, high unemployment, and are thus deprived of sources of regular incomes that can cover basic necessities such as food, shelter and clothing (*see Figure 13*). Between 1987 and 1995, the percentage of the population below the national income poverty line (of US$2 per day) was virtually unchanged at about 58 percent. Because

Percentage of Population below the National Poverty Line

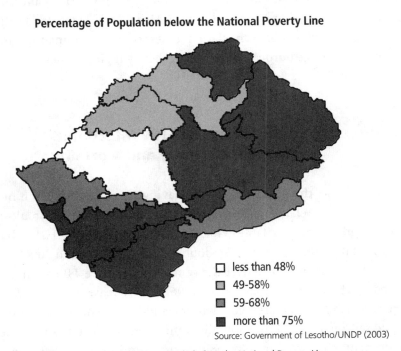

- ☐ less than 48%
- ▨ 49-58%
- ▨ 59-68%
- ■ more than 75%

Source: Government of Lesotho/UNDP (2003)

Figure 13. Percentage of Population below the National Poverty Line.
Distribution of income poverty in the 10 districts

HIV/AIDS stands to deepen poverty further by reducing productivity and incomes, and increasing health-related costs at the household level, there is a danger that a recurrent cycle of poverty and enhanced vulnerability to HIV infection will become entrenched, with dire consequences for the population.

In addition, Lesotho, along with several other countries in the SADC sub-region, is currently going through a severe food crisis. It is estimated that some 760,000 people—a third of the total population—may require targeted food aid in the year 2003/2004. Of these, more than 200,000 are children under 5 years of age. The immediate causes for the humanitarian emergency are the combined effects of reduced agricultural output due to adverse weather conditions, and steep increases in prices for staple foods. These trends have weakened the purchasing power of poor households, thereby excluding them from bridging the food gap through market channels.

These underlying causes of vulnerability (including vulnerability to HIV/AIDS) are a reflection of the country's extreme vulnerability to structural shocks. The food crisis further threatens to intensify and prolong the HIV/AIDS pandemic. A report of the recent UN mission of Special Envoys Morris and Lewis to Lesotho, Malawi, Zimbabwe and Zambia notes, in relation to Lesotho: "The humanitarian emergency has resulted in a large burden of disease, driven by high prevalence of malnutrition and HIV/AIDS."[3]

Consequences of HIV Infection: Increased Morbidity and Mortality

HIV/AIDS attacks the immune system, leaving the infected person more vulnerable to succumb to related opportunistic infections, such as Tuberculosis (TB) and other chest infections. Available evidence shows that since the HIV/AIDS epidemic in Lesotho, TB incidence more than doubled between 1993 and 2000, TB death rate increased by nearly one third over the same period, while TB case notification has increased by 15 percent annually since 1996. The increase in recorded TB cases can in part be attributed to increased advocacy and health education, which has led to increased self-referrals. At the same time, the incidence of TB can also be co-related to the deepening levels of poverty, poor housing and/or over-crowding and, in particular, to the spread of HIV/AIDS. For example, in some urban centres, 50 percent of TB patients were infected with HIV. It is estimated that in 2001, 54 percent of all incidents of TB in ages 15-49 and 68 percent of TB deaths were related to HIV/AIDS. Furthermore, death rates in TB patients undergoing treatment have progressively increased from 10 percent in 1993 to 14 percent in 2001. Therefore, effective HIV/AIDS control in Lesotho will have a positive effect on the control of TB, and vice versa.

HIV/AIDS and associated illnesses have rapidly increased mortality in Lesotho since the first days of the pandemic. As a consequence, life expectancy of the Basotho has already been reduced by more than a decade. In 1986, the average life expectancy was 55 years. At the time, it was expected to rise steadily to 60 years by the year 2001. Now, life expectancy at birth has been cut to 49 years (*see Figure 14*). Because the pandemic has a greater impact on women, life expectancy for women has been reduced to 48 years, compared to 51 years for men. Since there is a time gap of typically five to seven years between HIV infection and HIV/AIDS-related illnesses and death, the number of deaths is expected to increase significantly over the coming years as those who are currently infected, yet are a-symptomatic, will fall ill and die, possibly lowering life expectancy even further. Already, it is estimated that

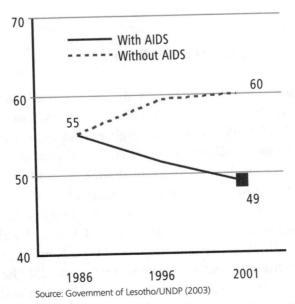

Source: Government of Lesotho/UNDP (2003)

Figure 14. Lesotho: Life Expectancy with and without AIDS, 1986-2001.
Consequences of HIV Infection: Increased Morbidity and Mortality

an average of 70 Basotho die every day of HIV/AIDS-related diseases. This is a very high number for a country with a population as small as Lesotho. It is for this reason that radical steps are needed to more decisively manage and control the pandemic.

Impact on Individuals, Households and Communities

Although there is a paucity of data to quantify these impacts in Lesotho, there is no doubt that HIV/AIDS has a devastating impact on individuals, families, communities and society as a whole. The increased incidence of ill-health, the increasing number of funerals being attended every week—with most of the deceased being younger people—bear testimony to this. The recent UN mission of Special Envoys Morris and Lewis to countries worst affected by food shortages found that, in Lesotho, those infected and affected by HIV/AIDS are unable to devote the necessary extra effort to agricultural cultivation. It further found that HIV/AIDS is depleting both skilled and unskilled labour. As the mission noted, these factors, coupled with the current food shortages, lead to a decline in the nutritional status of people living with HIV/AIDS and affected households.

Impact on Children

One of the most disturbing features of the HIV/AIDS pandemic is the disproportionate effect it has on children. As one or both parents become sick or die as a result of HIV/AIDS-related illnesses, children increasingly have to become caregivers to sick parents, younger siblings and/or other relatives. This threatens their prospect for attaining quality education, because frequent absenteeism and/or school dropout negatively affects their human development and their longer-term prospects for employment and self-reliance. It is estimated that 73,000 Basotho children under the age of 15 have either lost one or both parents due to HIV/AIDS.[4] This is equivalent to about one in ten children between the ages of 0-14. However, recent studies would indicate that this is an underestimation (*see Chapter 13*).The traditional extended family system, which offers care and support to orphans and other vulnerable children, is fast crumbling and thus unable to cope with this rapid increase in the number of children in need. In the absence of adequate support and care, orphans become neglected, abused, or take to life on the street. All these scenarios do, in turn, render children more vulnerable to contracting HIV. The increase in the number of orphans could also aggravate the problem of child labour in Lesotho.

In many communities, people living with HIV/AIDS are stigmatised, discriminated against and possibly cast out. The stigma is often extended to their relatives, friends and caretakers. These experiences of prejudice and rejection add to the emotional distress of those infected and affected by the pandemic. Moreover, it discourages people from seeking to know their HIV status so as to seek appropriate health care if infected. As a result, communities are hesitant to respond to the HIV/AIDS epidemic, leaving it to spread unchecked.

Long-term Impacts: HIV/AIDS and Development

Again, there is little data available regarding the long-term impact of HIV/AIDS on development in Lesotho, because there have not been specific impact studies on the public sector (except for the Education Ministry) or on the private sector, for that matter. However, based on current trends, it is envisaged that the long-term effects on Lesotho's development prospects will be significant. For example, there is already evidence of the impact of HIV/AIDS on Lesotho's demographic profile, as indicated by the drastic cut in life expectancy as mentioned above. It is also evident in the increase in the number of households headed by children, which is a direct result of the loss of productive adults and parents.

In addition, the Ministry of Health in Lesotho estimates that 50% of patients in hospitals, and one out of four outpatients, have HIV/AIDS-related conditions. The Morris and Lewis Mission was informed that 80% of all admitted patients in the Queen Elizabeth II Hospital in Maseru (the country's premiere hospital) were infected with HIV. The demand for medicines and care is already outstripping the capacity of the hospital. It is obvious that health care facilities will find it increasingly difficult to cope with increasing demands for treatment and care due to HIV/AIDS.

Another example comes from a survey conducted by the Queen Elizabeth II Hospital itself, in 1999, which suggested that 28 percent of teachers might be infected with HIV. Increasing levels of ill-health and death among teachers have major implications for the quality and quantity of education. Combined with increasing school dropout rates by children affected by HIV/AIDS, this situation poses fundamental challenges to the education system. Similarly, the World Bank has estimated that the impact of the HIV/AIDS pandemic will reduce GDP in Lesotho by almost one third by the year 2015, which significantly reduces the prospect of realising national development objectives.

These observations point to an increased demand for public services, the erosion of public sector capacity through loss of staff and associated skills, and an anticipated decline in economic growth. Combined with deepening household poverty, these factors will increase the scale of poverty in society even further. Moreover, the erosion of traditional social support systems and greater levels of scarcity are likely to induce higher levels of conflict over public resources, which could further undermine social cohesion.

HIV/AIDS and the Millennium Development Goals

The Government of Lesotho is a signatory to the Millennium Declaration, which was adopted by all 189 United Nations Member States in September 2000. The Millennium Declaration sets out the key challenges facing humanity, outlines appropriate responses to these challenges and establishes concrete measures for assessing performance. These measures are the Millennium Development Goals (MDGs), a set of inter-related goals on development, governance, peace, security and human rights. Within the context of the MDGs, the Government has set an interim target to reverse the HIV/AIDS pandemic by the year 2007, and bring down the HIV prevalence rate to 25 percent. However, the Government's draft Progress Report on the MDGs indicates that progress is slow and much more needs to be done if this target is to be achieved.[5] Moreover, as highlighted through the joint Government of Lesotho/United Nations process of systematic monitoring of the MDGs, the HIV/AIDS epidemic represents the single most important threat to attaining these goals (*see Table 2*).

Based on current national trends and the experiences of other countries, the multiple impacts of HIV/AIDS will be far-reaching and will leave no sector unaffected. Ongoing monitoring of current and prospective impacts of HIV/AIDS at different levels (household, community and society) and on different sectors is essential for an effective national response to HIV/AIDS.

Table 2.	Linkages between HIV/AIDS and the MDGs
GOALS/TARGETS	**LINKAGES**
EXTREME POVERTY Cut by one third the proportion of people living below the national poverty line by the year 2015.	HIV/AIDS drastically reduces incomes at the household level through illness and death and lowers the productivity of those who fall ill. Moreover, households have to divert scarce resources away from basic needs to cater for medicine, care and funerals. High levels of poverty and inequality in Lesotho have made the country more susceptible to the accelerating epidemic.
HUNGER Halve the proportion of the underweight among under-five year olds by 2015.	HIV/AIDS erodes traditional methods of households to cope with food insecurity by reducing capacity to produce and purchase food, depleting household assets and exhausting social safety nets. In Lesotho, the food crisis threatens to intensify and prolong the epidemic, as women and children, for instance, are being forced to barter sex for jobs, food and other basic essentials. Children are also leaving school to find work or forage for food.
UNIVERSAL PRIMARY EDUCATION Achieve universal primary education by the year 2007.	Young women are increasingly dropping out of school as they are expected to assume additional responsibilities in the household in terms of caring for the sick, and for generating additional income.
GENDER EQUALITY Achieve equal access for boys and girls to primary and secondary schooling by the year 2005.	The impact of HIV/AIDS disproportionately affects young women. Not only are they more susceptible to infection and suffer higher levels of infection rates, but they are expected to care for the sick and orphaned, often sacrificing their education in the process. The epidemic is integrally linked to issues of gender in terms of sexual rights and practices, children and family care, and the coping strategies of households, communities and societies.
CHILD MORTALITY Reduce infant mortality by one third by the year 2015.	The increasing mortality rate of newborn babies during the 1990s is a direct result of the adverse effects of the transmission of HIV/AIDS from HIV-positive mothers to their children during pregnancy, birth or breast-feeding. Most children infected will not survive their fifth birthday.
MATERNAL HEALTH Reduce maternal mortality ratio by three-quarters by the year 2015.	Complications associated with pregnancy, delivery and induced abortion tend to be more prevalent and severe among HIV-positive women. Pregnancy may also serve to increase the rate at which HIV-positive women develop AIDS. HIV/AIDS, combined with other indirect causes of maternal death and morbidity (including anaemia and tuberculosis) can also have dire consequences.
BASIC AMENITIES Halve the proportion of people without access to safe drinking water and sanitation.	Unsafe water and sanitation increases the likelihood of those with HIV/AIDS contracting opportunistic infections. Such infections further undermine the immune system and can accelerate the progression from HIV to full-blown AIDS.
GLOBAL MARKET ACCESS Develop further an open, rule-based, non-discriminatory trading and financial system.	The recent boom in the textile sector as a result of the African Growth and Opportunities Act (AGOA) has led to increased migration of predominantly female workers who are leaving behind their social networks. This migration represents a source of further HIV transmission, just as the Basotho migrant miners in the South African mining industry have proven to be. On a positive note, globalisation also provides opportunities for combating the epidemic through transfer of knowledge, skills and drugs, as well as through increased financial assistance, for instance, through the Global Fund.

Source: Government of Lesotho/UNDP (2003).

The National Response

As highlighted earlier, an appropriate national response to HIV/AIDS is the kind that combines multi-faceted strategies in relation to the four critical domains for action; namely, prevention, treatment and care, impact mitigation and addressing systemic development factors, to reduce vulnerability/risk and to strengthen coping capabilities. Let us now review the extent to which the response in Lesotho is covering these four domains, which are so essential for bringing about an HIV/AIDS-Competent Society.

Prevention and Behavioural Interventions: The Core of the National Response

A cursory assessment of Lesotho's current response to the pandemic in relation to the four domains of action shows that the majority of reported programmatic activities are concerned with prevention (*see Table 3*). In fact, 61 percent of all recorded HIV/AIDS-related projects taking place in Lesotho (46 out of 75 projects) are focused on prevention. Government activities are even more exclusively focused on prevention (22 out of 27, or 81%), through awareness raising, communication for behaviour change, as well as condom distribution. Of the remaining HIV/AIDS-related projects, 13 (or 17%) are concerned with treatment and care, eight (or 11%) with capacity building, six (or 8%) with mitigating social impacts, and two (or 3%) with reducing vulnerability. This shows an urgent need to broaden the national response beyond prevention efforts to address the various consequences of the pandemic (including the need for appropriate treatment and care) as well as the systemic development factors that constitute a context of vulnerability, risk and reduced capability.

From the perspective of HIV prevention, information, education and communication (IEC), based on health education or behaviour change models, is a core component of the national response. However, peer education approaches in the prevention of HIV/AIDS are still weak and are not an integral part of IEC programmes. Also, although the promotion of the use of condoms is part of IEC programmes, condoms are not sufficiently accessible and affordable to the public. In addition, it is not easy to find and buy condoms and many people feel embarrassed to ask for them at clinics or to buy them over the counter. Furthermore, cultural and religious beliefs are at odds with the promotion of condom use. In some instances, this

Table 3.	Ongoing HIV/AIDS-related Initiatives in Lesotho				
Implementing Agencies	Reducing Vulnerability	Prevention	Care, Support and Treatment	Impact Mitigation	Capacity Building
State Agencies	1	22	2	1	1
Development Agencies (bilateral agencies and international NGOs)	1	19	8	3	5
UN Agencies	None identified	4	3	2	2
Other (community/ informal organisations and the private sector)	None identified	1	Not measured	Not measured	None identified
Totals	2	46	13	6	8

Revised from LAPCA (2002): 7

involves myths about condoms (such as that condoms develop worms when placed in the sun), which need to be addressed.

Voluntary Counselling and Testing (VCT) is a proven preventive strategy and is recognised as an integral part of HIV prevention by the Government of Lesotho (*see Figure 15*). As outlined in the National AIDS Strategic Plan and the proposal submitted to the Global Fund to Fight AIDS, TB and Malaria (GFATM), VCT in Lesotho is expected to contribute to a comprehensive response to the HIV/AIDS epidemic by promoting HIV prevention as a key public health goal; by helping reduce stigma, fear and anxiety around HIV/AIDS and increasing openness in the community; by providing an entry point for future support through early knowledge and referral; and by helping parents prevent transmission to their babies. However, work on this is really at a rudimentary stage in Lesotho. Efforts must be stepped up to ensure that voluntary counselling and testing is implemented throughout the country as soon as possible. As more and more Basotho become HIV/AIDS competent, the demand for these services will significantly increase; it would be best if the supply side could keep pace with the demand side.

Finally, another intervention related to HIV prevention concerns the prevention of MTCT. In late 2002, the Government of Lesotho introduced the anti-retroviral drug, Nevirapine, to prevent MTCT. This is an excellent first step. Implementation needs to be more vigorously implemented and scaled up.

VCT as an entry point for HIV prevention and care

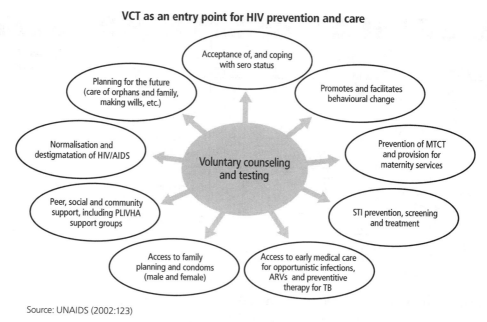

Source: UNAIDS (2002:123)

Figure 15. VCT as an entry point for HIV prevention and care

Treatment, Care and Support

As the situation analysis has shown, hospitals are faced with considerable demand for appropriate treatment and care for HIV/AIDS-related infections. Due to the lack of basic medicines and qualified personnel, health facilities are struggling to cope with the provision of appropriate treatment and care.

Overcrowding at hospitals and other health facilities, lack of essential drugs and a shortage of qualified health workers, combined with limited household assets to pay for hospital costs, have shifted the responsibility and focus from institutional care to home-based care (HBC). As a result, various NGOs, religious organisations and community groups are involved in this area. There is a need for greater coordination between these organisations, better coverage throughout the country and more extensive support to people living with HIV/AIDS (PLWHA), as well as affected households. LAPCA has proposed a plan of action to expand the network of Home-Based-Care providers from five in 2002 to 30 in 2007. However, a clear and detailed implementation plan is needed to ensure that this activity does not duplicate the work of the Ministry of Health and Social Welfare in this area.

Faced by the devastation of HIV/AIDS on individuals, families, communities and society, the provision of anti-retroviral drugs (ARVs) to people infected with HIV has become a critical issue. Yet, the prohibitive prices of ARVs have made the provision of such treatment in public health facilities unaffordable. For this purpose, the Government submitted a proposal to the Global Fund for AIDS, Tuberculosis and Malaria (GFTM2) in October 2002, which allows for a rollout treatment programme over the next five years. Some of the funds have been duly granted. Financial implementation should accordingly be accelerated to offer post-exposure treatment to health care workers, not least because at this point, ARV treatment is only made available at two public hospitals and in some private clinics.

Impact Mitigation Efforts

In 2001, the Department of Welfare commissioned a study on orphans in Lesotho, which identified a rapidly growing number of children who had lost either one or both parents to HIV/AIDS, leading to a significant increase in households headed by children, incidences of child labour and the number of street children. Some programmatic interventions have been developed to respond to the plight of AIDS orphans. The Government, through the Ministry of Education, and some churches are currently giving scholarships to orphans, including AIDS orphans, from Standard 4 to Form 3. In addition, one of the focus areas of the Ministry of Agriculture's Impact Mitigation Programme is to support households headed by children, whilst the Department of Welfare is providing foster care training and income-generating projects to foster parents of double-orphaned children. Her Majesty The Queen and Her Excellency The First Lady have also taken the plight of orphans to heart by supporting a number of projects directed at their needs. However, a comprehensive policy and programme, which address the needs of orphans and vulnerable children (OVC) in an all-inclusive manner, has not been developed. This is definitely an area of need, which has a great deal of sympathy from the international donor community.

Another area of impact mitigation concerns income-generating activities. As mentioned above, the Department of Welfare is providing income-generating projects to foster parents of double-orphaned children. The Ministry of Agriculture is also implementing income-generating activities. Yet, it is obvious that the scale and reach of these projects is limited and does not correspond to existing and growing needs.

In addition, the Ministry of Agriculture, the Office of The First Lady and the Chinese Embassy have collaborated and mobilised the Chinese business community to donate about 1,000 food parcels to OVC and PLWHA in six districts. Whilst this initiative provides immediate relief, there is still a need for a concerted effort to address the right to food security of PLWHA and OVC in a sustained and sustainable manner. Furthermore, the Ministry of Health and Social Welfare has implemented a number of pilot projects aimed at addressing the nutritional needs of people infected with HIV/AIDS. Such projects need to be scaled up to meet current and future needs.

In general, impact mitigation interventions in Lesotho are currently rather limited, largely haphazard and poorly coordinated. A much wider range of supportive measures is needed to provide the necessary support to those infected and affected by HIV/AIDS. There is also a need for forward-looking interventions that seek to pre-empt and mitigate the future impacts of the pandemic on social, economic, political and institutional systems.

Systemic Development Factors:
Risk, Vulnerability and Reduced Capability

One of the main reasons that the national response to HIV/AIDS has not been sufficiently comprehensive lies in the inadequate analysis of systemic development factors that constitute an environment of risk, vulnerability and reduced capability to cope with the epidemic. Although public statements by political leaders and critical policy frameworks, such as the National AIDS Strategic Plan (NASP), the National Vision and the Poverty Reduction Strategy Paper (PRSP), almost routinely refer to underlying factors in the socio-political and economic environment that help to facilitate the spread of HIV, evidence suggests that they do not translate into an indepth analysis of the factors or into appropriate programmatic interventions.

For example, the National Vision, which spells out the overarching development agenda of Lesotho, and the PRSP, which is the overall mechanism for implementing development programmes, both cite the creation of an HIV/AIDS-free Lesotho as a priority. In particular, HIV/AIDS has been identified as a key national challenge to poverty reduction and development in the ongoing PRSP process. However, an assessment of both policy documents and the process to date reveals that there is significant scope for improvement to ensure that the causes and consequences of HIV/AIDS feature as integral parts of the poverty analysis and policy prescriptions. The PRSP has the potential to become an effective tool for mobilising resources and ensuring action and involvement of all stakeholders in the fight against HIV/AIDS. However, it will only realise this potential once its policy analysis is strengthened and more specific policy interventions in the areas of prevention, care and support, impact mitigation and the determinants of risk, environment and reduced capability (that is, systemic development factors) are formulated. The NASP suffers from similar conceptual and programmatic weaknesses and therefore should be reviewed as a matter of urgency.

This is not to suggest that the Government or other stakeholders are not concerned with critical development challenges, such as poverty reduction, gender inequality, sustainable economic growth, meeting human rights needs and the equitable distribution of resources and opportunities. Quite the contrary. However, so far, interventions responding to systemic development factors that are determinants of HIV/AIDS, are formulated and implemented without a clear and explicit conceptual understanding of their inter-linkages with HIV/AIDS. The key challenge is to put the fight against HIV/AIDS at the core of all development plans and activities at government, non-government and community levels. By undertaking the consultative process that has led to the compilation of this document, the Expanded Theme Group on HIV/AIDS hopes it will be making a contribution, albeit modest, to this process.

The Way Forward

A proper assessment of the impact of HIV/AIDS on both the public and the private sector is an important first step in scaling up the national response to the HIV/AIDS pandemic in Lesotho. Whereas it is possible to start the process of core streaming HIV/AIDS into development plans and budgets simply on the basis of one third of the population being infected, the reality may be very different among working people, as we saw with the garment industry workers whose estimated prevalence rates are likely to far outstrip the national average rate. It would, therefore, be crucial for more specific data to be available at the earliest possible time in order to facilitate better planning and resource allocation. In addition, gaps in the reporting system have also resulted in a considerable underestimation of the severity of the HIV/AIDS epidemic in the country. For example, based on reported AIDS cases since 1986, official records show that, by the end of the year 2000, a cumulative total of 14,640 AIDS cases were reported in the country. Yet, estimates from the *UNAIDS 2002 Report on the Global HIV/AIDS Epidemic* suggest that by the end of 2001, 360,000 people were already living with HIV/AIDS in Lesotho and that 25,000 Basotho died of AIDS-related deaths in 2001 alone. Lack of qualified personnel, inadequate community health systems and a limited number of testing kits are among other main factors that lead to under-reporting. In short, an integrated disease surveillance response system does not yet exist in this country. This also needs to be addressed as a matter of urgency.

It is also crucial to recognise that the HIV/AIDS pandemic reinforces and reproduces certain systemic development factors that constitute a context of risk, vulnerability and reduced capability to cope with the consequences of HIV infection. The issue is not just to acknowledge that this is the case, but rather to actually understand **how** and **why** this is so in order for appropriate action to be taken.

In particular, as long as interventions related to the four domains of the national response to HIV/AIDS (prevention, treatment and care, impact mitigation and addressing systemic development factors) are not sufficiently comprehensive, the new approach is unlikely to be successful. In other words, understanding and commitment have to be translated into action.

Finally, the Government of Lesotho has been the main driving force of the national response against HIV/AIDS, together with some NGOs and development partners. It does need to be pointed out, however, that an assessment of responses at the household and community levels is most likely to reveal the central roles played by women, children and the elderly, extended family networks and community groups. However, a comprehensive national response to HIV/AIDS requires the involvement of a wide variety of stakeholders, including political leadership and the government at all levels, People Living With HIV/AIDS (PLWHA) and affected households, civil society organisations (including religious organisations and churches), communities, traditional leaders, the private sector and international development partners.

NOTES *for Chapter 4*

1. The statistics in this section are drawn from: Government of Lesotho (2000); Government of Lesotho/UNDP (2003) and UNAIDS (2002).

2. "Sero" is a technical term that relates to someone who could test negative, but is in fact positive, because of what is called the *window period*—the time between contracting the virus and the development of antibodies, the trademark of which allows the easy identification of one's positive status. The window is three months in duration.

3. UN *Report of the January Mission to Lesotho, Malawi, Zimbabwe and Zambia*, Geneva, Switzerland, 31 January 2003. [www.undp.org.Is/New_Events/index.htm]

4. *Report on the Global HIV/AIDS Epidemic 2002*, UNAIDS, Geneva, Switzerland, 2002.

5. Government of Lesotho/UNDP, *The War Against AIDS. Draft Progress Report: Millennium Development Goals, Lesotho*, Unpublished Report, Government of Lesotho and UNDP, Maseru, 2003.

5

Social Mobilisation for an
HIV/AIDS-Competent Society

Mobilisation of all sectors of society in striving for an HIV/AIDS-competent society has to be the core operational strategy if Lesotho is to succeed in scaling up the response to the pandemic. In many ways, it has thus far been the missing link between the Government's declared intentions since the year 2000 to fight HIV/AIDS as a national disaster and the low levels of achievement to-date. In other words, although the allocation of resources (2% of all sectoral budgets), the drawing up of a National AIDS Plan (NASP) and the establishment of an AIDS Coordinating Body (LAPCA)—that is, the **supply** side of the equation—are important, they are insufficient, in and of themselves, unless they are coupled with measures to create **demand**. Only such a duality could forge partnerships with individuals and communities, without whose participation it would be virtually impossible for the Government to deliver on the four domains of prevention, treatment, care and support, and impact mitigation, let alone address systemic development factors that constitute a context of risk, vulnerability and reduced capability.

Mobilising Basotho Society Towards HIV/AIDS Competence

So, what would it take to mobilise Basotho society towards HIV/AIDS competence? It would take the realisation of the need to engage a mobilisation strategy that embraces the principles of **community participation**, **social marketing** and **social mobilisation** to guide the urgent revision of the *National AIDS Strategic Plan*, to be immediately followed by the drawing up of an *Annual Business Plan* that prioritises which actions should be undertaken, in what sequence or manner of complementarity between and among the different actors, and with what resources. This would require taking full cognisance of the various actions and actors currently operational and seeking to generate the best possible synergy among them. This is a major undertaking that needs to be embarked upon as a matter of the utmost urgency.

In the meantime, it may be prudent to dwell a little bit on both the theoretical underpinnings of this rationale for a social mobilisation strategy, as well as on key international experiences that justify its serious consideration by the Government and people of Lesotho and, indeed, by any others wishing to embark on the quest for an HIV/AIDS-competent society. It also needs to be stated at the outset that there are various definitions and interpretations of the three core concepts of community participation, social marketing and social mobilisation. However, rather than engaging in any of these here, a deliberate choice has been made to utilise those definitions that are deemed useful in Lesotho's desire to come to grips with the pandemic in the quickest, most effective and efficient manner.

For the purposes of this discussion, *Community Participation* is seen as the educational and empowering process in which people, in partnership with those able to assist them, identify problems and needs and increasingly themselves assume responsibility to plan, manage, control and assess the collective actions that are proved necessary. *Social Marketing*, on the other hand, is seen as the design, implementation and control of programmes calculated to influence the acceptability of social ideas involving considerations of product, planning, pricing, communications and market research. *Social Mobilisation* is viewed as the process of bringing together ALL feasible and practical, inter-sectoral social allies to raise people's awareness of, and demand for, a particular development programme, to assist in the delivery of resources and services, and to strengthen community participation in the interest of sustainability and self-reliance. In other words, it is a process that is concerned with mobilising human and financial resources through five main approaches:

- *Political Mobilisation* is aimed at winning political and policy commitment for a major goal and the necessary resource allocations to realise that goal. The "targets" are national policy and decision-makers. The communication methods include advocacy, lobbying, using 'goodwill ambassadors', as well as the extensive use of arts, culture and the mass media.
- *Government Mobilisation* is aimed at informing and enlisting the help and cooperation of service providers and other government organisations that can provide direct or indirect support. The communication methods include training workshops and programmes, study tours/exchange visits, as well as extensive engagement of the mass media in raising awareness about the subject matter.
- *Community Mobilisation* has the express objective of informing and gaining the commitment of local political, religious, social and traditional leaders, local government agencies, non-governmental agencies (NGOs), youth as well as women's groups and cooperatives. Useful communication methods for achieving these objectives include training, participation in planning and extensive coverage of the activities by the mass media, arts and other cultural groups.
- *Corporate Mobilisation* is targeted at securing the support of national or international companies in promoting appropriate goals, either through the contribution of resources or the use of appropriate messages as part of their advertising or product labelling.
- *Beneficiary Mobilisation* has the express intention of informing and motivating the programme beneficiaries through training programmes, the establishment of appropriate community groups, as well as communication through traditional methods, including the arts and other forms of folk culture, and the mass media.

For a social problem as pressing and urgent as the HIV/AIDS pandemic, it may be prudent for Lesotho to immediately embark on a social mobilisation campaign as part and parcel of gearing up to the *programme acceleration mode*. For those who may be quick to criticise "campaigns" as a programme acceleration strategy, it would be important to note the following:

- Campaigns should be viewed as peaks in a continuous process rather than as discrete events in themselves;

- Capturing national imagination around one programme can have a very positive impact on other programmes;
- Through campaigns, ordinary people can come to regard themselves as the *subjects* rather than the *objects* of the programme, itself a major achievement; and
- Social mobilisation can break down the "special mystique" of officials and enhance the capability of social allies, making them integral and powerful dimensions of the permanent infrastructures, without whose willing involvement no social change can occur.

Social Mobilisation Actors

Social Mobilisation Actors can be many and varied, based on the social and political context of any given country. So, the following checklist is offered for the purposes of illustration and is by no means exhaustive.

Mobilisation of National-Level Partners for building inter-sectoral alliances and participation:

- National Leadership;
- Donors and the United Nations System;
- Inter-Ministerial Support;
- NGO Leaders;
- Service Clubs, such as the Rotary, the Round Table and the Lion's Club;
- Professional Associations, such as Medical and Dental Associations, Nurses and Midwives Associations, Teachers Associations, and more;
- Cultural/Traditional Leaders;
- Religious Leaders;
- Business Leaders;
- Leaders of Arts and other forms of Popular Culture; and
- Mass Media Decision-Makers.

Mobilisation of Mid-Level Partners/Channels for service delivery, communication, motivation, training, supervision, monitoring and evaluation:

- Government Supervisors and Field Workers;
- NGO Supervisors and Field Workers;

- School Systems;
- Cooperatives; and
- Traditional Media.

Mobilisation of Beneficiaries for increased community participation:

- Local Leadership Identification; and
- Group Formation.

Decentralisation for HIV/AIDS-Competent Communities

Fresh from the experience of the groundbreaking General Elections of May 2002, the government has recommitted itself to the establishment of elected local councils, marking a concrete move to introduce local democracy. This represents another step in consolidating democracy throughout Lesotho and bringing government closer to the people. In a yet unpublished government document, *Voices of the People: Report on Community Consultations for the National Vision and the Poverty Reduction Strategy Paper Draft, December 2002*, a woman from the village of Ha Rantsimane, Thaba-Tseka district, said:

> We need local government... we ought to be making our own plans and programmes. Government should not be making decisions for us. We should be doing things for ourselves.

The commitment to local government is driven by a belief that decentralisation increases popular participation in decision-making, creating a more accessible government, which is more knowledgeable about local conditions and more responsive to people's demands. However, these structures are only effective if they increase service delivery, especially in relation to the provision of basic social services to the poor. The decentralisation process provides a unique opportunity for scaling up the national response to the HIV/AIDS crisis in every village: creating HIV/AIDS-Competent Communities. While local government structures are considered essential elements of societies committed to good governance, such structures should not be seen as an end in itself. Essentially, they are about improving service delivery and should be judged on their capacity to do so. Local government structures are not a panacea: they have the potential—in societies with high levels of inequality—to reinforce local elite structures and, by extension, the marginalisation of the poor.

Moves by government to achieve real local democracy have the potential to bring the fight against the HIV/AIDS pandemic to all corners of the country. This provides a unique opportunity to create HIV/AIDS-Competent Communities with community and personal accountability. Such communities, as part of a HIV/AIDS-Competent Society, will ensure that everyone takes responsibility for fighting the pandemic: each community will facilitate testing; each community will develop a plan with clear benchmarks to ensure that those with the virus live long and productive lives; each community will have a child-safety and security plan; and each community will commit itself to ensuring that those who are not infected remain uninfected. How can this be done? Following are some suggestions:

- It is essential that there be clear structures at the local level, which are responsible for the implementation of anti-HIV/AIDS strategies. Already, there are district HIV/AIDS task forces and local community groups dedicated to the fight against the virus, supported by the Ministry of Local Government. These can be developed in every village in the country.

- In the post-election phase, there is a need for a comprehensive training programme for all newly elected counsellors to enable them understand their role as leaders in the fight against HIV/AIDS.

- The Ministry of Local Government can develop guidelines for HIV/AIDS-Competent Communities as part of its core streaming activities.

When one examines the above summary description of social mobilisation processes and actors in light of Lesotho's efforts thus far to tackle the pandemic, it will become increasingly clear why the investment of energy, financial and other resources have thus far not yielded the desired results. It should also be clear what now needs to be done, by whom, at what levels and with what objectives and possible outcomes. In truth, so far, it is the national leadership, primarily His Majesty King Letsie III and The Right Honourable Prime Minister, who have been consistently urging the Government and its people (with the support of donors, the UN and other international organisations) to leave no stone unturned in finding and implementing effective ways to fight the pandemic. It is now up to all of us, in our respective capacities, to take full cognisance of the importance of social mobilisation as a core strategy for the scaling up effort; that is, the required programme acceleration mode.

Importance of Folk Media for Successful Social Mobilisation in Lesotho

Although the country has a relatively fair number of radio stations and newspapers, there is still a huge gap in the availability of mass communication channels. Existing conventional media channels hardly reach half of the country. Most of the publications reach only a sector of the country, mostly in urban areas. However, it must be noted that the country has 12 weekly newspapers owned variously by the Government, the private sector and political parties. Radio is the most popular and widespread mass medium, with *Radio Lesotho* having a powerful transmitter that reaches deep into the country's mountainous terrain and well beyond the borders of the country. Its popularity varies considerably according to programmes, with phone-in programmes covering politics and current affairs being the most popular. In recent years, airwaves have become more open and several Radio Stations are now able to broadcast over FM frequencies. There are five FM radio stations, but *Radio Lesotho* remains the only radio station with a truly national outreach. Music stations are very popular amongst the youth. Interestingly, just as many Basotho who tune into radio stations in Lesotho also tune into the South African *Leseli Stereo* among a variety of other radio stations with different programmes of mixed educational and entertainment value. Lesotho has one television Station, *Lesotho TV*, which broadcasts local news and other programmes for about three hours every evening. Those who can afford it have access to round-the-clock broadcasting of more than 50 TV channels from *DSTV South Africa*, with varied news, entertainment, and other programmes, none of which is Lesotho-specific.

Given this limited reach of conventional channels of mass communication in Lesotho, it is crucial that a comprehensive Social Mobilisation Strategy for HIV/AIDS competence in Lesotho be strongly based on Folk Media. Basotho have a rich culture steeped in traditions like story-telling, poetry/praise-singing, choral and other forms of music, singing and dancing, which culminate in a prestigious national event—*The Morija Festival*—that takes place in Morija every October. Folk media channels of communications are also best suited for effectively raising awareness about HIV/AIDS, not least because they offer enjoyable ways of receiving otherwise tough messages about the pandemic and what can be done to stop its spread, to stop those who are not yet infected from getting it, as well as to prolong the lives of those who already have it. The school system can also be mobilised to use drama, intra/inter-school debating competitions, art competitions and similar vehicles as a means of making sure every Mosotho is HIV/AIDS competent.

Communication and Lesotho's Current Response to HIV/AIDS

The main force behind the response against HIV/AIDS in Lesotho has been the Government of Lesotho, Non-Governmental Organisations (NGOs) and the United Nations system UN Theme Group on HIV/AIDS. The national response to HIV/AIDS prevention and care in Lesotho focuses on the following:

Information, Education and Communication (IEC) and Advocacy

- Peer Education,
- Women's Groups,
- Men's Groups,
- Cultural Groups,
- Song and Drama Groups,
- Material Production,
- Condom Social Marketing, and
- Ministry of Education pilot schools and the Lesotho College of Education (LCE).

Counselling

- Provision of mass counselling, for example, through Pitso[1] meetings on HIV/AIDS, Church Gatherings/Mass Services, Counselling Seminars and Workshops,
- Training of different cadres in basic counselling techniques and services, and
- Counselling services provided in most health service provision centres, primarily hospitals and clinics.

Home-Based Care (HBC) Services

- Availability of Service Providers trained in Home-Based Care,
- Families and caregivers trained in care and support,
- Availability of support groups,
- High competency in orphan care, and
- High competency in viable income-generating projects.

Surveillance and Laboratory Services

- HIV/AIDS sentinel surveillance system, with a view to measuring the magnitude of the pandemic and monitor trends,
- Sustained screening of blood and blood products for HIV/AIDS,
- Procurement of equipment and reagents for HIV/AIDS testing sustained, and
- Studies conducted on knowledge, attitude, behaviour and practice (KABP) during the period.

Multi-Sectoral Response

- Ministers and Principal Secretaries Task Force on HIV/AIDS,
- HIV/AIDS focal points in all Government Ministries, NGOs and Private Sector institutions established,
- Nationwide youth anti-AIDS organisations and clubs,
- Community mobilisation through various structures,
- Campaigns against HIV/AIDS by the Prime Minister,
- AIDS commemoration days, and
- Drama, songs and charity walks.

Communication Approaches Against HIV/AIDS in Lesotho

The Lesotho AIDS Programme Coordinating Authority (LAPCA) spearheads a national goal whose vision is to have an HIV/AIDS-free society, with high levels of awareness, behavioural change, safe blood supply, safe sex practices, and equitable access to quality care and support for both the infected and the affected.

Currently, most HIV/AIDS communication strategies are based on health education or behaviour change models, such as those designed to improve immunisation coverage or to eradicate polio. Their rationale is that the successful delivery of information (in the form of messages) will cause individuals to change their behaviour. It is accordingly assumed that sexually active people, once they understand how HIV/AIDS is spread, would willingly change their sexual behaviour and protect themselves. Table 4 highlights ongoing Communication Interventions by various organisations.

Table 4. Highlights of On-Going Communication Interventions in Lesotho	
PREVENTION	
Project	**Implementing Organisation**
i. HIV/AIDS materials development.	i. Positive Action, MOHSW.
ii. Mitigation in HIV/AIDS in Lesotho.	ii. CHAL, MOA World Vision.
iii. IEC on HIV/AIDS and Life Skills Training for Youth.	iii. Lesotho Scouts Association
iv. IEC on HIV/AIDS for People with Disability.	iv. Lesotho National Assoc. for the Physically Disabled (LNADP).
v. HIV/AIDS awareness workshops and counselling training.	v. Lesotho Women's Institute.
vi. Training of trainers of member organisations.	vi. Lesotho National Federation of Organisations of disabled (LNFORD).

Table 4.	Highlights of On-Going Communication Interventions in Lesotho
CARE and SUPPORT	
Project	**Implementing Organisation**
i. Improvement and extension of services in Home-Based Care and Counselling to PWAs and their families.	i. Tšosane Tšosane Seli La Lefatše.
ii. Resource centre for Maseru, Maputsoe and Mafeteng.	ii. CARE SHARP project
iii. Lesotho Clinical Pastoral Education Project.	iii. Christian Health Association of Lesotho
iv. Nutritional assistance and establishment of self-help groups.	iv. Positive Action.
v. Improving quality of care for PLWA.	v. MOHSW, MOA and CHAI
vi. 24-hour toll-free HIV/AIDS help line.	vi. Positive Action
vii. Improving access to HIV/AIDS information and care (National Health and Youth policies).	vii. GOL, MOHSW.
viii. HIV/AIDS staff development and community/ capacity building.	viii. Lesotho Preschool and Day Care Association.
ix. Home-based care and training.	ix. Thusanang Lifeline.
IMPACT MITIGATION	
Project	**Implementing Organisation**
i. Population Policy review.	i. GOL, MODP.
ii. Health sector reform.	ii. GOL, MOHSW.
iii. Capacity Building for LAPCA.	iii. LAPCA.
iv. Baseline study for the establishment of Youth Centre in Quthing.	iv. GoL.
v. Regional AIDS response.	v. GoL, Ministry of Agriculture

Rationale for the Strategy

Recognising the need to improve the effectiveness, coverage and coordination of communication and advocacy efforts in support of the national response to HIV/ AIDS, LAPCA and its partners in the national response have developed a communication strategy with the following objectives:

- To provide a common framework and direction from which all communications planning and implementation in the national response will take place;

- To provide LAPCA with a tool for the coordination of communication and community mobilisation efforts in Lesotho;
- To support the development of high impact and low cost communication and advocacy interventions, which should include the identification of specific strategies to address discrete target audiences and the positioning of thematic areas such as care and support, impact mitigation, and home-based care, among others; and
- To identify and mobilise the support of non-traditional partners, such as the Ministries of Local Government and of Tourism, Environment and Culture, businesses, traditional leaders, religious leaders, and other institutions of civil society, so as to increase community capacity to respond to HIV/AIDS.

HIV/AIDS, Communication and Human Rights

A comprehensive communication strategy for scaling up the national response to the HIV/AIDS pandemic should adopt a human rights approach that regards communities as a vital resource rather than treating them as victims and, thus, passive recipients of development projects and inputs from benevolent outsiders. Such a strategy would be able to take into account the fact that communication occurs constantly within communities as people make daily decisions and discuss norms and standards to apply in their daily life. This continual "communication buzz" reflects existing power relationships and can therefore either support or constrain people's choices. People adapt and change their survival and coping strategies as the communication buzz around them makes new information available, or places it in a different context. An effective communication strategy should encourage people to discuss issues amongst themselves (and with outsiders) and assist in translating analysis into action.

But most people have fewer options for action and are disadvantaged, depending on their social position. Disadvantaged groups include most people coping with HIV/AIDS: orphaned children, sexually exploited young people, and women who care for the young, the elderly and the sick. Communication strategies that build their capacity to speak on their own behalf and be heard should be the ideal, under any circumstances. An understanding of communities and the power relationships within them is crucial to the design and delivery of communication strategies within a human rights perspective.

UNAIDS provides us with a contextual framework to better understand communities in *Communications Framework for HIV/AIDS: A New Direction*.[2] It establishes five interrelated domains of context that should be considered in developing communication strategies for HIV/AIDS prevention, care and support. These domains are directly related to the life of a community and to the relationship between a community and outside stakeholders, such as government departments, corporations or development agencies.

The domains are:

- *Government policy*: the role of policy and law in supporting or hindering intervention efforts;
- *Socio-economic status*: collective or individual income that may allow or prevent adequate intervention;
- *Culture*: positive, unique or negative characteristics that may promote or hinder prevention and care practices;
- *Gender relationships*: the status of women in relation to men in society and community, and the influence of gender on sexual negotiation and decision-making; and
- *Spirituality*: the role of spiritual/religious values in promoting or hindering a community's development of positive health actions.

Such a strategy should facilitate the delineation of the following key areas of strategic approaches, which will create the shift from a *supply/expert-driven behaviour* change process to a *demand-driven* intervention rooted in community processes that sustain behaviour and social change. These are:

Giving a Voice to the Voiceless

- Conducting participatory analysis of vulnerable groups such as orphans, other vulnerable children, people living with HIV/AIDS, females (especially young girls), and more.
- Supporting channels of communication from the voiceless to the more powerful community members and national decision-makers.

Giving the voiceless a voice is a process of ensuring that community members who are usually marginal to the process become part of the response. Often, community members are rendered marginal to the processes that they are expected to be part and parcel of. Many issues in HIV/AIDS, such as voluntary counselling and testing, condom use and prevention of mother/parent-to-child transmission, touch on critical human relationship issues. Individuals who are supposed to articulate HIV/AIDS need to be heard from the very beginning of the process to the end, so that their voices and input are fully taken into account at all times.

Facilitating Community Conversations

- Define community capabilities in communication.
- Create safe places for dialogue and conversation.
- Develop participatory action plans based on community conversations.

Communication workers should adopt and devise more open-ended approaches to dialogue so that conversations flow more freely and in more culturally sensitive ways. Conversations should be held in and between all the groups in the community; the role of external facilitators can be especially important in starting this process and in supporting it to maturity.

I. In facilitating community discussions, it would be important to cover:
   - inclusivity—who should participate?
   - key issues and priorities—what do community members want?
   - visions—what could be?
   - causality—why are things as they are?
   - identification of duty bearers and rights holders (role/pattern analysis) and capacity gaps—who can do something and what will it take for them to do it?
   - implications for government, agency, district and community partnerships.
   - feedback.

II. Connecting community plans and priorities to national plans and priorities:
   - ensure appropriate services at community level; and
   - base policy decisions on community action plans.

III. Defining a management role for communities when action plans are implemented:

A community-based approach to the management of information systems (CBMIS) can improve the management of the Triple-A—assessment, analysis, and action—processes. Years of accumulated experience have shown that the act of performing a collective Triple-A is in itself empowering.[3] Communities may need support to incorporate their own indicators and monitoring systems into existing mainstream data systems, such as school enrollment or growth monitoring of infants. If they can do so, the data they collect may be more accurate and more useful to community members.

Unlike conventional information systems, CBMIS has the potential to focus directly on children and young people as units of data analysis, rather than 'children's institutions,' such as schools or health centres.[4] The conventional focus on institutions can exclude not only many important issues, but also those who are not members of the institutions—a growing number of people, as the impact of HIV/AIDS increases. The development of CBMIS should consider:

- ways in which communities can develop their own pictures of reality—their own baselines;
- participatory monitoring and evaluation processes that include qualitative reflection as well as quantitative analysis. Have we developed effective community support structures? Have we reduced HIV infection?
- mechanisms for sustained community action.

Participating in CBMIS provides development professionals with a way of keeping in touch with the reality of the pandemic, thereby permitting programmes to be responsive to reality rather than the analyses of outsiders. Here, the role of the communication specialist is crucial in ensuring that the most vulnerable—usually most marginalised—interest groups are included in the process and that their views are retained through all levels of the decision-making process.

Management

Local people cannot 'own' projects that are managed outside their community or in which they have not been properly involved. Capacity—authority, responsibility and resources –should be explicitly developed so that communities can manage their own projects. From a human rights perspective, the professional from outside the community can no longer be considered to 'know best'. The community knows more about its own situation—what should be done about it and how—than one often gives it credit for. However, ways in which community competencies could be strengthened could include advanced negotiation and facilitation skills. Skills in conflict resolution will also prove useful as issues embedded in the power structures of communities arise and must be addressed.

Communication Strategy for the Four Domains of Conventional HIV/AIDS Responses

The Lesotho National Strategic Plan delineates four strategic areas that currently guide the national response: prevention; care and support; impact mitigation; and special issues. Under each of these issues, there are specific programme areas that form the communication strategy. Below are highlights of what falls under each of these four components:

Prevention

- youth involvement,
- peer group approaches (school-based life skills),
- promotion of the use of condoms, and
- prevention of mother-to-child transmission.

Care and Support

- people living with AIDS,
- home and community-based care,
- support to PLWA organisations,
- counselling,
- care for orphans and other vulnerable children, and
- increased access to anti-retrovirals.

Impact Mitigation

- voluntary counselling and testing,

- policy development dialogue,
- traditional resource development (traditional healers, drama, dance, chiefs), and
- service provider capacity-building.

Cross-cutting Issues

- stigma and discrimination,
- cultural practices,
- poverty, disparity and social exclusion,
- labour migration,
- surveillance, research and data collection/dissemination, and
- coordination and accountability mechanisms and responsibilities.

Guiding Principles for HIV/AIDS Communication

This chapter cannot (and was not intended to) present a comprehensive social mobilisation strategy or a comprehensive communication strategy for social mobilisation. This is a subject that is vast and deserves to be treated in a separate, comprehensive document of its own. However, it seems prudent to highlight, here, some guiding principles that should be borne in mind by those who will be charged with the responsibility of drawing up a comprehensive communication strategy for an HIV/AIDS-competent society in Lesotho.

In principle, an HIV/AIDS Communication Strategy should:

- *be accurate.* Information should be technically accurate, and consistent with international and national research findings.
- *be culturally relevant.* Whenever possible, messages should be developed by those with first-hand knowledge of the Basotho culture.
- *be presented in the local language, (that is, Sesotho).* Research has demonstrated greater credibility and accessibility of information when presented in the first language of the listener.
- *be appropriate to the literacy and comprehension level of the intended audience.* This requires a clear understanding, supported by research, where necessary, of demographic and other data related to target audiences.

- *seek to promote HIV/AIDS-related information and services.* Communication alone cannot influence prevention, care and support. Individuals and communities thus require information about resources that support particular actions, for example, consistent availability of condoms, counselling services, STI treatment resources, and the like.
- *strive for consistency* in terms of presentation and content, particularly with regard to icons, symbols, resources, and the like. This includes, for example, the use of red ribbons for HIV/AIDS awareness activities.
- *be non-alarmist.* Research has demonstrated that fear-based campaigns have had little success, and are particularly inappropriate at the mass media level. It is possible, however, to address issues of fear and denial within dialogue-oriented approaches, such as counselling, workshops, and the like.
- *be non-moralistic.* As it is often a result of sexual behaviour, HIV/AIDS infection has often been moralised in the same way that sexual behaviour itself has. This only serves to further stigmatise the disease and those living with it. Communicators should be cautious of disempowering, undermining or blaming individuals based on their gender, race, or sexual habits.
- *combat stigma.* As long as those living with HIV/AIDS are forced to do so in silence and live with discrimination, true dialogue about prevention will not take place. Healing of the nation must go hand-in-hand with a reduction of the stigma related to HIV/AIDS.
- *incorporate the perspectives of those living with HIV/AIDS*, being careful to be non-discriminatory. For example, referring to those with HIV/AIDS as "victims," "carriers" and "sufferers" creates the perception that people living with the disease are unable to take proactive steps regarding the virus.
- *recognise basic human legal rights.* Increasingly, international legislation is being passed to take into account the special needs of those with HIV/AIDS. Communicators should familiarise themselves with the growing body of legislation, and incorporate these aspects where applicable.
- *be cost effective.* Communication is a complex and costly activity and must use a variety of mediums (mass media, group and interpersonal communication). Every effort should be made to work through existing channels. Formats should be appropriate to target audiences and use appropriate technology whenever possible.

- *incorporate research, evaluation and monitoring wherever practical.* Communication takes place in an ever-evolving context, and messages must shift and change as the receiver's knowledge and attitudes change. Communications interventions that are informed by theoretical frameworks and seek to measure impacts have greater potential for success.

Monitoring and Evaluation

Monitoring and evaluation are crucial for the success of any project activity. As one has long learned, development is not a precise science. When one plans, one makes certain assumptions, some of which may be correct, and others which may be completely off the mark. In addition, the development situation in any given community and society is dynamic, changing all the time. Therefore, one has to make allowances for learning from the experiences of how a project activity is progressing, as well as by being prepared to make periodic adjustments, the necessity of which is manifest from the monitoring of developments on the ground.

Proposed Indicators

Prevention

1. Youth Involvement
   - Number of youth associations.
   - Number of members in youth associations.
   - Number and type of youth-friendly centres/corners and services.
   - Per capita budget on youth activities.
2. Peer-to-Peer Education
   - Number and ratio of peer educators.
   - Number of peer education approaches used.
   - Number and type of organisations providing peer-to-peer education.
3. Condom Usage
   - Number of condoms sold or distributed.
   - Evidence of number of people using condoms through demand.

4. Prevention of Mother-to-Child Transmission
   - Number of mothers participating in MTCT programmes.
     - voluntary counselling and testing.
     - anti-retroviral drug use, such as nevarapine.
     - nutritional strategy for infants born to HIV-positive mothers.
   - Reduction in drop-outs through MTCT programmes.
   - Number of community-based MTCT support groups.
   - Number of men and family members, such as mothers-in-law, attending community-based MTCT support groups.

Care and Support

5. People living with HIV/AIDS (PLWHA)
   - Number of PLWHA who have access to ARVs.
   - Number of PLWHA who receive nutritional advice.
   - Number of PLWHA who receive treatment for opportunistic infections.
   - Number of people trained in home-based care (HBC).
   - Number of community-based HBC support groups.
   - Number of nurse-trainers in HBC.
   - Number of HBC kits distributed.
   - Number of PLWHA using HBC kits (survey).

6. Orphans and Vulnerable Children
   - Number of orphaned children (definition of orphans).
   - Number of orphaned children cared for in institutions.
   - Number of orphaned children cared for in communities.
   - Number of households headed by children.
   - Government budget per orphaned child.
     - percent of budget allocated to institutions.
     - percent of budget allocated to communities.
   - Quality of care for orphaned children in communities.
     - number of orphaned children in schools.
   - Quality of care for orphaned children in institutions.
     - number of orphans in institutions.
     - number of children per staff member (trained and untrained).
     - condition of institutions compared to national standards.

7. Access to Anti-retrovirals (ARVs).
   - Covered in a previous section.

Impact Mitigation

8. Voluntary Counselling and Testing (VCT)
   - Number of VCT centres.
   - Number and availability of rapid test kits.
   - Number and availability of Elisa test kits.[5]
   - Number of people using VCT centres.
   - Percent of population tested for HIV/AIDS.
9. Public Discussions of Policy on HIV/AIDS
   - Number of Pitso meetings on HIV/AIDS.
   - Number of small group discussions on HIV/AIDS in communities.
   - Number of media stories on HIV/AIDS.
   - Ability of people to express views on HIV/AIDS through the media.
   - Number of media stories expressing community viewpoints.
   - Number of media stories expressing government or national viewpoints.
   - Number of media stories expressing special interest (such as PLWHA) viewpoints.
   - Number of Members of Parliament trained on HIV/AIDS issues.
   - Number of meetings of DATF (District AIDS Task Force).
10. Use of Traditional Governance in HIV/AIDS Communication
    - Number of chiefs trained on HIV/AIDS issues.
    - Number of Pitso meetings addressing HIV/AIDS.
    - Number of traditional healers trained on HIV/AIDS.
    - Number of people seeing traditional healers for counselling or treatment.
    - Number of traditional birth attendants (TBAs) trained on HIV/AIDS.
    - Number of people seeing TBAs for counselling or treatment.
11. Capacity Development—Service Providers
    - Number of NGOs or Community Based Organisations (CBOs) providing care or support for HIV/AIDS.
    - Number of nurses trained in HIV/AIDS-prevention and care.
    - Number of village health workers trained in HIV/AIDS prevention and care.
    - Number of community-based counsellors trained in HIV/AIDS prevention and care.

12. In addition, indicators could be developed for the following cross-cutting issues:
    - Stigma and discrimination;
    - Cultural practices;
    - Poverty and disparity;
    - Labour migration;
    - Surveillance, research, and data collection; and
    - Coordination and accountability.

Communications for Development Model

Table 5 illustrates how some of these development communication strategies can be applied to planning. It gives examples of target audiences, activities and outcomes for each strategy.

Table 5.	Communications for Development Model Strategies	
Participants/Targets	**Activities**	**Outcomes**
Advocacy		
Political leaders Decision makers Opinion leaders	*Advocacy with them*: Negotiation Joint planning/review Lobbying Special events Seminars	*Advocacy by them*: Political will Resource allocation Policy changes
Social mobilisation (of Partners in service delivery)		
Ministry of Health Other ministries NGOs Service clubs Media producers Advertisers Artists and intellectuals Curriculum developers	*Advocacy through*: Orientation programmes Joint planning Regular meetings Joint events Workshops Study tours	*Advocacy/action by them for*: Alliance formation Organisational motivation Multisectoral collaboration Institutional agreements

Table 5.	Communications for Development Model Strategies	
Participants/Targets	Activities	Outcomes
Social mobilisation/Behaviour Development Communication (Partners in the community)		
Political, traditional and religious leaders Administrative authorities CBOs Women's/youth organisations Economic organisations Cooperatives	Training Community mobilisation, organisation and participation Participatory research, planning, implementation and evaluation Strengthening of existing structure, monitoring/feedback	Community participation Service utilisation Community ownership Community financing Empowerment
Behaviour Development Communication (Users/clients)		
Parents Men Women Individuals	Audience research Behaviour analysis Development and use of educational materials and media Health education and/or promotion by field workers Training Dissemination of messages/materials	Change in knowledge, attitudes and behaviour Increased and sustained demand for services Adoption of appropriate technologies Accelerated programme achievement Increased uptake of MTCT services Disease/mortality reduction
Behaviour Development Communication (Field workers/other partners in service delivery)		
Health workers Teachers Extension workers Cooperative agents	Interpersonal communication training Organisational motivation Recognition Feedback Supervision	Improved communication with clients Improved planning High-quality services Attitude changes

The Lesotho AIDS Programme Co-ordinating Authority (LAPCA)

LAPCA is the national coordinating body, established in March 2001, to serve as a Secretariat for a National AIDS Commission, and tasked to update national policies, strategic plans and guidelines in HIV/AIDS. It is based at the 4th Floor of the Post Office Building in Maseru.

November 1999 saw the beginning of a series of consultative meetings involving the Government, led by the Ministry of Health and Social Welfare, and involving other ministries, young people, NGOs and members of the public. Two documents were produced (the National HIV/AIDS Strategic Plan and the National HIV/AIDS Policy Framework) and adopted by the Government of Lesotho (GOL) in October 2000.

These two documents indicated that one of the objectives of Government—the establishment of an institution or a body (LAPCA) within the Prime Minister's Office—would be to coordinate all activities nationally and make sure that the strategic plans were implemented. In March 2001, the Chief Executive for LAPCA was appointed, with the following mandates:

- Facilitate the development of sectoral plans;
- Make sure that the policies and strategies agreed upon are implemented, and hold regular meetings with various organisations and individuals within the country that have programmes designed to fight HIV/AIDS;
- Manage research activities relating to HIV/AIDS and sexually transmitted infections (STIs) in the country to make sure that they are relevant and lead to the production and popular dissemination of educational information to prevent and control the spread of HIV/AIDS;
- Mobilise and allocate available resources based on the need and institutional capacity on clearly set criteria;
- Monitor and evaluate the national HIV/AIDS programme; and
- Facilitate effective input of all stakeholders.

The Goals of LAPCA

The following are the goals of LAPCA:

- To delay young people's first sexual experience and promote abstinence;
- To protect sexually active people from being infected by the virus and infecting others, through promoting monogamy and the use of condoms;
- To empower individuals to protect themselves and loved ones, through promotion of Voluntary Counselling and Testing (VCT);
- To endeavour to reduce susceptibility of high-risk groups (sex workers, mineworkers and migrant labourers), through prevention campaigns, promotion of access to condoms, and more;
- To campaign for the human rights, humane treatment and protection of those infected by HIV/AIDS by dispelling the myths and fighting the stigma that create hate and shame;
- To promote that everyone strive towards quality care and treatment of the infected at all levels of care, through mobilising the relevant drug supplies and materials;

- To ensure continued support of the infected and affected through support for ongoing counselling; and
- To have an HIV/AIDS-free society in Lesotho.

The Case for a National AIDS Commission with LAPCA as its Secretariat

Since its inception, LAPCA has experienced a number of teething problems. First and foremost, it took a rather long time for the Chief Executive Officer, Dr. Mpolai Moteetee, to be appointed. Then it took almost a year before other professional staff were brought on board, and even now that they are, it is taking a lot of time for the office to operate at the expected level for its mandate and level of responsibility. In addition, it has become increasingly clear that LAPCA has two conflicting mandates: a strategic mandate and an operational mandate. In this case, LAPCA seems to be engaged far more in its operational mandate than in its strategic mandate, resulting in it establishing district offices and actually implementing HIV/AIDS plans and activities that may best have been undertaken by the Ministry of Health.

In addition, LAPCA's establishment within a Government Ministry seems to have sent a wrong impression to the other Ministries, who now feel that the 2% annual budget for HIV/AIDS for each Ministry should instead be allocated to LAPCA for implementation, a perception that threatens to inadvertently side-line HIV/AIDS from the core responsibilities of each Government Ministry. Furthermore, there are many (both inside and outside Government) who feel that at its current structure, LAPCA does not command the clout and influence required to mobilise the Basotho people and Nation behind a scaled up national response to the HIV/AIDS pandemic. Rather, it is strongly felt that it would be advisable for the Government to establish, as a matter of urgency, a National AIDS Commission, with LAPCA as its Secretariat, as was originally intended, and as a crucial pre-requisite to efforts to scale up the national response to the HIV/AIDS pandemic.

The Way Forward: Catalytic Actions by Government

Government should appoint a National Commission on HIV/AIDS (with LAPCA as the Secretariat) to bring on board all key stakeholders of Basotho Society: representatives of the Church, of traditional leadership, of business, of the network of People Living Positively with HIV/AIDS, of Arts and Culture, as well as of the Mass Media.

This Commission would have to oversee the following immediate actions, among others:

- urgently commission the revision of the National HIV/AIDS Strategic Plan;
- also commission the drawing up of a comprehensive Social Mobilisation Strategy as an integral component of the revised National Strategic Plan;
- urgently draw up an Annual Business Plan, prioritising those components of the National Strategic Plan to spearhead and support national and community-level actions for scaling up the fight against the pandemic; and
- define its own mandate and *modus operandi.*

It must be clearly stated here that a National AIDS Commission (NAC) does not need to have an extensive structure, from national and district levels all the way to community levels, especially since its responsibilities will be of a strategic, advocacy, oversight, monitoring, resource mobilisation and evaluation nature rather than of undertaking programme/project implementation. As stated everywhere in this document, the key strategy for scaling up the national response to the HIV/AIDS pandemic in Lesotho is for everyone in this society to make HIV/AIDS their business if we are going to achieve HIV/AIDS competence. Under the circumstances, each of the key stakeholders—Government, the Church, traditional leaders and healers, PLWHA, other organs of Civil Society—will be responsible for establishing and/or streamlining its own structure of policy formulation, planning, budget allocation, implementation, monitoring, reporting as well as evaluation. The NAC would NOT be responsible for coordinating these activities. Rather, its role would be to determine whether or not each and every stakeholder is keeping its end of the bargain by scaling up its fight against HIV/AIDS and receiving available resources in support of such action. The NAC would also hold those who are lagging behind accountable, including helping them to overcome discernible hurdles and have direct access to both the Head of Government (the Prime Minister) and the Head of State (The King), in order to seek their intervention as the situation may warrant.

Lessons Learned From Other Countries

Before we move forward to propose the roles and actions of the various stakeholders in Lesotho, let us take a minute to reflect on the experiences of other countries. In

Africa, Uganda and Senegal stand out as two countries that give us hope that indeed mobilising all social allies to fight HIV/AIDS can be effective in reversing[6] and containing their epidemics, as each of them respectively did. Uganda's HIV prevalence rate fell from 21.1% to 9.7% between 1991 and 1998, according to evidence obtained from 15 ante-natal clinic sites as well as studies conducted of the army and of blood donors,[7] while Senegal contained its epidemic at 1.7%.

Both Uganda and Senegal combined several of the five main *social mobilisation* approaches outlined above to achieve the success story that they did.[8] Here is how they did it.

The first was *Political Mobilisation*. It is by now a well-known fact that in Uganda the political leadership—in the person of President Yoweri Museveni, as Head of State—pioneered the nationwide campaign against HIV and AIDS. President Museveni's approach combined advocacy for the active participation and commitment of national policy and decision makers and the encouragement of prominent PLWHA (People Living with HIV/AIDS) acting as "Goodwill Ambassadors" throughout the country. Strong political leadership was complemented by strong *Government Mobilisation*, which involved new government policies and programmes that placed

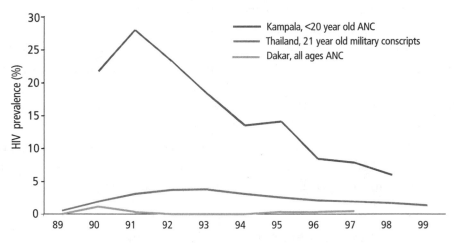

Trends in HIV prevalence in selected populations in Kampala, Uganda; Dakar, Senegal; and Thailand; 1989 to 1999

Source: National STD/AIDS Control Programmes, Senegal and Uganda
Armed Forces Research Institute of Medical Sciences, Thailand

Figure 16. Trends in HIV Prevalence in Selected Populations in Kapala, Uganda; Dakar, Senegal; and Thailand; 1989-1999.

the responsibility for action squarely in the hands of every sector so as to ensure the participation of the entire society in containing the spread of HIV, and thus ensuring the care of those already infected and affected. The fact that the Ugandan Government service delivery is comprehensively decentralised was itself immensely empowering as it facilitated the rapid allocation of resources to where it was most needed and that way demonstrated how *Government Mobilisation* could be extended to every corner of the country.

Community Mobilisation was indeed one of the greatest strengths of both countries' response to HIV and AIDS. As of 2001, there were 700 reported organisations working on HIV/AIDS issues across all districts in Uganda.[9] Religious leaders also played a frontline role, including speaking openly about their status and mobilising their congregation through HIV/AIDS education and prevention activities. Youth groups and traditional institutions, including women's organisations, were active stakeholders in the mobilisation of the society throughout the nation.

An important approach that ultimately yielded results in each and every Ugandan was *Beneficiary Mobilisation*. Using various mass media approaches, including local drama and music, the general population in both rural and urban areas made actions against HIV and AIDS their "patriotic duty"![10] They had learned that HIV was avoidable if they each made a personal decision to avoid risky sexual behaviour. To be able to mobilise the entire population in this manner required a decentralised approach to communicating for behaviour change involving "mass communication, which was community-based, face-to-face, and culturally appropriate." What is unique about Uganda that worked in its favour is that informal communication channels of friends and families are stronger than in many other societies (according to research) and that by the start of the campaign, knowledge of someone with AIDS was over 80%.

All these factors contributed to heightening action by the entire population. In addition, there has been a reduction in non-regular sexual partners by 60% over the period 1989-1995 and a reduction in its sexual networks,[11] as follows: When Ugandans were asked how they had changed their behaviour due to AIDS by 1995, they responded with the following: 48% of the men and women reported that they stuck to one partner; 11% of the women and 14% of the men stopped all sex; and 2.9% of the women and 12.5% of the men started using condoms.[12] Essentially, Ugandans took behavioural change decisions to "zero graze," and used "love carefully," as their communication campaigns urged.[13]

In some instances, several social mobilisation approaches were combined, and yielded results. *Political Mobilisation* was used to promote the noble goal of gender equality and the increased role of women in politics at both national and decentralised levels, while *Government* and *Community Mobilisation* were used to implement the objectives of the empowerment of women and girls and the responsibility of boys and men. This contributed significantly to behaviour change. In addition, youth in and out of school were targeted with a strong campaign to delay sexual debut, while teachers were made HIV-literate.[14]

One key lesson from the Senegalese response is a very simple one. The Senegalese used the *Beneficiary Mobilisation* approach to develop a targeted response. They took the time to learn who was most at risk and vulnerable to HIV, where they were, and why. Having identified commercial sex workers and their clients as the most vulnerable group, they then acted decisively to establish aggressive prevention programmes that targeted this group. Thailand titled their response, *The 100% Condom Use Programme!*

What Can We Learn From the Social Mobilisation Experience of Other Countries?

The lesson from these stories of hope is that we can prevent HIV infection, and that AIDS does not have to be a death sentence. Specifically, the key lessons from the examples above are, as follows:

HIV and AIDS is Everyone's Business

Our knowledge and experience of the pandemic is growing and changing faster than our blueprint responses, which generally recommended that HIV is the business of some parts of government and a handful of civil society organisations. When the pandemic is over 30%, we can assume that every institution, every civil society organisation, every school, every community and every government ministry will be affected by AIDS-related illness and death. In Lesotho, the message has been communicated several times (by His Majesty the King and by the Prime Minister) that HIV/AIDS requires the participation of everyone. But this has been slow to permeate throughout government and local institutions. Yet the clear message from Uganda must be that in order to succeed in reversing the pandemic, HIV and AIDS must be everyone's "Patriotic duty".

Build on Social Institutions and Group Formations to Mobilise the Country

Actions and strategies should be designed to exploit the communal and institutional structures and the cultural/behavioural strengths of each country. In Lesotho, the fact that there are 1,000 or so traditional leaders is a strength that can be exploited to mobilise every Mosotho against HIV and AIDS. Over 90% of Basotho are active members of Christian churches. This is an opportunity that can be exploited to ensure that messages of hope, of care and of prevention are shared with congregants every Sunday, and that the church uses its resources to care for orphans and those infected. The culture of community pitsos to deal with issues concerning the community-at-large presents another important avenue that is already being exploited and can have far reaching impact if used effectively.

Business-As-Usual is Not an Option

The global blueprint for HIV/AIDS strategies has to be adjusted to respond to local realities. The lesson here is that there really is no blueprint on how to respond to HIV and AIDS. Rather, each country is unique and, to be effective, requires that actions are designed to respond to the particular context and dynamics of the epidemic in that country. In the case of Lesotho, the National HIV/AIDS Strategic Plan for the period 2000/2001 to 2003/2004 was developed when the pandemic was about 25%.[15] By 2002, it had reached 31%, and is increasing by all accounts. According to the Plan, young Basotho women are at least 4 times more infected than their male counterparts, because they have sexual relations with older men in exchange for income, security, or marriage. In addition, 70% of those infected are married. Yet, neither the National Strategic Plan nor most other programmes have strategies to deal specifically with these groups. An approach that reflects an effective response, based on an understanding of the context and dynamics of the pandemic, would demand that married households are targeted for behaviour change and condom promotion campaigns. Similarly, strategies need to be designed that specifically target older men who often are themselves unaware of the deadly implications of their sexual relations with younger women.

Target and Localise Responses to the Particular Context

In Lesotho, the data on HIV/AIDS illustrate clear differences between regions, with Mokhotlong at 17% and Maseru at 42%. The data illustrate that the pandemic is multi-faceted. There are different pandemics occurring in Maseru than in Mokhot-long, with different drivers and dynamics. Within Maseru, there are likely different "hotspots" where infections are much higher than others, depending on the socio-economic conditions and sexual networks. Locations, such as Tetsane and Roma that report high levels of STIs, are likely such hotspots and would require a targeted response using a combination of VCT, communicating for behaviour change, condom promotion and peer education and support.

Another example that calls for a targeted and localised response is the recent food crisis. In devising strategies to respond to the food crisis, the country recognised that while the rains were late, the impact of AIDS on the lives of farmers had a devastating effect on the capacity of communities to grow their own food. An emergent strategy approach to the national response to HIV/AIDS would immediately revise its actions to ensure that the impact on the farming community is mitigated.

Building An Effective and Comprehensive Response to HIV/AIDS in Lesotho

How can we apply these important lessons of social mobilisation to building an effective and comprehensive response in Lesotho? In this document so far, we have proposed that to achieve an HIV-Competent Society would require that all Basotho engage actively in all four domains of a comprehensive response: prevention, treatment and care, impact mitigation, and dealing with systemic development factors that enhance risk, vulnerability and capability. Before we examine some actions for each sector, let us look at how we might apply some of the lessons from those countries of hope to the four domains of a comprehensive response.

Prevention

- To build an HIV-Competent Society requires that every Mosotho know how he or she can be infected and therefore how to protect himself or herself. To do so would require *Community and Beneficiary Mobilisation* (for example, door-to-door campaigns) where options for prevention are presented and information shared on where and what resources are available. Using community organisations, such as traditional leaders, church groups, *kgotlas,*[16] *stokvels,*[17] and youth groups, for this purpose is possible and necessary, and would signal a commitment by all to scaling up the national response to the pandemic.

- Using *Community Mobilisation* approaches, every community, institution or group has to identify its own strengths to respond to the challenges above. At the village level, this may be a committed Chief, a network of active community health workers, or strong churches with resources and commitment to family values, or a network of agricultural extension workers, or teachers (in the case of the public service). All these resources can then be re-trained and used to deliver counselling and testing services, as well as to offer face-to-face counselling for each and every Mosotho in that community.

- Using *Community and Beneficiary Mobilisation* approaches, every community, institution or group has to take the time to analyse and understand the drivers of HIV-infection in their particular context, and design targeted prevention strategies. In other words, if, in a particular village, HIV is spread, say, between older men and young women, mostly because of the need for income, then a localised prevention programme should involve community leaders who might offer options that enable the young women to pursue economic activities without placing them at risk, and get agreement in the community that older men take the responsibility to protect young women (and others) from infection.

- Each community, institution or group has to identify the most vulnerable sexual networks related to its particular context (for example, commercial sex workers and transport workers, or married men and single young women). Using *Beneficiary Mobilisation* approaches, an appropriate localised prevention response would target these particular groups and offer alternatives that recognise their particular situation. For commercial sex workers and transport workers, a 100% condom-use prevention strategy can be adopted, while married couples can be counselled to commit to either mutual faithfulness or, if not possible, to the use of condoms in extra-marital relations. In all cases, VCT is a critical component as it alerts all to their status and enables informed decisions by community members.

- *Pitsos* are useful homegrown *Community and Beneficiary Mobilisation* approaches that can be used effectively for communication at the community and even national levels. This can be exploited to serve as a forum for "communal counselling," where a community or group is able to discuss and agree on values and activities that it will commit to promoting, to deal with stigma and discrimination, and to agree on community testing.

- New industries and construction, such as the textile factories in Mapotswe and Tetsane, are likely to contribute to increased HIV-infection by attracting workers from all over Lesotho who are likely to establish new sexual networks in their new work locations. *Corporate and Government Mobilisation* would be necessary to ensure that every new or existing industry has both an impact assessment and a prevention campaign designed for the new workers to ensure that positive developments, such as job creation, do not result in negative results, such as increased HIV infections.

Treatment and Care

- To build an HIV-Competent Society requires that each and every Mosotho understand what to do once he or she, or a loved one, is infected. It would require that one knows where to seek medication and correct nutrition, and that one has the requisite support from health workers. In Lesotho, in addition to government health workers, there are over 1,000 community and church health workers who can be re-trained to provide such direct support to households, including monitoring compliance in the use of ARVs.
- Home-based care has been the primary responsibility of all. Lessons from Uganda and Zambia point to the use of *Community Mobilisation* approaches using local community churches and other social groups who organise themselves to provide home-based care on a rotational basis and to offer additional support to households in order to enable those who are well to pursue economic activities. Social workers in churches and other community organisations can also be so mobilised.
- Using the 1,000 community and church health workers to offer VCT, treatment and care using existing local facilities, such as schools, polling stations and church buildings, would boost the overstretched capacity of government health workers and at the same time reach every Mosotho rapidly.

Impact Mitigation

- An HIV/AIDS-Competent Society requires that each and every Mosotho understand that HIV and AIDS cause illness and death and will, therefore, impact on household capacity, on families and on all local and national institutions. It means, therefore, that every Mosotho has to commit himself or herself to take responsibility to care for those children who are without parents, to stand in by assisting colleagues in the workplace, and to ensure that institutions do not collapse as a result of AIDS-related illnesses.

- Orphans and Vulnerable Children are increasingly heads of households. Building on local assets and structures, communities might design localised solutions on how to care for these OVCs in a manner that enables the community leaders and members take responsibility to ensure that they are watched over by an adult and have the necessary support required. In Lesotho, the Church is already providing some support. But this can be scaled up to ensure that every OVC is well-cared for in terms of parenting, love and support. On this issue, the Government has already taken steps to alleviate some of the financial burden of schooling by offering limited bursaries to OVCs, but this has to be made available to all.

- Following our lesson of the 2002 food crisis in Lesotho that was linked to the loss of farming capacity due to AIDS-related illness and death, it is important that communities and government alike plan ahead for similar impacts. It is feasible, for example, that where several households are vulnerable to food shortages due to AIDS-related illness and death, the Chief can organise for support groups to rotate in establishing communal gardens for these households.

- The impact of AIDS-related illness and death is experienced throughout the civil service, leaving many dependent households more vulnerable and poorer than ever. In an HIV-Competent Society, *Government Mobilisation* at all levels and throughout all sectors would be necessary to develop far-reaching policies that reduce the impact at the household and institutional level. Within government, this requires that comprehensive HIV workplace policies and programmes are developed that ensure that every worker has access not only to prevention, treatment and care, but also to adequate pension and other insurances to enable his or her family to cope. Within government itself, systems are redesigned to reflect the reality that HIV and AIDS introduce changing patterns and the size of demand for services from communities affected.

Systemic Development Factors: Creating an Enabling Environment that Reduces Risk and Vulnerability and Enhances Capabilities

- In an HIV-Competent Society, government and policy makers are aware that factors, such as poverty, gender inequality, migration and even socio-cultural factors, drive the epidemic. They are also aware that the impact of HIV and AIDS is long-term and will have a far-reaching effect on the future demographic pattern of the society.
- As policy makers, government and parliament have the responsibility to ensure that vulnerability to HIV caused by poverty is well understood, and urgent measures are taken to implement poverty reduction efforts as a matter of urgency. Gender equality, in particular at the household level, has to become a national priority and a campaign needs to be developed that illustrates how inequality between men and women can exacerbate HIV infection. Policy measures should be adopted so that any initiatives that might require migration patterns should have an aggressive prevention, treatment and care programme. All government policies that are related to poverty reduction, gender equality and long-term economic growth have to be examined through an HIV/AIDS lens to ensure that they do not inadvertently drive the spread of HIV.
- Building on local structures and mechanisms, it is possible for community leaders to invite their communities, through Pitsos, to dialogue on designing a new society that promotes values that would not place some members at risk. These initiatives already exist in Zimbabwe, where communities identify the vulnerable groups, the reasons for their vulnerability (for example, poverty or gender inequality), and then take a community decision to protect these particular groups and change their behaviour in order to sustain the community.

These are some of the ideas that have emerged from global lessons over the past 20 years of the epidemic in Africa and point to some useful lessons for Lesotho.

NOTES *for Chapter 5*

1. Sesotho word for general public gatherings, usually called for the purpose of creating awareness of HIV/AIDS, plural form of *Pitso* is *Lipitso.*

2. UNAIDS and Pennsylvania State University, *Communications Framework for HIV/AIDS: A New Direction,* UNAIDS and Pennsylvania State University 1999.

3. See, for example, Viviene Taylor, *Social Mobilisation: Lessons from the Mass Democratic Movement* (SADEP, 1997).

4. Judith Ewen, *Developing Indicators for Monitoring Children's Rights: Manual for Training Trainers,* Draft, 1996.

5. There are an increasing number of rapid tests for HIV that are user-friendly and appropriate for use in remote rural areas.

6. Janice A. Hogle (ed.), '*What Happened in Uganda? Declining HIV Prevalence, Behaviour Change and the National Response*', Uganda, USAID, Synergy Project, September 2002. Contributors: Edward Green, Virand Nantulya, Rand Stoneburner, John Stover, and Daniel Lowbeer.

7. Ibid.

8. Alan Whiteside, with Nkosinathi Ngcobo, Jane Tomlinson and Alison Hickey, *What is Driving the HIV/AIDS Epidemic in Swaziland? And What More Can We Do About It?* For National Emergency Response Committee on HIV/AIDS (ERCHA) in Swaziland, ERCHA and UNAIDS 2002. Not published.

9. Ibid .

10. Whiteside et al.

11. Ibid.

12. In Alan Whiteside et al—By marital status: among unmarried men; 38% stopped all sex; 17% stuck to one partner; and 20% started using condoms. Among married men, 65% stuck to one partner, 1% stopped all sex, and 8% started using condoms. In all these situations, 55-65% of the people reported changes in primary sexual behaviours. This conforms with the Ugandan AIDS policy, which focused on delaying sex among youth and sticking to one partner among adults.

13. Ibid.

14. Ibid.

15. Government of Lesotho, National AIDS Strategic Plan 2000/2001-2003/2004, Government of Lesotho, Maseru, 2000.

16. Sesotho term for male gathering place to discuss issues of concern to men and development.

17. Term (not Sesotho) for fundraising activities performed mainly by women.

CHAPTER

6

Information and Communications Technologies and HIV/AIDS
Powerful Tools in the Response to the Pandemic*

ICT and National Development

The enabling capacities of information and communications technologies (ICT) have become so fundamental to the daily social, economic, political, administrative and cultural life of any society and the joint pursuit of individual self-actualisation and a better quality of life for all society, that they effectively constitute basic tools of national development. Those who have the appropriate ICT infrastructure and the corresponding applications, software and content to derive the full benefit of the products and services they provide continue to experience rapid development, even when the fortunes of the ICT companies themselves hang on the balance.

Those who, on the other hand, do not have adequate ICT infrastructure and the corresponding applications and contents, and therefore cannot avail themselves of the benefits of ICT products and services, risk marginalisation of a substantial scale sufficient to be marooned on the wrong side of the "digital divide". For those countries, like Lesotho, that are already at the receiving end of the asymmetrical

---

* This chapter is culled from *Information and Communication Technologies and HIV/AIDS* by Joseph O. Okpaku, Sr., Ph. D., a work-in-progress on the role of ICT in support of the effort to combat the HIV/AIDS epidemic, copyright © 2004.

dispensation of global wealth and opportunities, the risk of further marginalisation through the failure to embrace ICT and capture it for quantum development is a stark reality.

ICT has a duality of capacities: as a basic infrastructure for information and communications, that is, as a utility; and as an enabling capacity that supports and, in many cases, drives practically all other sectors, through its own products and services. In other words, there is a dual challenge: that of ICT development, as well as that of ICT for development. Both aspects of this duality are compelling challenges to the Government and people of Lesotho as the Kingdom constructs its long-term strategies for national development within the framework of its key strategic policies, such as the draft National Vision, its Poverty Reduction Strategy Paper and other policy frameworks it is putting in place to achieve its primary development goals. ICT can greatly advance prospects of overcoming the HIV/AIDS pandemic, eradicating chronic poverty (replacing it with sustainable wealth), as well as achieving and entrenching food security within a healthy and protected environment and ecosystem. It can also provide a critical platform and supporting tools for the achievement of sustainable popular democratic governance and the national stability that comes with it, as well as enhance the overall social and economic well being of its people.

The Challenges

To meet the challenges of ICT development, the following issues and capacity needs must be addressed:

- Definition and determination of specific objectives of ICT development through appropriate assessment and policy formulation;
- ICT infrastructure needs assessment and related needs, such as reliable and affordable energy supply;
- Resource identification, mobilisation and deployment;
- Human resource capacity development;
- Science and Technology development (especially through research and development capacity building);
- Industrialisation at appropriate, sustainable and beneficial sectors and levels;
- Capacity building in software and applications development;
- Local content development for domestic use as well as for export;

- The building of technical competence in such areas as systems design and integration as well as in infrastructure design, building, management and maintenance;
- The access to, the capacity to select and, when possible, the ability to develop, appropriate technologies to provide more, better and more affordable products and services to meet specific local needs, conditions and usage culture;
- Popular and public education regarding both the benefits of ICT and how to utilise its specific products and services for enhancement and self-development;
- The courage and ability to embrace the new way of doing things inherent in the adoption of ICT as a new and pervasive platform for the systemic operation and management of business, government, health, education, agriculture and the various other aspects of national life;
- The courage and willingness to undertake the re-education necessary to take the fullest advantage of the facilities of ICT, even at high levels of authority where the appearance of the need to know is often considered a threat to the preservation of old-fashioned authority and power; and
- The wisdom to identify the limitations and potential downside of ICT, and the corresponding courage to hold the line where the primacy of indigenous culture and desirable lifestyle is threatened by the wholesale adoption of technology—in other words, the constant recognition of the primacy of cultural and human priorities over technology for technology's sake, and the compelling need to subjugate technology to the commanding dictates of human priorities.[1]

Opportunities for Innovation

While meeting some of these challenges might be daunting at first, the benefits they accrue to society and the people far outstrip the concomitant commitment of political will and material resource, and the necessary modifications in *modus operandi*. Some of these benefits and opportunities include:

- The ability to transform a national economy from poverty to equitably distributed wealth, through the development and deployment of intellectual capacity and resource even in the absence of much material resources;
- The opportunity to create a niche market for which the country could become the first port of call for investment seeking opportunities in such a niche market;

- The opportunity to build new and modern infrastructure, systems and processes without the burden of rapidly obsolete legacy infrastructure and practices;
- The opportunity to reach far-flung communities to deliver quality goods and services, thus overcoming the current limitations of distance and isolation;
- The delivery of critical services, such as health and education, to urban as well as rural and remote communities, stretching the capacity of limited material and human resources, as well as expertise through the benefits of network technologies;
- Improved democratic and transparent governance by virtue of easy access to public information and resources, and the ability to establish a two-way dialogue between the citizens and those who govern, and the improved prospects of political stability that come with such public enlightenment;
- Improved productivity by virtue of the simplification of energy and time-consuming exercises, which ICT deployment can drastically reduce if not completely eliminate;
- The ability to create a massive united effort behind a common cause such as, in the case of Lesotho, the War against HIV/AIDS;
- Access to the world and its vast knowledge, culture and information, and the reciprocal exposure to the world of local knowledge, culture and information;
- Opportunities to create well-paying job opportunities in ICT, especially for the young and ambitious, as a way to also stem the tide of emigration in search of more fulfilling opportunities and challenges; and
- National integration, which comes from a higher level of shared ideas, values, dreams and ambitions on the basis of a common people with a common dream and purpose and reasonable expectation of their fulfilment.

ICTs As Powerful Tools in the Response to the HIV/AIDS Pandemic

The challenge of the HIV/AIDS pandemic in Lesotho, and indeed in much of the SADC region where the level of infection is variously placed over 30% of the adult population (15-49 years), cannot be fully understood and conceptualised, unless portrayed in their vivid dimensions.

- Lesotho is already experiencing a negative population growth due to HIV infection. This means, theoretically, that it can conceivably have its population reduced to a point of virtual non-existence.
- The inversely proportional rate of increase in the incidence of orphaned children itself constitutes a major obstacle to the family, and to the social and cultural health of the Basotho. The end result is a scenario of uncles and aunts and, in fact, ill-equipped grandparents, looking after lots of young children, in addition to their own. Ultimately, it results in children raising children. The direct impact of this on school populations and the quality of education is glaringly self-evident.
- If we factor in the rate of infection of children by HIV-infected mothers, the picture dims further. We will have fewer healthy children becoming adults, an age group that is experiencing a declining and weakening population.
- Given the fact that men and women are naturally at their most virile and productive in their youth, the sapping of energy caused by HIV infection threatens to render the population drastically non-productive at what should be its most productive phase.
- The direct impact of this on the numbers and strength of the labour force and its productivity, and their combined impact on the national economy, are equally unimaginable.
- From an economic point of view, this means that businesses, from micro to small and medium-size enterprises, and all the way to corporate entities, will not only experience low productivity due to illness and absenteeism, but will also be faced with a declining market, as the large and revenue-earning population it needs to constitute a market will itself decline. This means that the compulsion of the economic sector to take an active role in the War against HIV/AIDS is not altruistic, as some might think, but a matter of active self-interest and survival.
- The social and cultural impact of this scenario is that society, as we know it today, might become so embattled, that the norms, which have been the underpinning of the culture, risk being shredded.
- From the point of view of poverty reduction and food security (the two other key foci of the Lesotho national development priorities, in addition to the War against HIV/AIDS), it is clear that these goals cannot be achieved without a

radical reversal of the infection process and its devastating impact on all aspects of social and economic life, productivity, quality of life and *joie de vivre*.

This is the downside of the HIV/AIDS pandemic in Lesotho; the challenge, if you will.

The Opportunity

As with all significant challenges, the compelling need to respond to this pandemic and the threat it poses, offers the Government and people of Lesotho, the private sector and civil society, and indeed the country's friends and development partners, a unique opportunity to rise to the clarion call by galvanising and unleashing their genius in meeting this threat head-on in a comprehensive and sustained manner.

From the point of view of long-term strategic planning, there is the collateral compulsion to craft policies and strategies, which permit the mobilisation of all available resources, in all their possible configurations, to forge a comprehensive, coherent, holistic and eminently effective drive to reverse the HIV infection process in Lesotho. This, is turn, will restore the natural process of growth and development to the land and population. This will also permit Lesotho to pursue the best possibilities of development, taking advantage of the best of its human and natural resources, on the backbone of its eminent historic and cultural heritage.

ICT Deliverables Against HIV/AIDS

In such a comprehensive and holistic thrust, the unique array of facilities and deliverables of information and communications technologies offers a significant opportunity for jumpstarting the process of a vigorous campaign against this unacceptable challenge to human health and development, and indeed, to the very posterity of man.

These deliverables may be classified as follows, in accordance with the areas of their potential impact:

- Knowledge and Information;
- Culture, Perceptions and Definitions;
- Information and Data Collection;

- Public Enlightenment;
- Dialogue vs. Instruction—Relinquishing the Disposition to Didacticism;
- HIV/AIDS-specific Health Management, Education and Training;
- Diagnostic and Treatment Support via eMedicine Solutions;
- Support for Compliance with Medication Regimes;
- Global Outsourcing—Online Employment for HIV/AIDS Patients; and
- Innovation through Research and Development.

Knowledge and Information

The dynamics of contemporary existence require a much higher level of individual and group knowledge and information than used to be the case when such capacity was considered to be necessary only for the professional. In the case of HIV/AIDS, there is a need to create a minimum threshold of everyday knowledge about the disease, its cause, prevention, nature, symptoms, impact, consequences and management, as a basic public knowledge. The failure to pursue the creation of this knowledge threshold is a major flaw in the battle against the disease. The capacity of ICT, especially through broadcast as well as network information access and diffusion, offers a simple and relatively inexpensive way to create this basic HIV/AIDS knowledge threshold.

Culture, Perceptions and Definition

Another major flaw in the current established approach to the drive against the disease is the assumption, perhaps presumption, that the campaign against the disease and its management are "scientific", by which, in common parlance, it is understood to be culture-neutral. Besides the fact that science and technology are both intimately culture-determinant, the management of, and response to, the disease (especially one that is so intimately tied to social behaviour and subject to cultural perceptions and the resilience of traditional norms and practices), the pedigree of HIV/AIDS, and the response to it, are significantly culture-dependent.

Furthermore, the unfortunate political, social and regional bias in the earliest efforts at determining the origin of the disease (a bias which promptly "blamed" the origin of HIV/AIDS on Africa) created a resistance to the strategies and policies that have been established in the fight against it. The natural instinct to resist being typecast as the cause or source of any major disease and, therefore, to be suspicious of the solutions propagated by people who are also perceived as coming from the same source and heritage as those perceived to be the architects of such "blame", the African resentment of the unfair stigma, has been under-estimated with devastating consequences. Apropos this, for example, many traditional healers in Lesotho are said to consider HIV/AIDS to be an alien mischief, and the condom, an instrument of a "plot" to destroy the Basotho.

The failure of the condom campaign in much of Southern Africa would seem to suggest that there are additional problems of culture and perception. One such suggestion might be the cultural differences between Africans and the West with respect to the acceptability of explicit discussions of sexual matters, especially across generational boundaries (*see Chapter 7—Culture, the Message and the Messenger: The Role of Culture in the Communication of Critical Social Messages*).

In all of this, in the definition and analysis of these cultural differences and sensitivities, the public dialogue on their implications and consequences, the crafting of a new and more efficacious approach to the challenge, and the dissemination of the resulting strategies and the policies and programmes for their implementation, ICT offers tremendous tools for a Lesotho-specific approach to the War against HIV/AIDS. Such a solution offers a greater promise of constituting a significant and sustainable counterforce against the disease. ICT does so in all its modalities: broadcast, print, telephony, networked education, SMS (Short Messaging System) and other personal information-sharing applications, and more. The result will also be one that is easier to accept and engage in by the Basotho, because they can take ownership of it, being that it would have derived from their cultural and social norms, perceptions and practices, craftily and inconspicuously modified, if necessary, to serve the eminent purpose of literal self-preservation.

Information and Data Collection

A major challenge in the War Against HIV/AIDS is the paucity and accuracy of information and data (both statistical and episodic) on all aspects of the infection, spread, impact and control. Although this is part of the general problem of statistical information-gathering in Lesotho and throughout much of the developing world, the urgency of the response to the disease compels the crafting of a better way to obtain accurate data and information, especially from rural and remote areas where the impact of the disease is no less devastating than it is in urban centres like the capital city, Maseru. ICT offers the best response to this challenge. Innovative use of broadcast technology, especially of radio, as well as the establishment of the infrastructure for online or networked information gathering through the Internet and Intranet, would greatly enhance the scope and quality of such information and data collection mechanisms and processes.

Similarly, the same system, driven in the opposite direction, can enhance the dissemination of information and data about the disease to the Basotho population across the country, from urban dwellers to rural populations.

Public Enlightenment

While there is general agreement that in order to even have a fighting chance of combating HIV/AIDS and rolling back its prevalence and debilitating impact the public must become knowledgeable about it, there is equally general agreement that few people have functional knowledge of the basic facts about it. In fact, it can be said with reasonable accuracy that most people have more erroneous notions about HIV/AIDS than facts. This plays a major role in the difficulty of getting the fundamental message of the true enormity of the threat of HIV/AIDS to humanity's future to the Lesotho public-at-large. Most of the programmes that have been implemented to advance public enlightenment have essentially failed.

Why has the message failed to get across? What must be done differently and how? Our best hopes of finding efficacious answers to these questions just might lie in the crafty deployment of ICT's versatile applications in the HIV/AIDS battlefield. For example, those who are most affected by the disease, either directly as victims, or indirectly as family, friends and employers who must care for them, belong to a totally separate group from those who design and deploy the public enlightenment programmes. With no commonality of understanding and instinct, communication atrophies, leaving the messenger marooned with his or her message, while the audience is left alone at the dusk of despair to ponder listlessly in private how best to cope with a personal and ever so lonely and intimate perpetual nightmare.

To undermine this strategic fault, a deliberate programme of promoting local content development in all aspects of the media must be crafted and implemented. The very act of doing so, providing local ownership of the message and the means for its delivery, especially within the context of commonality between the messenger and the audience, will leapfrog this gulf of understanding, and help bring home the HIV/AIDS message the way it badly needs to. The intellectual basis of this is the importance of identifying with the messenger in order to be most receptive to the message.

With the support of community and communal leaders, storytellers, local chiefs and traditional healers combining to form the local corps of HIV/AIDS messengers, and backed by broadcast (especially radio, and in Sesotho), this local content initiative could transform the playing field of public enlightenment, even creating an eagerness to learn about and openly discuss the disease, its cause, prevention, management and ultimate cure.

Where the infrastructure might prove to be a limitation, innovative deployment of IP-based rural and community radio broadcasting could fill the gap. The same infrastructure can then double up to provide other services, such as education, and administrative and routine health services.

From a cultural point of view, traditional myths, narratives, beliefs and norms could be cleverly adopted and skillfully yet imperceptibly modfied to support the process, taking advantage of the human penchant for seeking a little public attention, a fact most true of traditional healers, chiefs and storytellers.

Such an effort, spearheaded by Basotho youth (both male and female) and drawing on the familial affection basic to the culture, and deployed with a thorough knowledge of, and sensitivity to, the respect of traditional attitudes towards public discourse of sexual matters, would have the additional value of enhancing urban-rural and cross-generational integration. This would prove to be a critical means of disseminating information on prevention from infection and the care of the infected.

Dialogue vs. Instruction: Relinquishing the Propensity for Didacticism

A related concern is the fact that the flow of ideas, information and knowledge about HIV/AIDS is in one direction, from the AIDS worker to the infected or populations at risk. This comes down as instructions (and sometimes pontifications), with the presumption that those infected or at risk are ignorant or have nothing to say or share. The approach, therefore, becomes didactic, often coming across as condescending. And yet, who knows more about the experience of HIV/AIDS than those who either have it, or have to care for those who have it?

A programme to learn lessons from the experience of the infected, those at risk or those who care for them, holds the promise of a new world of insight into how to fight the War against the pandemic. ICT applications offer the best instrument for such an effort. For example, given the fad of mobile telephony amongst the young who also constitute the largest HIV-infected or at-risk population, a simple programme of using SMS to share HIV/AIDS information or to broadcast short reminder messages of caution and protection could have dramatic instantaneous impact that can then be sustained by broader programmes.

HIV/AIDS-Specific Health Management, Education and Training

Given the level of HIV infection in Lesotho and the challenge of HIV/AIDS management, there is a need to train a much larger number of care-givers, from the level of nurses and home-care providers to family members, who could use some basic knowledge and training. ICT applications, from radio and television, to online and storage and retrieval training programmes, offer tremendous opportunities in this regard.

Diagnostic and Treatment Support via eMedicine Solutions

Furthermore, given skewed proportions between patients and healthcare facilities, in addition to the reality of remote small populations with little medical facilities, electronic health (or eHealth) programmes provide the only affordable means of delivering critical services, from diagnostics to prescription and monitoring. There is so much innovation in the eHealth field that new and versatile services should rapidly become more affordable by the day.

Support for Compliance with Medication Regimes

A much-debated issue with regard to the provision of HIV medication in Africa as a whole, including Lesotho, is that of how to monitor the medication regimes so critical to achieving the benefits they provide. In the absence of the battalion of nursing aids that will be required to administer such medication individually to every HIV-infected, or full-blown AIDS, patient, simple and innovative use of common ICT facilities and applications can be devised to serve this purpose.

Global Outsourcing–Online Employment of HIV/AIDS Patients

A major part of the challenge of HIV/AIDS is the economic, social and psychological debilitation it foists on the patients and their families. The physical and psychological aspects, including especially their condition in the advanced stages of the disease, confine patients to the isolation of the home, hospital or other healthcare facility. The loss of income creates poverty which, in turn, increases the vulnerability to the disease as a result of the increased malnutrition. Furthermore, given the fact that a good number of these patients once had productive employment, the psychological consequences of being rendered both unemployable and without gainful activity, erodes the emotional fortitude and fortification of the patients. This, in turn, drastically increases their vulnerability to the disease by undermining hope and their psychological fortitude, two attributes proven to be critical to the healing process, in addition to faith.

A bold, innovative and comprehensive programme to provide skills development and online employment for HIV/AIDS patients in a public/private partnership holds immense possibilities in this regard. Given the network capacity of ICT technologies, support participation for such an initiative could be global, reaching well beyond the national boundaries of Lesotho, through job outsourcing.

Innovation Through Research and Development

Above all, there is no way to combat a disease so prevalent in Lesotho without a comprehensive research and development programme in any one of the myriads of areas where innovation could make a difference. Such research with respect to how to use ICT applications to support various aspects of the War against HIV/AIDS would suggest itself as a worthy area of strategic national investment.

A Compelling Priority

Overall, scaling up the national response to the HIV/AIDS pandemic in Lesotho is a compelling priority if the promise of development and the quantum expansion of the quality of life and self-actualisation for the people are to have meaning and efficacy. ICT, in its versatility and nimbleness, constitutes an area of possibilities, the embracing and deployment of which should greatly enhance the fighting capacity of the nation and its people. Fortunately, in the process, it will also promote greater national integration and the benefits of nation-building that come with it.

NOTES *for Chapter 6*

1. See Joseph O. Okpaku, Sr., "Information and Communications Technologies as Tools for African Development," in *Information and Communications Technologies for African Development: An Assessment of Progress and Challenges Ahead*, pp.11-12, UN ICT Task Force, New York, 2003.

Culture, the Message and the Messenger
The Role of Culture in the Communication
of HIV/AIDS and Other Critical Social Messages*

There is little that we do or engage in that is serious or meaningful that is not predicated on, or influenced by our cultural foundation. From the way we perceive nature and its phenomena and interact with it and with each other, through our reasoning process, to what and how we communicate, and the meaning we derive from so doing, our behaviour is driven to a large extent by our culture and the way it has shaped us and determined our worldview. In this context, and outside of genetic and other such factors, variations in individual choices and behaviour depend, to a great extent, additionally, on our individual knowledge, experience, exposure and the extent and degree of mastery of (and accommodation with) our culture or cultural background. They also depend on the extent to which that context plays against our exposure to, and influence by, other cultures which we come in contact with, directly or indirectly. Put differently, our behaviour, perception, perspective and actions are shaped to a large extent by the dialectical tussle between our innate and

---

* This chapter is culled from *Culture and the Challenge of Modernisation* (working title) by Joseph O. Okpaku, Sr., Ph.D., a work-in-progress critique of global development strategies and their legacy vis-a-vis African culture and socio-cultural tenets, priorities and popular paradigms, copyright © 2004.

heritage culture, on the one hand, and, on the other hand, often competing cultures which we embrace or are otherwise exposed to.

In this what might be called the battle of cultures for control of our mind and soul, and implicitly our worldview, preferences, perceptions and behaviour, claims and images of global absolutes are conjured up and deployed, even if inadvertently, to undermine our inner strength and resilience in the expectation that in order to be "recognised" as being truly global, to come of modern age, so to speak, we must ourselves first perceive our heritage culture as obsolete and antithetical to progress, and thus reject it. And yet, because our heritage culture, especially as Africans, is one of the oldest and most resilient in the history of man, we become vulnerable to global uncertainties only in direct proportion to the extent of our cultural alienation.

The most powerful weapons in this cultural battle for global prominence and absolutism, which is what we really are talking about when we talk of the challenge of globalisation in more common parlance, are the mass media, those instruments of the propagation and diffusion of information and opinion that create mass cultures which in turn, challenge heritage culture to the drumbeat of modernisation. At the most critical level, control of the mass media, especially the global mass media, becomes simultaneously the instrument for, and yardstick of, cultural domination, and the presumption of a single global standard, culture and development path. The resulting mass culture, or the disjointed hybrid which is often the only achievable outcome of this process, not only imposes the notion of commonality of human understanding and acceptance of a single system of vision, perception, behaviour or communication (glaring evidence to the contrary notwithstanding), but also leads to the presumption that we all speak the same language and therefore have a common understanding.

When, then, messages are presumed to have been communicated in what we might call the "cultural language" of one party, and the evidence suggests that the message is not getting through, every avenue of denial of the glaring lack of efficacy of the language and mechanism of its delivery is pursued, anything to avoid the obvious fact that the message is simply not configured to be accepted, or even considered.

But perhaps we should first lay a common platform for understanding of this discourse by establishing a handful of definitions, especially of what precisely we mean when we talk about information, knowledge, culture, society and civilisation, living, learning and the quality of life.

Knowledge, Culture, Society and Civilisation–Living and Learning

In a presentation to the ASEAN Regional Workshop on Building Knowledge Societies held in Kuala Lumpur, Malaysia, in January 2000, and subsequently in a presentation in Coventry, United Kingdom, in August 2001, one had made the following postulation:

"Next to the Universe, mankind, and the human spirit which drives it, remains one of the most durable phenomena of history. The context within which mankind pursues its existence is *society*. The environment within which this pursuit takes place is *culture*. The substance of culture is *knowledge*. The process by which man interacts with knowledge, extracting from it and enhancing it, is what we call *learning*. The process by which the human spirit prosecutes its survival is *living*, and the extent to which man succeeds or fails in achieving self-enhancement and the advancement of society and enrichment of culture is called the *quality of life*.

Culture, the accumulation of human experience and creativity, is, therefore, the pre-eminent context of human existence, the sustaining substance of which is *knowledge*. Contrary to popular assertions, *knowledge* does not derive from *learning*. *Learning* is a process by which we access knowledge. *Learning* is the tool with which we acquire *education*. *Learning* is a process, not a foundation. *Knowledge* then is the tool for building societies, and the foundation for that process is *culture*".[1]

Information and Knowledge

One has also sought to distinguish between information and knowledge thus:

"Too often, *information* and *knowledge* are used as if they were synonymous. This confusion inhibits our ability to address the true nature and challenge of our knowledge society. *Information* is simply a body of facts and data, with no compelling intrinsic value or meaning. *Knowledge*, on the other hand, is the crystallisation of lessons learnt from the study or experience of the phenomena of history. Knowledge derives from culture; and the history of knowledge within a culture becomes *civilisation*. Knowledge, therefore, embodies not only the mastery of the phenomena of life and man's innovation, but the ethics, morality and traditions of a given society and its culture."[2]

Where knowledge spills over beyond a given society onto a global platform, its context becomes *global culture*. Building a knowledge society, therefore, compels the entrenchment of the essential qualities of a given culture or civilisation as the core of a new configuration of future society. Access to information, while an important component of acquiring knowledge, does not in itself constitute learning. This would suggest severe limitations in the power we implicitly grant to Internet access as the magic tool of transforming society. It must be remembered that the essential value of Internet access is the ability to access much larger chunks of information much faster and, hopefully, much more easily.

Culture, Credibility and the Message

Each society has its own set of attributes with which it expresses, determines and recognises credibility. In Africa, for example, and perhaps in most older cultures and civilisations, credibility, with respect to the person, requires touch and visual contact. It is commonly presumed, especially by older Africans, that you cannot look them in the face and lie. In younger and even not-quite-so-much-younger societies, on the other hand, in modern society, as the common parlance goes, credibility, and therefore trust, is predicated on agreements, documentation, and authentication. This dichotomy, which is not merely a matter of development, has serious and complex implications when we try to communicate or transmit critical social messages across cultures and societies, implications which lend themselves to fascinating analysis in broader space. For us, therefore, the one critical implication is that Africans, perhaps in their presumed naiveté, still believe that, "If I cannot trust you, I cannot believe anything you tell me." In other words, trust precedes credibility which, in turn, is a necessary condition for literally "opening up" to allow a message come in, or to penetrate our natural defense mechanisms.

The Cultural Immune System (CIS)

In reviewing development strategies and their mixed legacy vis-à-vis African culture and socio-cultural tenets, priorities and pre-eminent pillars, an exercise that was instigated by the recognition of a constantly lingering touch of recalcitrance in the record of the accomplishment of development assistance and intervention in the struggle against HIV/AIDS in Africa, one has come to the preliminary view, that a major reason for some of the remarkable flaws in aspects of the efforts to convey the HIV/AIDS message to Africans, is possibly, quite possibly, the fact, or so it would seem, that there is a cultural gulf between the messenger and the target audience. Behind the communication effort, albeit inadvertently, there appears to be invariably embedded in the very fabric of the message, a set of invisible ancillary cultural messages with no direct bearing on the HIV/AIDS issue (similar to "cookies" in computing), and with questionable relevance or authenticity.

Put differently, when messages of critical public import are being communicated to Africans primarily from outside, such as relate to public enlightenment in the fight against HIV/AIDS, the cultural priorities and "biases" of the messenger tend to be bundled with the message, and "sold" wholesale to the African.

Almost equally invariably, such efforts tend to fail, or fall short of common sense expectations. The message either does not come through (that is, it fails to penetrate the skin of the society), or if it does, it has no staying power and is hardly absorbed and internalised. In other words, it fails to achieve relevance and resilience. The people deny the message package any licence of due consideration because, in their view, the package lacks authenticity. They refuse the message package because they cannot take ownership of it without, in their view, exposing their cultural priorities to uncertain invasion. (See *Chapter 16—Conclusion: Taking Ownership of the HIV/AIDS Challenge*).

A close examination of this phenomenon, one which has bedeviled the legacy of development assistance for decades, suggests, fascinatingly, that there is a systematic and systemic resistance to such message packages being communicated. The message package is "blocked" from penetrating the protective skin of the culture and from entering the system.

On further examination, one discovers that as an older culture, Africa has built, through the centuries, its complex ways of blocking or fending off what it suspects to be cultural subterfuge, ways of resisting cultural influences which it considers alien or hostile to its interests, and which threaten its culture and domain. The inherent attribute which drives this process, the mechanism for doing so—this inherent instinctive cultural self-protective mechanism which is akin to our biological immune system—is what one has chosen to call a *"Cultural Immune System"* or *"CIS"*.

The Cultural Immune System (CIS) and the HIV/AIDS Message:
A Cultural Communications Challenge

If this thesis has efficacy, even if only slightly so, then the question arises, is it possible that the resistance to the critical message of HIV/AIDS derives from the fact that the message comes heavy-laden with other cultural baggage such that the African cultural immune system jumps automatically to "protect" the centuries-old norms from "invasion" by the cultural "threat" embedded in the fabric of the HIV/AIDS message?

If this is the case, then perhaps we can circumvent this "throwing the baby out with the bathwater" situation by seeking to separate the message from the culture of the messenger, and once having isolated the message, "injecting" it, by itself (that is, in its essentially pure or "naked" form), into the cultural mechanisms and traditions Africans themselves use for conveying critical social messages, especially those concerning situations that threaten the life and very survival of the society.

Traditional Indigenous African Channels for
Communicating Critical Social Messages

If this theory of a Cultural Immune System has efficacy, then certain questions arise:

- What are the traditional ways in which Africans, and specifically for the purpose of this effort at scaling up the fight against the HIV/AIDS pandemic in Lesotho, the Basotho, convey and transmit critical and significant social messages?
- Who enjoys the most trust in conveying what kind of messages?
- Do different people play this role in different sub-cultures, different age groups, different genders?
- Do traditional social clubs, cults and similar cultural or even so-called "secret societies" play a critical role in this process, and if so, how?
- What role do traditional leaders, healers and elders play in this process?
- What roles do grandparents, parents, aunts and uncles, siblings and other relatives in the extended family play in this process?
- Overall, what roles do these people and institutions play in communicating and preserving critical social messages, lessons learned and acquired knowledge and

information for the present and future benefit of the community and society-at-large?

Adopting Traditional Mechanisms of Communicating Critical Social Messages in Support of the Response to the HIV/AIDS Challenge

If, indeed, this theory of a Cultural Immune System is valid, which one believes it is, given the preponderance of evidence and the almost total consensus about it by many Africans old and young with whom one has engaged in a discourse on the subject, then we stand at the threshold of a possible major breakthrough in the conduct of communications and public enlightenment in standing up to the HIV/AIDS pandemic and to other social, economic, health and overall quality of life challenges.

What we need to do would be simply to get back to our age-old and time-tested traditional channels of social communications, adopt them and adapt them to contemporary exigencies, and deploy them innovatively as the avant garde of our defensive as well as offensive strategies and thrust. In so doing, we would gain additional significance and benefit in that we would be restoring respect, relevance and value to our traditional peoples, our elders, embracing them to embrace us in a unified African Family march of progress for a comprehensive self-development.

In the process also, we might even invoke our ancestors to look upon us and intercede for us, their descendants, as we struggle hard to protect, preserve and promote the heritage and legacy they bequeathed us, and which we are in grave danger of losing. The process of this phenomenal unleashing of our cultural and traditional latency is boundless. Its psychological, morale and inspirational attributes and benefits, especially in a struggle such as this one in which psychological and inspirational support and faith are critical, could go a long way to cushion the harshness of the fight, and help uplift our spirit at a time when we must fight without despair and disillusionment.

We are, therefore, duty bound, with the promise of immense value accruing from doing so, to devise a mechanism for placing the HIV/AIDS message in the hands of our traditional agents of critical social message transmission, and to empower them to do what they traditionally do best, namely, pass on such critical messages (on the rapid knowledge and understanding of which the security and survival of society depends), authoritatively to the rest of society, especially to young ones.

The Process

The process of adopting and adapting traditional channels for communicating critical social messages can be summarised in a few steps:

1. *Isolating the message from its embedded cultural baggage;*
2. *Identifying the indigenous traditional and contemporary channels of transmitting significant and urgent messages;*
3. *Injecting the stand-alone message into the indigenous cultural "conveyance mechanism";*
4. *Popularising the message throughout the extensive network and system of traditional public enlightenment and education;*
5. *"Modernising" the process in order to cater to those, mostly urban peoples, whose communal connections might have slipped through time, without undermining the fundamental value, nature or efficacy of the process;*
6. *Using the process to promote internal and national integration, not only vertically through the various classes but horizontally between rural and urban populations, the young and the old, thus promoting the restoration of the unified family as the fundamental unit of survival, progress and self-defense in African society.*

The above requires that the traditional culture take ownership of both the problem and the message it is propagating to address the challenge.

Crafting an Indigenous HIV/AIDS Message for Lesotho

In resuscitating traditional channels of communicating critical social messages for the fight against HIV/AIDS, especially on the premise of the need to isolate the message from its alien cultural baggage, the need arises to craft indigenous HIV/AIDS messages to deliver through the traditional pipes. Doing so will involve careful research and content development, which itself would be empowering and promote capacity building. The key is to take the scientific message, at its most accurate possible, and to infuse it with the most efficacious traditional means of messaging, including story telling, dance, music, art, and other forms of creative and innovative communications.

Mobilising Traditional Lesotho Culture in Propagating and Promoting the HIV/AIDS Message[3]

Lesotho Culture

Culture is of the utmost importance to the people of Lesotho, as it is to most African peoples. Lesotho culture has been under assault many times in its history, from the church, from apartheid, but it has survived all of them. In fact, culture was at the very core of the creation of the Lesotho nation by King Moshoeshoe.

The people of Lesotho are very proud of being Basotho. Everyone talks about the Lesotho nation. This has its pluses and minuses. But the pluses out-number the minuses. This pride in Sesotho culture is the basis of their identity and resilience. It is that resilience which enabled them to resist the onslaught of apartheid, and even of the rugged climate. As a mountain country, the climate of extreme temperatures, high winds and dust can be quite challenging. Surviving it requires fortitude, and that survival has further increased the resilience of the Basotho. As a case in point, the Basotho have a special breed of horses which, unlike most others, can survive in a harsh mountain environment.

The Initiation Schools

Basotho have a complex tradition of social education, the most relevant of which are the Initiation Schools. Initiation Schools are a very important institution in Lesotho culture and society. Professor F.Z.A Matšela, in an unpublished paper, provides the following description of the Lesotho Initiation Schools:

> Matšela & Motlomelo (2000) found in their recent research that (the Initiation Schools) had a well-defined set of educators, students of a minimum age, a specified curriculum, clearly defined management, and instructional

environments, and approaches. It was the formal culmination of a long period of non-formal education characterised by work-based apprentice-type instructional activities with various other learners, under varied but mainly senior adult educators and assistant instructors. In all cases, the initiation processes took place towards the close of puberty and at the onset of adulthood. The chief educator (principal) of the initiation academy (*mophato*) is a highly respected person of irreproachable character and outstanding knowledge of (and dedication to) Lesotho cultural values and their responsible practice. While initiated males are considered experts in the arts of war, farming and the bovine-based economy, initiated women are also expected to be specialists in house crafts and home economics. They all had to teach by both example and precept and not by the latter alone, and to them, cultural maturity implied responsibility and dedication to a life of fruitful service to one's family and community or nation.

The initiation curriculum consists of both an open and a secret phase. The latter's clandestine character is due to its socio-political demands, religious doctrines and military acumen. The former consists of understanding critical elements of national history, theology, economics, philosophy, sociology, kinship genealogies and pragmatics all welded together into lessons of life taught through ancient sacred songs (Sheddick, and Makara, 1953). Among other things, the curriculum is composed of lessons on values including truth; justice and peace; mercy; discipline and commitment to service; patriotism; problem-solving; poetry; and song and dance. Initiates learn to work amicably together; they compose their own poetry under the expert guidance of their master-teacher (*Mosuoe*); they are introduced to basic handicrafts, as well as to the art of war (for men) and the family crafts (for women). This implies an inbuilt capacity in the system's training to produce armies of motivated and action–oriented men and women, committed to saving their nation culturally and economically. It also implies a commitment to discipline in the pursuit of cultural values and with this commitment, the initiated men and women can become leaders of change in their communities.

The initiated elders of today complain that some of today's initiation academies (*mephato*) have lax discipline and produce immature "semi-adults" (*makoele*) in place of the expected men and women capable of handling socio-cultural and communal/national economic problems seriously and effectively. The essence of Sesotho initiation rites is its religious dogmatic character; it had to be carried out to produce God's people under the keen eyes of the Sacred Spirits/Shades (*Balimo/Liriti*) and the chiefly leadership. They, therefore, had a powerful system of prayer-rites for various purposes (*Makara, 1960, Ellenberger & McGregor, 1969*). Discipline and the ability to live and display exemplary values-changed behaviour, are critical for Basotho adults.[4]

Given these attributes, the Initiation Schools potentially can play a key role in the fight against the HIV/AIDS pandemic. The ideas which young men learn during initiation, they hold onto dearly for the rest of their lives—more than even church teachings, and definitely more than what they learn in schools from the classroom and from books. So, if basic knowledge and information about HIV/AIDS (its cause, how it is transmitted, prevention, protective measures for self and for partners, the need for testing, treatment and care of the infected and the full-blown AIDS patient) is taught through the Initiation Schools, chances are that the men will hang on to such lessons and apply them more diligently and faithfully than whatever they could be taught in school.

Since information and knowledge about HIV is about sexuality, what better place to learn about HIV and sexuality than through the very institutions in which sexuality, from childhood through puberty to manhood, is traditionally taught?

Re-engineering the "Curriculum" of Initiation Schools

Given the attributes of the Initiation Schools, it should be possible to undertake a comprehensive study of its specific *modus operandi*, and to re-engineer its curriculum to infuse it with the critical social HIV/AIDS message, duly isolated from attendant alien cultural baggage as discussed above, and to make it a major channel for communicating such critical messages throughout the country. As part of the curriculum, in teaching the boys about manhood, for example, that notion should be expanded to include the dignity and responsibility of protecting the well-being and health of the entire family, young women, their wives, as well as themselves and their children. Avoiding HIV infection and, therefore, avoiding the risk of ultimately having AIDS and suffering its debilitating consequences should be taught as an act of noble manhood, part of the same attribute as military acumen, virility or statesmanship. The congruence of manhood and sexual responsibility that will emerge from such a subtle re-engineering, or what one might describe as "a slight expansion of the attribute of manhood", to embrace sexual responsibility, offers a remarkable example of the adoption and adaptation of traditional channels for HIV/AIDS public enlightenment.

Gender Responsibility—e.g. Condom Responsibility

One of the challenges of battling HIV/AIDS is that the very subject of sexuality itself strikes at the heart of our privacy. This places the issue in the realm of intangible candour, from demure inarticulation through covert denial to blatant misstatement. Much of public sexual dialogue is predicated on grand-standing, whether on the moralistic side or on the brave and liberated side. There is, in today's modern discourse, no credible example of a popular open discourse of the intimacy of sexuality which covers the delicate last mile. Ironically, traditional cultures, especially of old and tested civilisations such as Africa, do have traditional means and avenues for dealing with such intimate privacy routinely and in commonly acceptable fashion and parlance. In some cases, resort is made to narrative, metaphor, ritual, song and dance, and even art, to undertake such discourse for popular involvement, education and absorption.

Gender, Culture, Sexuality and Negotiating Safe-Sex

Let us take, for example, the insistence that young African women be empowered to negotiate safe sex. Where is the efficacious precedence? How many educated, sophisticated, professional, even liberated women in the western world have been able to negotiate safe sex with their partners, even with their husbands? How then do we expect to teach and empower young African women, girls in fact, to negotiate safe sex with their male friends, not to talk about their husbands?

This is only one of the simple truths, albeit embarrassing, of the skewed global dialogue and policy about HIV/AIDS management and prevention which fall flat in the face of more rigorous analysis, especially from the point of view of a firm and informed cross-cultural or multi-cultural perspective. It is also another argument for the pressing need for Africans to take ownership of the HIV/AIDS crisis, develop their own authentic perspective on the challenge and craft efficacious paradigms for their solution, taking appropriate advantage of the best and most enlightened global information, knowledge and experience. In so doing, they can get the most out of collaboration with the development and donor community to implement a more coherent and relevant programme in genuine partnership. Uniquely, here is an example of where culture, tradition and traditional institutions can make a major positive impact.

Traditional Sex Education in African Society

One of the most common approaches to the efforts at taming the HIV/AIDS pandemic in Africa has been the strong advocacy that parents teach their children sex education. In particular, the pressure is on mothers to teach their daughters about sexuality. The problem is that traditionally, sex education is not undertaken by parents, but by aunts, uncles, and, most importantly, grandparents. These are the people with whom young men and women feel relaxed about discussing their sexuality. These also, especially grandparents, are those whom tradition has given the right to be explicit about sexual discourse, because they have earned it by experience. Young people will more readily share sexual anxieties with their aunts, uncles, and most especially their grandparents before they even contemplate approaching their parents. The cultural norms of respect also would preclude this.

The argument can, of course, be made that modern life compels a shift to sexual education by parents on the basis of a new nuclear family. But a counter-argument can be made as to why we should not make the most of a ready-made tradition which can deliver as much, if not more of what we need. Furthermore, such cross generational interventions have the collateral benefit of holding the family closer together, and providing a meaningful role for the elderly in the lives of the young. At the end of the day, a hybrid approach could be a reasonable compromise.

Eliminating the "Gender Guilt" Approach to the HIV/AIDS Effort

An issue which also calls for review in the search for greater efficacy in the HIV/AIDS campaign is the preponderance of gender guilt laid heavily on boys and men in Africa. This outgrowth, in part, of the gender efforts whose legitimacy are beyond question, could have the effect of introducing yet another conflict or contention in an already heavy-laden arena in which all are at risk, and where a united family approach is the only solution.

The argument to pay particular attention to the special needs and vulnerability of girls and women is irrefutable. In Africa, these arguments can be made even more effectively on the basis of the common cultural tenet that our women are the managers and caretakers of our society and its well-being, and that for society to be well and wholesome, our women must first be well, healthy, wholesome and fulfilled.

But the argument can also be made that at the present level of the HIV/AIDS crisis, of what value are differential gender statistics in a situation in which society itself, not just female society, is theoretically at risk of effective eventual extinction?

Furthermore, given the enormity of the challenge and its impact on virtually all society in Lesotho, for example, and the enormous emerging political buy-in at the highest and all levels, the clarion call must be for all hands on board, male and female. Risking defensiveness on the part of either group, male or female, amongst both the general population and the political and traditional elders and authorities, would be counter-productive. Furthermore, the automatic alienation of the genders, which has become common fare in the global power struggle in the battle of the sexes, does not hold much efficacy for Africa. What does is gender union and collaboration, using attributes inherent in the primacy of the structure and value of the institution of the African family to protect girls and women, young and not-quite-so-young.

Quite simply, the battle ahead will need all hands on-board, and even more. We need to bring men and women, boys and girls, closer together, so close, in fact, that the commitment to safe sex, for example, will become a routine joint action, a new aspect of enlightened love and romance, manhood and womanhood—that is, the coming of age. We cannot achieve this if we allow even the slightest room for the perception of guilt or culpability.

The pandemic has already undermined hope, faith and self-confidence as much of men as of women. Let us not forget, for example, that the impact of HIV on family survival, besides its direct impact of impoverishment, malnutrition and deprivation, also imposes the additional sense of shame of incompetence to deliver masculine responsibilities on the part of the man. Overloading his already fragile system with guilt runs the risk of totally overwhelming him, with even more drastic consequences for everyone including girls and women. Examples elsewhere in the world are instructive.

Meeting the Special Needs of Girls and Women

On the other hand, all of the above notwithstanding, there are special issues, concerns, anxieties and needs of women and young girls with respect to the HIV/AIDS pandemic, which require particular attention. This has been addressed in various places in this manual. Its importance, however, cannot be sufficiently emphasised.

Culture, Tradition and Development

At the end of the day, the national response to the HIV/AIDS pandemic in Lesotho is in itself, a struggle to preserve and enhance Lesotho culture and traditions. The protection and development of both is at the foundation of the development of the land and the people. Deploying the attributes of Lesotho's culture and traditions and engaging the people and institutions that embody them, therefore, in this major response, is not only necessary, but also inevitable if success is to be achieved. Our elders, the curators of our culture and tradition, embody a wealth of knowledge and experience of coping with the toughest challenges which we all need to learn and benefit from. What better arena to do so but in all of us joining forces to save and protect all?

NOTES *for Chapter 7*

1. Joseph O. Okpaku, Sr., *Designing Knowledge Societies: Challenges and Opportunities,* ASEAN Regional Workshop On Building Knowledge Societies, Kuala Lumpur, Malaysia Jan 26–27, 2000.

2. Joseph O. Okpaku, Sr., *eCulture, Human Culture and In-between: Meeting The Challenges Of The 21st Century Digital World,* ITU Conference on Creating New Leaders for e-Culture, Coventry, United Kingdom, August 2001.

3. This analysis benefits from engaging discussions with several people, including Mrs. Scholastica Kimaryo, Dr. Samuel Okpaku, Thomas Okpaku and Ms. Nepeti Nicanor, amongst others.

4. From unpublished paper by Professor F.Z.A Matšela, Secretary General of the Sesotho Academy, Maseru, Lesotho.

8

Personal and Institutional Transformation as Pre-requisites for Success

Capacity Building and Development

The commitment of the Government of Lesotho to defeat the HIV/AIDS pandemic is not in doubt. It is clear from the statements and actions of the leadership at the highest level that Government is deeply committed to addressing this pandemic in a sustainable manner. However, there is a gap between the announcement of a strategic plan to address the pandemic and achieving results: this is the delivery gap (*see Figure 17*). It is not only in relation to the fight against HIV/AIDS, but also in regard to other public sector priorities. This is something that needs to be addressed from the outset.

As we see the impact of the deepening of the problem of HIV/AIDS in Lesotho, undermining the entire system with responsibility for delivering on development priorities, essentially undermining the ability of the country to respond effectively to the challenges of the 21st Century, the answer here (as in some other countries) has been to focus on *capacity building*. There are, of course, gaps in different sectors of the public service, which need to be addressed. But if capacity problems are addressed only from the perspective that the problem is a lack of capacity, then the

Figure 17. The Delivery Gap in Public Service

institution is in danger of putting on a straightjacket, which immediately undermines innovative thinking, and looks for solutions from outside rather than from within.

As an important subtext of the development problem over the last decade, capacity building has been seen as a panacea for success. But it has an unimpressive record: the evidence of a continued need for capacity building indicates the failure, to date, of this approach. It is interesting that capacity building is almost exclusively used in the context of developing countries and is not part of the development discourse when dealing with problems in richer countries. For example, when major problems arise in the developed world, responses are often spoken of in terms of the need for institutional change and restructuring. But seldom is the term *capacity building* used. Yet, no project proposal or analysis of a problem in the developing world can be addressed without the ritual references to capacity building. There are a number of reasons for the status of the term in development discourse, which include:

- Concern about institutional effectiveness;
- The recognition of the need to increase the capacity of civil society organisations to increase their level of participation in the decision-making process;

- There has been a shift away from direct implementation of projects and pro-grammes by bilateral organisations as they recognise the need for local struc-tures to implement development activities;
- The understanding that certain sector ministries should operate in a specific manner and have certain structures, because their counterparts in the so-called developed world have such structures; and
- The increasing turbulent and unpredictable political and economic environ-ment of the 1990s has put significant pressures on organisational management capacity.[1]

The response has tended to be on individual training capacity building through skills development, especially through the vehicle of training.

During the visit to Lesotho, in December 2002, by the UN Special Envoy for HIV/AIDS in Africa, Mr Stephen Lewis, the Prime Minister expressed exacerbation about the constant refrain that this country has limited capacity, stating that he did not buy this argument, and that if Lesotho could pull off the world-class General Elections as it did in 2002—which involved the mobilisation of some 17,500 young volunteers to work in over 2,500 polling stations across the country—then why was it not possible to mobilise the whole country to fight HIV/AIDS?

Perhaps one of the problems is that the issue of capacity is always seen from the perspective of *capacity building* rather than *capacity utilisation*. What are the impli-cations of such an approach? Capacity building approaches organisation develop-ment from the perspective that something is wrong and solutions are to be found from outside. The international community takes comfort from what it can provide rather than what is required; providing what is tangible and quantifiable, because this suits the paradigm within which most operate. Government structures have learnt to ask for capacity building initiatives, because the paradigm demands this. The challenge is to understand the different and new environment within which all are operating worldwide, and by extension, in Lesotho. It is an environment of globalisation, where there has been a considerable shift in thinking (from financial to intellectual, from elite to the masses, from boundaries to no boundaries and from highly preserved knowledge to rapid obsolescence of knowledge) and in the way institutions work.

This is a country with a literacy rate of over 80% (including a substantial lit-eracy rate in the English language) and a hunger for education going back to the

19th Century and where girls have received education to the same or greater extent than boys, it can be argued that institutions that focus on skills training, especially where there is already a considerable reservoir of skills, completely miss the point about capacity utilisation. Development agencies need to look at structures and institutions and, most importantly, the people within them. Often, such agencies approach the issue of capacity building from the perspective of incremental change—approaches that do not bring change, but are dressed up in the language of change and which, in the end, contribute to strengthening the *status quo*.

Change must start with clear political commitment at the top and be implemented with change champions who lead the process in all institutions. Change that is incremental is appropriate for minor activities, but it is also about strengthening the *status quo*. Transformational change, on the other hand, involves breaking out of a mold to create a new and radically different environment. Peter Senge prefers to use the term 'profound change' to describe "organisational change that combines inner shifts in people's values, aspirations and behaviours with outer shifts in process"[2]. He goes on to say that "this is not about the organisation doing something new, but it is about building capacity for doing things in a new way."[3] This change is energised by the realisation that unless it takes place, current assumptions and delivery mechanisms will not *deliver* on meeting emergent development challenges and opportunities. In the context of the HIV/AIDS crisis, this means that the efforts will simply not deliver on reducing the infection rate in Lesotho, not because of the lack of political will, but because of the lack of understanding of the nature of the change required in the way the pandemic is addressed. In this regard, it is worth referring to the *Five Learning Disciplines* outlined by Senge which, amongst others, include *systems-thinking*, a discipline described by him as "enabling people to better understand interdependency and change and thereby deal more effectively with the forces that shape the consequences of our actions".[4]

In a resource-limited environment, agencies need to seek new solutions through drawing on ideas that point to new ways of addressing problems, and reduce the time between the generation of ideas and their implementation. It is clear that ideas can only be nurtured in an environment that focuses on the person and encourages new thinking and risk taking—one that is open to change, including structural change. In essence, the focus must be on the person within the institution, changing the way he or she relates to the institution and changing his or her role in relation to clients, in this case, the Basotho. This involves a focus on the total person with an emotional investment in relationships. There is a need to move from managing people to helping people to manage themselves. Within the public service and elsewhere, we have learnt that people are mobile assets that walk out the gate every evening and, with the access to the market in South Africa next door, it is particularly important that efforts are made to keep this asset at home to serve the goals of the nation.

If the delivery gap is to be bridged, it is essential to review the structures of the public service and the way it does business and, by extension, how the international partnership contributes to the *status quo. Institutional structures do not innovate; People do.* It is people within the institution, who are key to innovation, key to creating new ideas, and key to driving change through. But it is how we see people within the institution that is most important and, also by extension, how they see themselves. Just as we know from the private sector that innovation springs from the most unlikely companies and environments, so too does the public service hide deep untapped resources and talent. Just as the private sector needs ideas for change, which are reflected in new products and services, the public service not only needs to be open to new ideas, but also it needs to actively encourage an environment of innovation and the generations of ideas, and alongside this, establish structures that facilitate their implementation.

Focusing on resource constraints often puts people into a straight jacket—one that undermines new thinking and sometimes has a disempowering effect on individuals and institutions. But a resource-constrained environment, if managed properly, can empower and spur new thinking and ideas in addressing old problems. In this context, the old adage that *Necessity is the Mother of Invention* is perhaps appropriate. As Peter Senge points out in *Harvard Management Update* of May 2002, many private companies can become prisoners of their own success, even though circumstances have changed. Things that have worked in the past are often no longer appropriate in a fast-changing environment. This basic truth must act as a guild for those trying to change the way the public service responds to the needs of the people in this country.

Capacity building programmes are often an un-integrated mix of methods, models and tools (based on models from outside) trying to make something fit where it simply does not. For example, training provided in the project cycle or in participatory rural appraisal is seen as key in capacity building. But these are taught in two-week training programmes with little or no regard for the way the institution operates. It is difficult to see what can be produced from training someone in project management in an environment where the focus is not on projects, but on providing continuous services to the majority of the people. The focus of these training programmes is often on transmission of knowledge and the passive acquisition of such knowledge with, of course, mandatory jargon about the participatory learning environment.

Thus, the context and content of the training is often inappropriate for real capacity building. Little or no emphasis is put on learning-by-doing. Learning often happens in direct engagement with the environment, enabling people to perceive and make sense of changing patterns where the environment is unpredictable and changes all the time.

The Public Service: The Learning Service for the Public

What one is advocating is a person-centred approach: one that recognises the development of personal strengths and qualities; one that emphasises self-awareness and self-development. Capacity is not something that can be achieved or saved. Organisations in the true capacity development sense are on a continuous journey with a number of clear milestones represented by achievements. This understanding is necessary in an ever-changing world, and has led to the establishment of *The Learning Organisation*. This, according to Senge,[5] can be defined at two levels: the individual and the organisational.

At the Individual Level

- They innovate and initiate. They believe that their success in doing so will be rewarded and that failure will be treated as a step in the learning process.
- Individuals develop good learning habits. They ask questions, they carry out experiments and test their ideas, and they freely and openly pool information on what is working and what is not.
- Individuals thirst for data, and first-hand experience exceeds their deference to the opinions of persons in authority.

At the Organisational Culture Level

- The organisation is much more egalitarian than most. It treats people as valued contributors. It nurtures and rewards their creativity and initiative.
- People in authority support, expedite and facilitate the contributions of those who report to them and they bring a broader organisational perspective to the work of their units. They expect subordinates to be internally motivated and responsive to the needs of their peers, rather than motivated by rewards and punishments.
- People are expected to try things that do not work for the first time and learn from their mistakes and ensure that others learn from them. Making mistakes is not something to be frowned upon, but something which can be celebrated in a sense that it feeds through the institutions so that people can see where the mistake came from, how it evolved, and what action was taken to mitigate the impact of the mistake.
- Individuals are empowered to contribute in accordance with ability and developmental needs, rather than their position within the organisation. Ideas are judged on their merits, rather than on the status of the person who puts them forward.
- The norms and values of the organisation support cooperation and mutual support. People help one another beyond the formal demands of the job. People are valued for sharing their knowledge, expertise and talents, rather than devoting these qualities exclusively to individual achievement.

The Learning Organisation encourages an atmosphere of decision-making, rather than procrastination, which is often a characteristic of large bureaucracies. As David H. Freeman states,[6] indecisiveness is a fatal flaw—worse than making a mediocre decision, because a mediocre decision, especially if swiftly rendered, can at least stand a chance of achieving goals. Such an approach fosters decision-making by design, rather than by default. Often, people feel comfortable about not deciding on important issues and spend their time rationalising the decision to do nothing. The challenge and opportunity for the Public Service in Lesotho is to become an extensive network of learning units, which are result-orientated and which create an environment where people take risks and learn from failure: in short, a *Learning Service for the Public*. It can be a public service that leads the fight against HIV/AIDS and one that challenges the *status quo*. To do this, it must embrace change, transformational change, with senior staff leading the way in doing this. While we talk about change being led from the top, leaders talk often about change yet act as if everyone, but themselves, has to change. Leaders need, first and foremost, to understand that they do not have all the answers and clearly indicate this in their actions and thinking.

The Learning Organisation also encourages people to seek information, rather than wait until it is provided, and act on this in real time, without having to run questions up and down the hierarchy. This encourages a situation where people can understand their limitations and seek advice from those who may know more about a particular situation than they do, in effect encouraging a leadership style, which generates alternative opinions and is comfortable with opposing views. This demands an environment where authority is delegated and people are encouraged to see opportunities to achieve agreed-upon goals. Delegation of authority to subordinates does not mean leaving them on their own, but it does mean encouraging and willing them to succeed.

Collaboration is routinely spoken about in institutions as a key element of the approach to work. However, the reality is that action is often taken to undermine teamwork with special project structures, payment and reward systems. In some organisations, units, including project management structures, operate like fiefdoms with unit leaders avoiding cross-unit cooperation in the belief that success is a zero-sum game. This is a particular problem with project management structures in the business of aid. Parallel structures, called project management units or the like, are often established where they are unnecessary, and staffed with expensive expatriate of local professionals with counterparts appointed who are not clear about their roles and are often marginalised. This ignores the reality that project management is internationally unique in its code of practice with a body of knowledge based on international practice and governed by the International Project Management Association (IPMA). This body ensures that the codes of practice and the bodies of knowledge of the various national project management associations adhere to one standard, allowing for modifications on the basis of national circumstances.[7] Project Management associated with development cooperation tends not to fall within this understanding.

In a Learning Organisation, there is a focus on after-action reviews, which take place after each major event or at a particular time period: when something goes well or when something does not go well. Ideally, these sessions would normally be facilitated and blur the hierarchical differences that are part of any organisation. Most managers like to say that they give their subordinates room to fail, but some practise tolerance to the extent that they demand failure, the logic being that the person who does not fail is not pushing the boat out far enough to try new approaches. Often, institutions claim they want their people to be innovative, but if mistakes are made, the person is made to pay. This relates directly to the level of risk-taking within an institution. Risk-taking is something that is always part of successful organisations as they move to learn from the mistakes of the past and push the boat out in terms of learning. A risk-avoidance mindset is understandable, especially in the public service. But, paradoxically, it too carries risk, and where the country faces enormous challenges like that of the HIV/AIDS pandemic, one can see where this lack of risk-taking can lead to inaction and a sense that little can be done.

This is not to suggest that institutions should tolerate all types of failure. There are two kinds of failure—those failures from which one's organisation ultimately benefits and those that result in the kinds of activities that do not work. There are situations where risks are insufficiently monitored and these have the potential to spin out of control; they have to be avoided. How does one foster the former while avoiding the latter? This can be done by creating a psychologically tolerant, secure and safe organisational culture, one that is conducive to the questioning, information sharing and risk-taking that innovation requires.

Competencies

Key to working with a person-centred approach is the development of competencies. Experience indicates that enhanced performance can be best achieved and maintained if people focus not only on the knowledge and skills required for the job, but also on the behaviour and the attributes. The combination of knowledge, skill, behaviour and attributes determines whether people handle situations appropriately and professionally at work. Of greater importance, they determine whether institutions move towards achieving goals and objectives as set out in organisational plans and whether they can bridge that delivery gap that we all know exists within the public service. The development of the necessary behaviours and attributes as well as the knowledge and skills required in order to do the jobs well and in a way that facilitates the realisation of one's potential, is important.

A competency framework must be at the centre of the management framework so that we can move from a focus on skills and gaining knowledge to one where we build competencies and seek to develop centres of excellence within our public service.

Transformational change, or profound change, can lead to centres of excellence. Such change is about building a situation where people are able to understand their role, not just as health workers or teachers or accountants or engineers from the professional sense, but also from the point of view of their contribution to achieving objectives. To do this, they must start with themselves. Aiming for centres of excellence within the public service is a decision for the Basotho, driven by the clear knowledge that the capacity is within the country to achieve this. The centre of excellence is not about improving the skills and knowledge of personnel; it is a commitment to the development of a new institutional culture of teamwork, sharing and learning, communication, relationship-building, and a commitment to the core values of the Government of Lesotho, as well as the achievement of the goals and objectives as set out in the National Vision.

What are the implications of this? One key implication is the need to develop abilities, such as:

- The ability to find the right questions to enable the organisation to take the first step forward towards change;
- The ability to manage tensions that arise from ambiguity and uncertainty;
- The ability to observe and listen;
- The ability to use metaphor and imagination;
- The ability to reflect on our own interventions;
- The ability to conceptualise and thus analyse; and
- The ability to overcome cynicism.[8]

But perhaps of greatest importance is the ability to believe in oneself. If one thinks it can be done, it will be done. If one thinks the tasks at hand are impossible, they will be impossible. With a lack of belief in oneself comes the growth of cynicism one of the most corrosive influences on any institution, and one that undermines the very structure and motivation of the people who make up the institution.

In order to bridge the delivery gaps, which are so obvious from the manner in which the HIV/AIDS crisis has been addressed, we need to take a good hard look

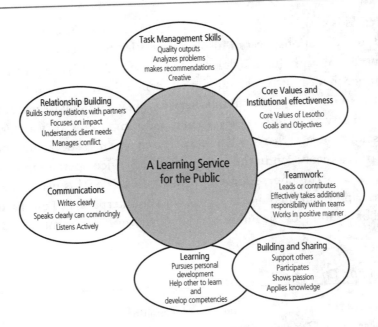

Figure 18. Competencies and The Learning Service for the Public Sector.

at the way our Public Service is managed. Turning the crisis into an opportunity demands a totally new look at the way the Public Service operates in this country, perhaps starting with an undertaking that the Public Service commit itself to refraining from using the term, *We Have No Capacity,* and adopting a can-do approach to dealing with problems. The Poverty Reduction Strategy Paper (PRSP) and Vision 2020 represent key opportunities for the Public Service to determine how it will change the way it does business. These, combined with the commitment to fight HIV/AIDS, represent a commitment by government to a new Lesotho. However, these can only be implemented in an environment where there is a commitment to transformation and a commitment to developing accountability on a personal and institutional level.

But change can only come when there is a demand for change. We have up to now been talking about the supply side, which is about the government's commitment to a new reformed Public Service that is responding to the needs of the people. This can be addressed by establishing a compact with the people, through distilling the content of the Vision and PRSP into, say, ten or fifteen points, such as that every

Mosotho child is entitled to free education, up to Standard X; every Mosotho child is entitled to vaccinations; every Mosotho is entitled to a free HIV test, and more. These rights are meaningful, tangible, easy to grasp and, if disseminated in a meaningful manner that can be understood, then demand will be created for more services and thus a more responsive Public Service. They represent issues that people at all levels of society are comfortable with and, most important, they are *deliverables*.

This is not to suggest that it will be easy. The change must be lasting and in many ways demands a revolution in the way the Public Service operates in this country. There are a number of courses developed on the basis of this need. For instance, institutions can be commissioned to work with counterparts in Lesotho to develop a new kind of training for the Public Service. This would represent a good start.

NOTES *for Chapter 8*

1. Chapman and D. Harding, *Capacity Building*. Not published, 1999.
2. Peter Senge, *A Fifth Discipline Resource. The Dance of Change: The Challenges of Sustaining Momentum in Learning Organisations*, Doubleday/Currency Publishers, New York, 2002.
3. Ibid.
4. Ibid.
5. Peter Senge, *The Fifth Discipline: The Art and Practice of Learning Organisations*, Doubleday/Currency Publishers, 1990.
6. David H. Freeman, *Harvard Management Update*, March 2002, Vol. 7, No. 3.
7. Edinburgh Business School, Heriot Watt University, Scotland.
8. Community Development Resource Association (CDRA), *Capacity Building: Myth or Reality?* Community Development Resource Association, 1995.

9

The Role of Government in Scaling up the National Response to the HIV/AIDS Pandemic

The role of government is central in scaling up the response to the HIV/AIDS Pandemic. This chapter presents ideas on how governments can core stream HIV/AIDS into various sectors and development planning processes, thereby ensuring a long-term response to the vulnerabilities that derive from poverty and poor development, and the manifestations of AIDS. This chapter proposes the roles and responsibilities of duty bearers in Government and presents actions for all Ministries in response to HIV/AIDS. The concept of duty bearers is crucial to our understanding of what needs to be done in the fight against HIV/AIDS and is described in some detail in *Chapters 2 and 5*. In order to core stream HIV/AIDS effectively, it is crucial that civil servants understand how their core mandate is impacted upon and, therefore, how they will take responsibility to deliver their services as is appropriate to communities affected by AIDS. To do so will mean that *business-as-usual* is not an option. It means that every government ministry will need to examine how AIDS-related illness and death is affecting their core mandate, depleting their human resources and affecting their productivity.

In addition, for a country like Lesotho whose infection rate is already over 30% and climbing, the immediate reality is that the increased incidence of AIDS-related illness and death is rapidly transforming the core mandate and shape of each sector. Hence the need for each and every Government Ministry to transform its organisational arrangements and structures, and develop new business processes in partnership with other sectors so as to deliver its services effectively. This is what we refer to in this manual as **core streaming** HIV/AIDS into the policies, plans and budgets of every Ministry. This chapter suggests that core streaming in government should be at two levels: *Core streaming* HIV/AIDS into the policies, plans and strategies of each and every sector; and core streaming HIV/AIDS into the macro-policy frameworks—Vision 2020, the Poverty Reduction Strategy Paper (PRSP) and the Millennium Development Goals Report. *Core streaming*, therefore, draws heavily from the theoretical underpinnings of development planning and its relationship to planning for HIV and AIDS to deepen our understanding of the relationship between HIV/AIDS and development. The chapter then offers tools to guide the exercise of *core streaming* of HIV/AIDS into government sectors. Reference is made to the relevant global commitments expressed in the UN General Assembly Special Session (UNGASS) Declaration of Commitment on HIV/AIDS as a reminder of the global agreements and actions to which the Government of Lesotho is a signatory. These proposed actions are presented in box below.

UNGASS Declaration on Core Streaming

- By 2003, ensure the development and implementation of multi-sectoral national strategies and financing plans for combating HIV/AIDS that address the epidemic in forthright terms; ... fully promote and protect all human rights and fundamental freedoms; integrate a gender perspective; address risk, vulnerability, prevention, care, treatment and support and reduction of the impact of the epidemic; and strengthen health, education and legal system capacity (paragraph 37);

- By 2003, enact, strengthen or enforce ... legislation, regulations and other measures to eliminate all forms of discrimination against, and to ensure, the full enjoyment of all human rights and fundamental freedoms by people living with HIV/AIDS and members of vulnerable groups (paragraph 58);

- By 2003, integrate HIV/AIDS prevention, care, treatment and support and impact-mitigation priorities into the mainstream of development planning, including in poverty eradication strategies, national budget allocations and sectoral development plans (paragraph 38);

- By 2003, evaluate the economic and social impact of the HIV/AIDS epidemic and develop multi-sectoral strategies to address the impact at the individual, family, community and national levels; develop and accelerate the implementation of national poverty eradication strategies to address the impact of HIV/AIDS on household income, livelihoods and access to basic social services, ... review the social and economic impact of HIV/AIDS at all levels of society ... and adjust and adapt economic and social development policies ...

Core Streaming of HIV/AIDS into Government Sectors

The concept of "core streaming" refers to the process of making HIV/AIDS analysis and response part and parcel of all aspects of government, including policy development, planning and budgeting, service delivery, human resource management, as well as monitoring and evaluation. We have chosen in this manual to use "core streaming", rather than the more commonly used term "mainstreaming", to emphasise that HIV/AIDS should be placed at the centre of all plans within a given institution. It must not be seen as an ancillary activity, but be given the same prominence as core institutional activities. This applies not only to Government ministries, but also to the government system as a whole, which indicates the need for decentralised action within a national framework of cooperation and coordination.

> Core streaming demands that the issue of HIV/AIDS be located at the centre of all plans within a given institution. It must not be seen as an ancillary activity, but be given the same prominence as core institutional activities. This differs from HIV/AIDS mainstreaming, which is appropriate in countries where the situation is not so urgent. Core streaming demands a profound change in the way an institution operates and perceives its role.

Commitment to core streaming is a leadership decision. The UNGASS Declaration makes clear that leadership is more than just commitment; it is also expressed in concrete action. Thus, political leadership on HIV/AIDS is reflected in the adoption of specific programmes and plans, in the allocation of resources and in the support for national and regional initiatives on HIV/AIDS. Political leadership on HIV/AIDS must cascade across all levels of government.

Now let us return to the theoretical underpinnings for core streaming HIV/AIDS into development. The notion of core streaming is based on the recognition that HIV/AIDS is a development challenge, not merely a health concern, with the unique ability to undermine the development process, developmental outcomes and key mechanisms for development (that is, organisations, including public sector organisations). Further, it puts the onus on all sectors to develop strategies that put the fight against HIV/AIDS at the centre of their work.

Since the mid-1990s, many policy documents and plans concerning HIV/AIDS refer to the need for a multi-sectoral response. In practice, however, it is still proving difficult to get all sectors to comprehend the medium to longer-term impact of HIV/AIDS on their constituents and on the organisation itself, let alone to develop comprehensive programmes along the continuum of prevention, treatment and care and mitigation. When it comes to articulating interventions, there is a persistent tendency to revert to the traditional mainstay of HIV/AIDS programmes (limited impact mitigation, care and treatment, and prevention). As a result, the main responsibility for responding to HIV/AIDS is usually located within the health and education sectors and, to some extent, the social welfare sector (with regard to orphans, for example), as if other sectors are not affected by the pandemic or do not have a contribution to make in responding to the development challenges associated with HIV/AIDS. The UNGASS Declaration specifically mentions the need to ensure that HIV/AIDS is brought into the 'mainstream' of development planning to address the systemic development factors that either facilitate or inhibit the vulnerability of communities. This is what governments across the globe have committed themselves to do.

Development Planning and HIV/AIDS

Development planning is a core activity of governments to facilitate and enable development. In a recent publication on the link between development planning and HIV/AIDS, the UNDP makes a distinction between 'development planning for HIV/AIDS' and 'development planning aimed at realising specific development objectives', such as macro-economic growth, poverty reduction, food security, rural or urban development, quality education, and more.

Most countries affected by HIV/AIDS have adopted some form of 'development planning for HIV/AIDS.' Nowadays, the most common form is to adopt a National Strategic Framework for HIV/AIDS, which is intended to guide a country's multi-sectoral planning approach to HIV/AIDS, and to translate this planning framework into an action plan, with explicit targets and implementation steps. Some sectors have also developed their own plans for HIV/AIDS, usually to prevent HIV transmission among their constituents and/or to respond to a particular impact of the epidemic with direct relevance for the respective sector. For example, the Ministry of Education may have developed a plan that aims to raise awareness of HIV/AIDS among pupils through peer education and/or that seeks to ensure that orphans do not drop out of school. Similar examples may be found in other sectors.

Whereas 'development planning for HIV/AIDS' clearly is an important part of the national response to HIV/AIDS, it is also vital to review other types of development planning and the links with HIV/AIDS. Other types of development planning would include economic development planning, sectoral planning and urban/rural development planning, amongst others. These various types of planning are typically concerned with addressing one or more systemic development factors, as identified in *Chapter 4*. As the UNDP publication states:

"Often, these types of development planning include little or no reference to HIV/AIDS. Even if reference to HIV/AIDS is made, this hardly ever translates into a programmatic focus on HIV/AIDS. Yet, this broad category of development planning can significantly enhance or decrease the level of risk and vulnerability to HIV infection and the extent to which individuals, households and organisations are able to cope with the consequences of HIV infection."[1]

On the one hand, development planning can encourage migration, increase income inequalities, undermine food security or lead to economic underdevelopment, all of which could enhance the risk of HIV transmission. For example, apartheid planning in South Africa is an example of a deliberate government attempt to instigate economic underdevelopment in certain areas of the country. The migrant labour system, a cornerstone of apartheid urban planning, has been identified as a major contributing factor to the spread of HIV/AIDS, as it resulted in the fragmentation of families and communities.[2] Other examples of how development planning can contribute to the spread of HIV come from Ghana and Malawi. In Ghana, the construction of the Volta River Dam resulted in the displacement of local communities and reduced their economic security, which led many women to engage in sex work to generate income. In Malawi, road construction is seen to have contributed to the spread of HIV by enhancing mobility.[3] These last two examples show that development planning can *inadvertently* contribute to an environment of enhanced risk and vulnerability to HIV infection, even if the initial objective is to promote 'good' development.

The UNDP paper points out that since the 1980s, structural adjustment programmes have tended to exacerbate those systemic development factors that constitute a context of risk and vulnerability to HIV infection. Amongst others, structural adjustment led to loss of employment and other sources of income, increased poverty and reduced food security, reduced access to public services (through cuts in public services and the introduction of user charges) and entrenched the burden of care on women. Even though structural adjustment programmes did not cause HIV/AIDS, it is clear that these were introduced at a time when households, communities and societies were already quite vulnerable to external shocks. As the paper states: "It is at this time that HIV/AIDS started to emerge, first as a public health concern and subsequently as an epidemic with major implications for all dimensions of development."[4]

Global experience further shows that development planning, usually unintentionally, can undermine the capabilities of households and communities to cope with the consequences of HIV infection. For example, the cuts in public service provision and the introduction of user fees since the 1980s have made access to services like health and education more difficult, if not near impossible, for many poor rural and urban households. In the absence of adequate services, the burden of coping with the HIV/AIDS pandemic shifts to communities and households—and more particularly to women, children and the elderly. Likewise, trade liberalisation strategies that lead to a loss of permanent jobs in sectors, such as agriculture, are likely to erode the capabilities of affected households to cope with shocks and stresses, like HIV/AIDS.

On the other hand, development planning can also help prevent the spread of HIV and mitigate the impacts of the epidemic, for example, through deliberate efforts to reduce poverty, improve economic opportunities or food security, enhance the status of women, or support political voice and participation, especially of marginalised social groups. In other words, these are conscious attempts to address the systemic development factors that contribute to a context of risk and vulnerability and that reduce capability to cope with the consequences of HIV infection.

Thus, it is critical to review, firstly, how any type of development planning aggravates (or diminishes) an environment that enhances the vulnerability of men/boys and women/girls to HIV infection and, secondly, how it strengthens (or undermines) the capabilities of individuals, households, organisations and institutions to cope with the impacts of HIV/AIDS. This is particularly important for those types of development planning and the associated planning frameworks that are not commonly understood to be directly linked to HIV/AIDS, like the Poverty Reduction Strategy Paper (PRSP), the Medium-Term Expenditure Framework (MTEF), Rural or Urban Development Framework, and so on. The following box presents a guide to the stages for core streaming HIV/AIDS into Poverty Reduction Strategies.

Stages for Core Streaming HIV/AIDS into Poverty Reduction Strategies

Stage 0: *Poverty reduction strategy has no HIV/AIDS section or chapter.*

Stage 1: *Poverty reduction strategy has a section or chapter on HIV/AIDS with the following elements:*

- Evidence of *analysis* of the impact of AIDS-related mortality on society's capacity to achieve poverty reduction goals.
- Evidence of *analysis* of the impact of AIDS-related morbidity on society's capacity to achieve poverty reduction goals.
- Evidence of *analysis* of potential of poverty reduction strategies facilitating the spread of HIV.
- Evidence of *analysis* of potential of poverty reduction strategies inhibiting the spread of HIV.

Stage 2: *Poverty reduction strategy has HIV/AIDS treated as a cross-cutting theme with the following elements:*

- Evidence of *understanding* of the impact of AIDS-related mortality on society's capacity to achieve poverty reduction goals.
- Evidence of *understanding* of the impact of AIDS-related morbidity on society's capacity to achieve poverty reduction goals.
- Evidence of *understanding* of potential of poverty reduction strategies facilitating the spread of HIV.
- Evidence of *understanding* of potential of poverty reduction strategies inhibiting the spread of HIV.

Stage 3: *In addition to elements of Stage 2:*

- Policies developed to mitigate the impact of AIDS-related mortality on society's capacity to achieve poverty reduction strategy goals.
- Policies developed to mitigate the impact of AIDS-related morbidity on society's capacity to achieve poverty reduction strategy goals.
- Policies developed to mitigate those aspects of the poverty reduction strategy that will facilitate the spread of HIV.
- Policies developed to encourage those aspects of the poverty reduction strategy that will inhibit the spread of HIV.
- Financial resources made available to implement the above-mentioned policies.
- Organisational structures and procedures changed to implement the above policies.
- Plans developed by society to achieve the above.

Stage 4: *In addition to elements of Stage 3:*

- Evidence of structures for implementation of the plan.
- Evidence of structures to determine if there is learning in the society.

Source: UNDP Regional Project on HIV and Development in sub-Saharan Africa (2002).

Why HIV/AIDS is Not Adequately Integrated into Development Planning

The fact that most development planning frameworks that are not considered to be HIV/AIDS-specific, like the PRSP, do not adequately integrate HIV/AIDS is, to some extent, indicative of the lack of alignment between the various planning paradigms and planning systems. Such alignment between the key frameworks guiding development planning and the synchronisation of planning systems, including financial planning systems, is a crucial step towards a concerted national response to HIV/AIDS. Linked to this is the need to ensure that various development-planning frameworks are translated into annual plans with clear targets, implementation and budget allocations.

More importantly, perhaps, the inadequate integration of HIV/AIDS into development planning frameworks is an indication of how HIV/AIDS is conceptualised and understood. Although it is almost universally recognised that HIV/AIDS is a crosscutting development issue requiring a multi-sectoral response, more often than not, HIV/AIDS is relegated to a separate sphere of planning or to specific sectors. Thus, a critical challenge facing many countries is to move beyond formal recognition of the need for a multi-sectoral response to HIV/AIDS to the formulation of effective programmes and interventions within and across sectors, based on a sound analysis of the implications of the HIV/AIDS epidemic for specific sectors.

How To Core Stream HIV and AIDS into Development

The Pathways of HIV/AIDS: Morbidity and Mortality

In concise form, such analysis starts from the premise that HIV/AIDS primarily affects sectors through two main pathways: morbidity and mortality (illness and death). Mortality and morbidity will, in turn, affect demand, by increasing the complexity and quantity of services required of the given sector. It also affects supply, by reducing the number and quality of service providers. Eventually, the combined effect of these two forces will result in changes in the overall mandate, priorities and expenditure patterns of the respective sector. Because its capacity to generate income from service users will also decline, as people infected and affected by HIV/AIDS will have less disposable income, its ability to deliver on its mandate will be jeopardised. (For an example of how HIV/AIDS affects the education sector in terms of both demand and supply (see *Table 1 in Chapter 2—Turning A Crisis into an Opportunity: An Overview*).

Consequently, the operational questions to guide the government's revision of sector core mandates and plans in the context of HIV/AIDS include the following:

1. What aspects of development inhibit the spread of HIV and AIDS? Therefore, what policies, strategies and actions should be maintained?
2. What aspects of development encourage the spread of HIV and AIDS? Therefore, what policies, strategies and actions should be developed to minimise the spread?
3. What is the impact of AIDS-related illness on the capacity of a Sector to deliver on its core mandate? Therefore, what policies, strategies and actions should be put in place to minimise the impact of HIV/AIDS?
4. What is the impact of AIDS-related death on the capacity of a Sector to deliver on its core mandate? Therefore, what policies, strategies and actions should be put in place to minimise the impact of HIV/AIDS? [5]

These questions are critical to facilitate the process of core streaming of HIV/AIDS in all sectors and to bring HIV/AIDS to the centre of development planning. The following box illustrates the various stages for core streaming of HIV/AIDS into key sectors of government, in accordance with these key operational questions, and is a useful tool for monitoring the core streaming process.

Stages for core streaming of HIV/AIDS into key sectors of Government

Stage 0: At this stage, the sector has no HIV and AIDS plan (They may have condoms in toilets but still have no plan for the given sector).

Stage 1: The sector has developed an HIV and AIDS plan, which has the following elements:

- An analysis of the factors that put workers at risk of acquiring HIV.
- An evidence-based communication for behaviour change strategy.
- Systematic condom promotion.
- A trained focal point person on HIV and AIDS designated.
- Financial resources made available.

Stage 2: In addition to components in Stage 1, the sector HIV and AIDS plan has the following elements:

- A study to analyse the impact of AIDS conducted.
- Policies, strategies and actions to mitigate the impact based on the study developed.
- Evidence of the implementation of policies, strategies and actions to mitigate the impact of AIDS on the sector.

Stage 3: In addition to components in Stage 2, the sector HIV and AIDS plan has the following elements:

- A study conducted that examines the negative or positive impact of implementing sector policies on the spread of HIV in the community being served.
- Policies, strategies and actions developed that will inhibit the negative impacts developed.
- Policies, strategies and actions developed that will facilitate the positive impacts developed.
- Evidence of implementation of policies, strategies and actions that will inhibit the negative impacts.
- Evidence of implementation of policies, strategies and actions that will facilitate the positive impacts.
- A monitoring and evaluation framework developed and being implemented.

Stage 4: In addition to components in Stage 3, the sector HIV and AIDS plan has a consolidation process, which would include:

- Evidence of incorporating lessons learnt in sector policies, strategies and actions for mainstreaming HIV and AIDS.

Source: UNDP Regional Project on HIV and Development in sub-Saharan Africa (2002)

Actions for Core Streaming

The decision by the Government of Lesotho to allocate 2% of sectoral budgets to HIV/AIDS programmes and interventions is potentially a critical element of core streaming of HIV/AIDS. But it is not sufficient. Following are some key elements that illustrate the resources and level of commitment that Ministries must take to make a difference.

Key Elements of A Comprehensive Response to HIV/AIDS by Government

Role of the Minister:

- Provide political leadership on HIV/AIDS as core to the sector;
- Constant engagement with sector stakeholders to monitor progress; and
- Commit entire sector to core stream HIV/AIDS.

Role of Principal Secretary and Senior Management:

- Management support of political leadership;
- Operational support through commitment of resources of entire sector;
- Review sector plans and policies to reflect HIV/AIDS competency; and
- HIV/AIDS core streaming must be a key performance area of managers in entire sector.
- Technical Competence
  - Senior Technical Advisory team with strong HIV/AIDS Competency.
- Budget
  - 2% per sector useful to kick-start activities in the Ministry and initially pay for additional competencies where required.
  - Core stream HIV/AIDS into the recurrent budget.
- Enabling Policies
  - Review all policies using an HIV/AIDS Competency Lens to reflect an understanding of HIV/AIDS as central to core mandate.

Tables 6 and 7 highlight examples of what each sector can do in relation to the four domains of a comprehensive response to HIV/AIDS (i.e. prevention, treatment and care, impact mitigation and addressing systemic development factors). As a first step, let us look at the role of the leadership in government, which is responsible for leading efforts to core stream HIV and AIDS, as well as the role of Parliament, which is responsible for legislating and ensuring the allocation of adequate resources for HIV/AIDS and development (*see Table 6*).

The Cabinet

The Cabinet is, amongst other things, responsible for drafting policy and legislation and proposing such measures to the Legislature, for developing appropriate programmes for the effective implementation of policy and legislation and for ensuring adequate financial and human resource allocations for the effective implementation of these programmes.

Table 6 presents various options for interventions in relation to HIV prevention, treatment and care, impact mitigation and addressing systemic development factors that fall within the ambit of the Executive. The suggestions included here cover more generic options for the Executive to pursue, rather than specific examples per sector. Sector-specific examples are included in the next section on core streaming.

Parliament

Parliament's main areas of responsibility and competence revolve around passing legislation, allocating resources, monitoring the efficient use of resources and the effective implementation of policies, programmes and legislation. It also includes an oversight role with respect to the Executive.

Specific interventions in relation to HIV prevention, treatment and care, impact mitigation and addressing systemic development factors that fall within the ambit of Parliament are presented in the list below. Clearly, these are not exhaustive, but are meant to be illustrative. In addition, a number of actions can be identified that are not restricted to any of the domains of a national response to HIV/AIDS, but reflect foundational or structural options for Parliament to express leadership on HIV/AIDS. These actions include the following:

- Adopt the Greater Involvement of People Living with HIV/AIDS (GIPA) Principle as a cornerstone of all Government programmes on HIV/AIDS;
- Participate in (and support the work of) the Parliamentary Portfolio Committee on HIV/AIDS and ensure it has sufficient capacity and resources to fulfill its tasks effectively;
- Hold regular parliamentary debates on HIV/AIDS to review the magnitude of the pandemic, its impact and its implications for human and economic development in Lesotho;
- Review legislation and policy in line with the UNGASS Declaration of Commitment on HIV/AIDS (related to prevention, treatment and care, impact mitigation and addressing systemic development factors);

- Regularly review budgetary and human resource allocations to HIV/AIDS programmes and interventions, including the implementation of Parliament's stipulation that 2% of the national and sectoral budgets should be allocated to HIV/AIDS programmes;
- Adopt a comprehensive HIV/AIDS Workplace Policy and Programme for parliamentary staff in accordance with the ILO Code of Practice on HIV/AIDS and the World of Work.

Table 6.	Actions for Mobilising Leadership for an HIV/AIDS-Competent Society		
Prevention	**Treatment & Care**	**Impact Mitigation**	**Addressing Systemic Development Factors***
Leadership structure: The Cabinet			
Develop policies that prioritise HIV prevention in each sector. Adopt a policy requirement that all sectors carry out a rapid HIV Vulnerability Assessment[6] to ascertain which population groups require targeted support to reduce their vulnerability to HIV infection. Recommend the specific targeting of men in national prevention campaigns. Ensure the effective implementation of VCT and other prevention strategies in accordance with the proposal submitted to GFATM. Support the implementation of UVT	Consider the political and financial feasibility of taking an executive decision to make ARV treatment available throughout the civil service. Engage with SADC/Lesotho pharmaceutical companies and donor countries to provide assistance for HIV/AIDS treatment and care, including reducing the cost of ARV treatment and drugs for opportunistic diseases.	Regularly commission the review of the impact of HIV/AIDS and propose appropriate policy interventions to mitigate such impacts (e.g. Education policy in relation to orphan care, Policy on the redeployment of retired civil servants to replace capacity lost due to HIV/AIDS, etc.). Review the cost implications for comprehensive and proactive impact mitigation strategies (including the anticipated costs of non-intervention) and propose feasible and appropriate impact mitigation interventions for parliamentary approval. Commission an assessment of the institutional impacts of HIV/AIDS by sector and across sectors, including the impacts on human resources, productivity and financial cost implications.	Develop and implement national strategies for the empowerment of women in all spheres of life Develop and implement national strategies for youth development in accordance with the National Youth Policy, particularly in relation to employment opportunities. Commission a review of the distributive effects of economic growth trends and develop appropriate national strategies based on the findings of the review. Adopt a policy on support for small-scale enterprises and the informal sector as a major contributor to the economy (which could also include provisions for financial support to small-scale enterprises affected by HIV/AIDS)
*(Vulnerability/risk reduction & enhancement of capabilities)			

Table 6.	Actions for Mobilising Leadership for an HIV/AIDS-Competent Society		
Prevention	**Treatment & Care**	**Impact Mitigation**	**Addressing Systemic Development Factors***
Leadership structure: Parliament (National Assembly and the Senate)			
Monitor the effective implementation of national programmes of HIV prevention, including those approved by the GFATM (in particular, VCT programmes). Ensure adequate resource allocation for the Government's MTCT programme and regularly review its implementation.	Ensure that adequate resources are made available for comprehensive treatment and care programmes, including HBC. Engage with SADC, pharmaceutical companies and donor countries to provide assistance for HIV/AIDS treatment and care, including reducing the cost of ARV treatment and drugs for opportunistic diseases.	Prioritise the development of a comprehensive Orphans and Vulnerable Children programme with provisions for adequate resources Regularly review progress made towards the MDGs. Request regular reports from the Executive on the impact of HIV/AIDS on specific sectors. Ensure adequate resources are made available to sectors to proactively respond to the impacts of HIV/AIDS. Enact, strengthen or enforce legislation, regulations and other measures to eliminate all forms of discrimination against PLWHA.	Monitor the review of the PRSP and National Vision with an HIV competence lens. Review of the macroeconomic framework and the PRSP to assess whether it adequately addresses HIV/AIDS. Monitor the implementation of the Sexual Offences Bill and ensure adequate resource allocation for its implementation. Monitor the effectiveness of the National Youth Policy in addressing the developmental needs of youth in Lesotho. Enact, strengthen or enforce legislation, regulations and other measures to eliminate all forms of discrimination.
*(Vulnerability/risk reduction & enhancement of capabilities)			

Core streaming into Government Sectors

Table 7 focuses on actions that the various government sectors can take to core stream HIV/AIDS into their various development mandates. To take the case of Agriculture as an example, it is proposed that the Ministry develop a comprehensive HIV/AIDS workplace programme focusing on all four domains of the comprehensive response to HIV/AIDS for its entire staff (that is, in relation to the internal environment).

Clearly, the suggested actions reflected in the matrices are not exhaustive, but merely serve to illustrate how the various sectors need to approach the development challenges related to the HIV/AIDS epidemic. To enhance the involvement of all sectors in the national response to HIV/AIDS, there is a need for capacity development in areas such as policy analysis, planning and programme costing/budgeting for HIV/AIDS across government sectors. This will facilitate the process of core streaming in the country, where each sector will see it has responsibility for the fight against HIV/AIDS and will incorporate its contribution into its overall plan. To do this effectively, all sectors need to develop the capacity to involve People Living With HIV/AIDS (PLWHA) in all aspects of planning in order to reduce stigma and to ensure that their particular needs are met.

Table 7. Pragmatic Actions for Core Streaming HIV/AIDS by Government Sectors			
Prevention	**Treatment & Care**	**Impact Mitigation**	**Addressing Systemic Development Factors***
Sector: Agriculture			
Awareness-raising activities and condom distribution through existing structures and mechanisms (e.g. agriculture extension services). IEC campaign by extension workers and farmers as well as PLWHA—where possible from the local community. Peer educators within the sector (agricultural extension workers) who promote safe sexual practice. Using participatory rapid appraisal methodologies, assess sexual networks within the agricultural sector that might be fueling the epidemic. Design targeted prevention programmes to respond to identified sexual networks. Mobile VCT facilities as part of service provided by the Ministry in response to HIV/AIDS.	Appropriate Home-Based Care for affected households as part of emergency relief programme, including agricultural inputs and services. Training for service providers in Home-Based Care. Inventory of treatment and care centres for wide distribution throughout the Ministry. A guide on nutrition for PLWHA based on FAO/WHO model but specific to Lesotho.	PLWHA involved in all aspects of policy development, programming and implementation to reduce stigma and ensure their needs are met. Nutritional and food distribution programmes targeting affected households. Flexible arrangements and alternative sources of income-generation to accommodate changing nature of labour supply and reduced productivity. Labour-saving agricultural strategies (e.g. conservation farming) and access to credit and subsidies (for light mechanised farm equipment, less labour-intensive crop farming, etc.) to lessen the workload on HIV-affected households. Involvement in a comprehensive, cross-sectoral programme for orphans with agricultural messages designed for children and adults.	Emergency relief programme and early warning system linked to HIV/AIDS trends. Agricultural growth strategies combined with the creation of stable employment. Diversification of agricultural strategies away from mono-cropping. Policy measures to ensure equal access to employment and land for women. Assessment of gender roles, and vulnerability to risk sexual practice in the sector in relation to income distribution and access to agricultural inputs and services. Review agricultural policy to respond to outcomes of assessment
*(Vulnerability/risk reduction & enhancement of capabilities)			

Table 7.	Pragmatic Actions for Core Streaming HIV/AIDS by Government Sectors		
Prevention	**Treatment & Care**	**Impact Mitigation**	**Addressing Systemic Development Factors***
Sector: Communication			
Awareness-raising activities about prevention through a variety of media. Educational programmes on condom use. Develop face-to-face communication messages. Media campaign focusing on men and responsible sexual behaviour. IEC interventions on STIs, which encourage people to seek STI treatment.	IEC on available options for treatment and care, which de-stigmatise HIV/AIDS and encourage people to know their status and seek appropriate treatment and care. Door-to-door media campaign on availability of options for treatment and care.	Media campaign involving PLWHA to break the silence on HIV/AIDS and address prejudices and stigma. Information dissemination of effective community initiatives, which encourage other people to respond to HIV/AIDS in their community.	Comprehensive information, education and communication (IEC) programme targeting all Basotho, with particular focus on illiterate people and women. Media campaign on violence against women and gender-based discrimination.
Sector: Defence			
Information-dissemination, awareness-raising activities and condom distribution at army bases and patrol stations for surrounding communities. Voluntary Counselling and Testing campaign for all members of the defence force. Develop strategies for 100% condom-use in areas close to army bases. Design targeted prevention programme to respond to identified sexual networks.	Referral mechanisms at army bases and patrol stations for surrounding communities. Support voluntary work by military personnel in the area of assisting families affected by HIV/AIDS.	Military to be trained in and deployed to assist communities with distribution of goods and services as required.	Using participatory rapid appraisal methodologies, assess sexual networks within the defence sector that might heighten risk and vulnerability.
*(Vulnerability/risk reduction & enhancement of capabilities)			

Table 7.	Pragmatic Actions for Core Streaming HIV/AIDS by Government Sectors		
Prevention	**Treatment & Care**	**Impact Mitigation**	**Addressing Systemic Development Factors***
Sector: Education			
Awareness-raising activities in education institutions & society. HIV-Competency a requirement for all teachers through formal and in-service training. VCT services for all secondary school students and teachers. Condom distribution at education institutions and education on the use of condoms. Anti-AIDS clubs and peer support groups. HIV-competent curriculum development, e.g. sexuality education. Context-responsive school-based HIV prevention programme.	Counselling support and referral mechanisms at education institutions for children infected/affected by HIV/AIDS. School-supported clinic services for learners and educators living with HIV. School-feeding scheme to be extended to cover 3 meals a day for all vulnerable children, including those infected with HIV. Examine mechanisms to facilitate feeding of orphans on non-school days. Full-day programme at schools for orphaned learners in partnership with community organisations and teachers.	Directive on non-discrimination against AIDS orphans and children infected with HIV. Guidelines for staff on how to deal with children affected/infected by HIV/AIDS in a sensitive manner. Involvement of PLWHA and children infected/affected by HIV/AIDS in education activities to address prejudices and stigma. Design of education activities to accommodate the need for children to assist in the household to avoid dropouts. Full scholarships for AIDS orphans and vulnerable children. Extension of school-feeding scheme to child-headed households when schools are closed.	Policy measures to ensure access to education for all, regardless of ability to pay (e.g. scholarships or cross-subsidisation mechanism) Curriculum development, e.g. life skills education. Education-planning to ensure the education system is in line with the requirements of the country and the economy. Incentive system for teachers to work in rural areas. Review and assessment of vulnerability of girls and boys to the spread of HIV. Policy on preventing, sexual abuse of learners, which represents zero tolerance of such abuse.
*(Vulnerability/risk reduction & enhancement of capabilities)			

Table 7.	Pragmatic Actions for Core Streaming HIV/AIDS by Government Sectors		
Prevention	**Treatment & Care**	**Impact Mitigation**	**Addressing Systemic Development Factors***
Sector: Finance			
VCT for all staff in the sector. Provision of adequate resources for prevention of PMTCT in national budget. Provision of adequate resources for the institutional mechanisms for the national response to HIV/AIDS. Resources to reduce vulnerability of women through policy interventions (e.g. unemployment fund for women, adequate and secure boarding houses for school girls). Review budget requirements for HIV/AIDS-prevention including new policies that are designed to minimise vulnerability to HIV, e.g., the posting of civil servants as families rather than individuals.	Provision of adequate resources for proper health care, e.g. basic medicines, ARV treatment, personnel and infrastructure. Financial budgeting and planning for the resource requirements of the HIV/AIDS door-to-door campaign.	Resource allocation for national impact mitigation programmes, e.g. comprehensive orphan programme. Provision of national resources for social security and social welfare for infected/affected households. Development of a tool for costing of HIV/AIDS-related activities for sectoral planning and budgeting.	Provision of national resources for poverty reduction (e.g. social security and social welfare). PRSP and national vision to core stream HIV/AIDS with a view to reducing vulnerability, risk and loss of capabilities but also to recognise the new structure of communities as a result of HIV.
*(Vulnerability/risk reduction & enhancement of capabilities)			

Table 7.	Pragmatic Actions for Core Streaming HIV/AIDS by Government Sectors		
Prevention	**Treatment & Care**	**Impact Mitigation**	**Addressing Systemic Development Factors***
Sectors: Foreign Affairs			
VCT for all diplomats and staff of the Ministry. Information dissemination, awareness raising activities and condom distribution through foreign missions among Basotho living abroad. Training for diplomats and other staff on current thinking in regard to HIV/AIDS and ensuring that they are totally up to date on the situation as it affects Lesotho. Develop reporting formats, which are distributed within the Public Service in Lesotho on the fight against HIV/AIDS in other countries with particular reference to new approaches to fighting the disease.	Counselling and referral services at foreign missions. Support programme for Basotho living with HIV/AIDS in foreign countries (support groups).	Support programme for PLWHA and their families living abroad who face discrimination or seek to return to Lesotho. Negotiations on behalf of PLWHA and their families living abroad to ensure equitable access to appropriate services in the host country.	Agreements with other nations, which ensure that Basotho living abroad have equitable access to public services and associated information-dissemination to Basotho. Social programme with regular meeting opportunities for Basotho living abroad to strengthen social networks. Active participation in the SADC and NEPAD processes that are aimed at reducing vulnerability of those most poor. Review cross-border policies to core stream HIV/AIDS.
*(Vulnerability/risk reduction & enhancement of capabilities)			

Table 7.	Pragmatic Actions for Core Streaming HIV/AIDS by Government Sectors		
Prevention	**Treatment & Care**	**Impact Mitigation**	**Addressing Systemic Development Factors***
Sector: Health and Social Welfare			
HIV workplace programme for health and social welfare, including GIPA. VCT programmes to be prioritized. STI control programme and condom distribution (family planning programmes). PMTCT policy framework and programmes. Prophylactic treatment of rape victims. Blood safety. Close partnership with religious organisations and community groups to promote a culture of prevention and care. Prioritisation of Communicable Disease Surveillance. Measures to integrate traditional healers into the public health system. Training community-based workers on HIV/AIDS prevention	Treatment programme for opportunistic diseases, including access to basic medicines and preventive therapy for TB. Anti-retroviral therapy to be expanded to all hospitals. Counselling programme for rape victims, pregnant women and others infected with HIV. Policy framework and programmes in support of community and home-based care. Nutritional programmes and guidelines developed based on the FAO/WHO guidelines but relevant for Lesotho. Nutrition training programmes to be integrated into Home-based care. Capacity-building programme for Community Health Workers.	Involvement of PLWHA and affected households in all aspects of policy development, programming and implementation to reduce stigma and ensure their needs are met. Policy and comprehensive programme on orphan care, including support for community-based mechanisms. Policy and programme on financial support to affected households, including elderly caregivers and child-headed households.	Policy measures to ensure access to basic health care for all, regardless of ability to pay (e.g. exemptions or cross-subsidisation mechanism). Priority to be given to those health service areas considered hardest hit. Comprehensive social welfare and social security programme (e.g. universal school feeding scheme). Increase the capacity of social welfare workers as a matter of urgency. Shelters and income-generating opportunities for abused women and children. Community-based health planning with active involvement of local community. Incentive system for health workers to work in rural areas.
*(Vulnerability/risk reduction & enhancement of capabilities)			

Table 7.	Pragmatic Actions for Core Streaming HIV/AIDS by Government Sectors		
Prevention	**Treatment & Care**	**Impact Mitigation**	**Addressing Systemic Development Factors***
Sector: Justice and Law			
Voluntary Counselling and Testing for entire sector. Information-dissemination (rights-based), awareness-raising activities and condom distribution at courts. Review of feasibility and constitutionality of severe sentences of rapists who consciously infect their victims, as a deterrent. Specific measures to avoid the spread of HIV/AIDS including the provision of condoms to prisoners.	Referral mechanisms at courts. Counselling facilities for rape victims at courts. Information campaign to fight discrimination. Training for judiciary in relation to HIV/AIDS and human rights.	Review of legislation to ensure non-discrimination against PLWHA and their families. Promotion of anti-discrimination of PLWHA, e.g. through public media, community workshops and circulars to employers. Directive for judicial staff on legal recourse for PLWHA and their families. Policy guidelines for judicial staff on dealing with PLWHA in a sensitive manner.	Policy on equal access to justice and legal recourse. Consistent application of legislation in line with the principles of equality and fairness. Development of guidelines on human rights in the context of HIV/AIDS for PLWHA and society in general Alignment of legal instruments, such as the Gender Equality Bill, Sexual Offences Bill and on children's rights with the UNAIDS policy on "Criminal Law, Public Health and HIV Transmission".[7] Review of customary law and practice that might increase vulnerability and risk.
*(Vulnerability/risk reduction & enhancement of capabilities)			

Table 7.	Pragmatic Actions for Core Streaming HIV/AIDS by Government Sectors		
Prevention	**Treatment & Care**	**Impact Mitigation**	**Addressing Systemic Development Factors***
Sector: Labour and Employment			
Voluntary Counselling and Testing for all sector workers. Information-dissemination (rights-based), awareness-raising activities and condom distribution at workplaces (possibly targeting groups most at risk, e.g. migrant workers). STI programme for the public sector and employees. Policy requiring prevention programmes in ALL workplaces including for casual labour. Training for staff at the Ministry to build capacity in the fight against HIV/AIDS.	Referral mechanisms and counselling support programme at workplaces. Clinic services to care for those ill and requiring treatment of opportunistic infections.	Involvement of PLWHA to reduce stigma and ensure their needs are met. Workplace programmes protecting the rights of infected employees. Benefit schemes based on employer-employee contributions to support PLWHA. Policy on flexible working arrangements for infected/affected employees. Flexible use of leave-days, including the possibility of lending leave to those ill.	National employment-creation strategy that recognises the particular vulnerability of women and, therefore, targets them. Policy and programme on employment and income-generating opportunities for women. Minimum wage to support sustainable livelihoods of those affected by HIV/AIDS and including community caregivers. National policy on terms of employment protecting the rights of employees and establishment of appropriate negotiating forum. Policy on using GIPA Principle (i.e. Greater Involvement of People Living with HIV/AIDS).
*(Vulnerability/risk reduction & enhancement of capabilities)			

Table 7.	**Pragmatic Actions for Core Streaming HIV/AIDS by Government Sectors**		
Prevention	**Treatment & Care**	**Impact Mitigation**	**Addressing Systemic Development Factors***
Sector: Local Government			
Voluntary Counselling and testing for entire sector. Information-dissemination, awareness- raising activities and condom distribution at local/district offices and through local Counsellors. District-level mapping of sexual networks and vulnerability assessments to identify the hotspots and opportunities for effective prevention. Community mobilisation programme using locally available capacity from communities, churches and IEC part-time workers. Voluntary Counselling and Testing services at the District level.	Referral mechanisms at local/district offices. Community-based health care programmes for treatment of opportunistic infections. District level nutrition programme for those infected and affected by HIV/AIDS and food insecurity.	Community-based media campaign involving PLWHA and AIDS orphans to address stigma and prejudice in the community. Community mobilisation programme using the Volunteer Brigade to reach every affected household. Comprehensive impact mitigation programme for affected households. Housing policy and programme for affected households, including child-headed households.	Integrated development planning framework. Participatory planning mechanisms at local level. Policy review on patterns of land ownership and access to land for household food security. Local state support mechanisms (e.g. indigence policy or subsidies) to ensure poor households have access to essential services. Competency development for district structures including district -level AIDS Task Forces to become the local-level cornerstone of the response. Require that all submissions for tenders must have an HIV/AIDS impact assessment and proposals for HIV prevention .
Sector: Natural Resources			
Awarenes-raising activities and condom distribution through existing structures and mechanisms at district level.	Referral mechanisms and counselling support programmes at district level and in rural communities.	Programme targeting PLWHA and affected households to sustain and diversify their livelihoods.	Rural water supply programme, regardless of ability to pay (e.g. exemptions or cross-subsidisation mechanism). Situation analysis of the impact of the Lesotho Highlands Project on local communities.
*(Vulnerability/risk reduction & enhancement of capabilities)			

Table 7.	Pragmatic Actions for Core Streaming HIV/AIDS by Government Sectors		
Prevention	**Treatment & Care**	**Impact Mitigation**	**Addressing Systemic Development Factors***
Sector: Planning and Economic Development			
HIV/AIDS workplace programme including using GIPA. Information-dissemination, awareness-raising activities and condom distribution through family planning, reproductive and education programmes (in partnership with the Ministry of Health). Review of all development projects from an HIV/AIDS lens. Policy on what constitutes an HIV-Competent development project that will not increase vulnerability to HIV and will mitigate the impact of AIDS.	Basic health care and community health care programmes as integral part of development projects. Development projects and policies to be designed to build in care and support of affected communities. Development projects to be prioritised for communities that are worst affected by AIDS and most vulnerable to HIV.	Housing programme for affected households, including child-headed households (e.g. housing subsidy). Participatory mechanisms facilitating the Involvement of PLWHA, affected households and communities in decision-making concerning national economic development (e.g. PRSP process). Capacity assessments to inform needs in implementing macro-programmes including the PRSP. Policy on contracts for capacity replacement using retired civil servants.	Review of macro-economic policy framework and impact on employment creation and the distribution of wealth/income in light of HIV/AIDS. Policy measures on appropriate state support in the context of widespread poverty. Review of impact of market-oriented strategies (user fees, privatisation) on equitable access to essential services, including cross-subsidisation mechanisms for poor households. Situation analysis of household & community capabilities to provide essential services in the context of HIV/AIDS. Participatory mechanisms to inform implementation of PRSP, focusing on households affected by HIV/AIDS and food insecurity. Comprehensive socio-economic programmes in economic growth areas (e.g. family accommodation, education facilities, etc.). Impact assessment of infrastructure development projects on local communities.
*(Vulnerability/risk reduction & enhancement of capabilities)			

Table 7.	Pragmatic Actions for Core Streaming HIV/AIDS by Government Sectors		
Prevention	**Treatment & Care**	**Impact Mitigation**	**Addressing Systemic Development Factors***
Sector: Public Service			
Requirement that all civil servants make it their duty to engage in prevention activities as they meet the public. Guidelines on HIV/AIDS workplace programme across the public service.	Code for all civil servants to provide either guidelines or care and support directly in their interactions with the public. ARV treatment policy and programme for employees across the public sector.	Policy guidelines, training and sanctions to prohibit disrespectful behaviour and discrimination by public servants towards PLWHA and affected households. Policy guidelines for public service employees on dealing with PLWHA, affected households and AIDS orphans in a sensitive manner. Comprehensive policy on support for civil servants affected by AIDS in relation to funeral costs, care for orphans and those most vulnerable. Capacity-replacement using retired civil servants.	Transformation of the public service to create enhanced delivery and greater coherence in the public sector. Policy guidelines and sanctions system to prohibit sexual favours in exchange for government services. Policy guidelines on a public service ethos and code of conduct for engagement between public servants and citizens/local communities. Citizen-complaints mechanism (e.g. ombudsman) to report disrespectful or discriminatory behaviour by public servants. Review of National Policy on age of retirement to enable the civil service to utilise all available capacity.
Sector: Tourism, Culture and Environment			
Prevention campaigns for tourism workers. Information-dissemination, awareness-raising activities and condom distribution at hotels and tourist destinations and in surrounding communities. Requirement for all suppliers of services in the industry to have an HIV-workplace programme.	Referral services and counselling facilities at tourist destinations, targeting both tourists, workers and local communities.	Policy guidelines to prevent discrimination of PLWHA and affected households in income-generating opportunities. Involvement of PLWHA and affected households in information sessions with tourists to reduce stigma and prevent HIV transmission.	Policy on local employment creation at potential growth sites for tourism, including policy measures for the employment of women. Review of cultural practices that facilitate the spread of HIV/AIDS. Policy on irrigation and conservation farming.

*(Vulnerability/risk reduction & enhancement of capabilities)

Table 7.	Pragmatic Actions for Core Streaming HIV/AIDS by Government Sectors		
Prevention	**Treatment & Care**	**Impact Mitigation**	**Addressing Systemic Development Factors***
Sector: Trade, Industry and Marketing			
Agreements with business/ industrial sectors on policy/ programme on prevention for Basotho employees and their families. Information-dissemination, awareness-raising activities and condom distribution at Ministry's offices for small-scale entrepreneurs. Policy on requirement for HIV/AIDS impact assessment and prevention programmes for all industries.	Agreements with business/ industrial sectors on policy/ programme of treatment and care for Basotho employees and their families. Referral services at Ministry's offices for small-scale entrepreneurs. Policy requiring all industry to provide a minimum package of treatment and care for workers infected.	Agreements with business/ industrial sectors on impact mitigation programme for their workforce and local communities where they are located. Policy on financial support for small-scale entrepreneurs affected by HIV/AIDS (e.g. financial support for affected households or financial contributions towards funeral costs).	Agreements with trade partners about the terms of trade that strengthen local growth economies and balance domestic and external needs. Policy on support for small-scale entrepreneurs, including encouraging women in particular. Agreements with industrial sectors on corporate social responsibility programmes resulting in social investment in local communities Agreements with private sector on the provision of employment and on-the-job training programmes for Basotho.
Sector: Works and Transport			
Awareness-raising programme for taxi drivers, lorry drivers and the transport industry, including condom distribution at major transport hubs. Information-dissemination, awareness-raising activities and condom distribution at construction sites. Collaboration in ILO project on prevention in the transport sector in Southern Africa. Referral mechanisms for STI treatment of all workers in the industry. Policy on HIV/AIDS impact assessment and prevention by all public works programmes.	Referral services and counselling facilities at major transport hubs and at construction sites. Peer support programmes among taxi/lorry drivers and construction workers. Policy on treatment and care for all workers.	Public works programme designed for PLWHA and affected households. Policy on transport subsidies for PLWHA, affected households and AIDS orphans.	Public works programme targeting women and female-headed households with reports indicating the effectiveness of this. System of transport subsidies for poor households and disadvantaged social groups. Policy requiring that ALL public works programmes have an HIV-prevention programme for workers and drivers in the industry.
*(Vulnerability/risk reduction & enhancement of capabilities)			

Table 7.	Pragmatic Actions for Core Streaming HIV/AIDS by Government Sectors		
Prevention	**Treatment & Care**	**Impact Mitigation**	**Addressing Systemic Development Factors***
Sector: Youth, Gender and Sports			
Information-dissemination, awareness-raising activities and condom distribution using peer education and *pitsos*. Community mobilisation exercise to prevent HIV/AIDS should involve women's and youth groups as critical partners. Rapid assessment of sexual networks and most vulnerable behavioural patterns for women and youth. Gender policy and strategies designed to empower men to protect women and the society in general from HIV.	Peer support groups for youth. Support groups for women. Referral services at *pitsos* and other places of gathering of women and/or youth (e.g. sports facilities). Programme to support caregivers. Programme to review the possibility of targeting mothers of young children for ARV treatment.	Policy guidelines for support to female-headed households affected by HIV/AIDS. Policy guidelines for the involvement of women and youth living with, and affected by, HIV in decision-making processes (e.g. *pitsos*)	Strategy to publicise and implement the Gender Policy. Review of legislation and adoption of new legislation to enhance the status of women (e.g. sexual offences, legal status of women in customary marriages, sex with a minor). Policy guidelines for support to female-headed households. Policy on the participation of women in decision-making processes (e.g. *pitsos*). Policy on youth participation in national issues and policy dialogues. Comprehensive Youth Development Policy.
*(Vulnerability/risk reduction & enhancement of capabilities)			

NOTES *for Chapter 9*

1. UNDP Regional Project on HIV and Development in Sub-Saharan Africa. *Development Planning and HIV/AIDS in Sub-Saharan Africa*, Concept Paper, Pretoria, South Africa, 2003, para. 28.

2. UNDP Regional Project on HIV/AIDS. *Development Planning and HIV/AIDS in Sub Saharan Africa*. Concept Paper 2. Johannesburg, South Africa, 2002.

3. UNDP Regional Project on HIV and Development in Sub-Saharan Africa. *Development Planning and HIV/AIDS in Sub-Saharan Africa*, Concept Paper, Pretoria, South Africa, 2003, para. 28.

4. Ibid: 10

5. Taken from UNDP Regional Project on HIV and Development in sub-Saharan Africa. *Conceptual Shifts for Sound Planning: Towards an Integrated Approach to HIV/AIDS and Poverty*, Concept Paper, Pretoria, South Africa, 2002.

6. An HIV Vulnerability Assessment is a mapping exercise similar to that undertaken for food security, which seeks to determine which individuals and households are most vulnerable to the spread of HIV and their location. A comprehensive Vulnerability Assessment would also include those households already impacted on by HIV/AIDS.

7. Report on HIV/AIDS and Human Rights, Mission to Lesotho, Miriam Maluwa, UNAIDS Law and Human Rights Advisor.

10

The Role of Civil Society in Scaling up the National Response to the HIV/AIDS Pandemic

Global Lessons

UNGASS Declaration on Civil Society Mobilisation:

- By 2003, ensure the development and implementation of multi-sectoral national strategies and financing plans for combating HIV/AIDS that address the epidemic in forthright terms; ... involve partnerships with civil society and the business sector and the full participation of people living with HIV/AIDS, those in vulnerable groups and people mostly at risk, particularly women and young people ... (paragraph 37).

- The UNGASS Declaration further acknowledges "the particular role and significant contribution of people living with HIV/AIDS, young people and civil society actors in addressing the problem of HIV/AIDS in all its aspects... " and recognises "that their full involvement and participation in the design, planning, implementation and evaluation of programmes is crucial to the development of effective responses to the HIV/AIDS epidemic" (paragraph 33).

A national, multi-sectoral response to HIV/AIDS is not only contingent on the commitment and active involvement of individual leaders, leadership structures and government sectors, but also of religious organisations, NGOs, community groups and community-based organisations, cultural groups, the private sector and trade unions. Given the scale and nature of the epidemic, all sectors of society need to be mobilised to play their part in stemming the pandemic and turning the country into an HIV/AIDS-Competent Society.

Traditional Leadership

Lesotho is the only Constitutional Monarchy in Sub-Saharan Africa. It is estimated that the Traditional Leadership, represented by the Principal Chiefs in the Senate, have a widespread network of some 2,700 Chiefs down to the Village Headman.[1] The country also boasts of a wide network of Traditional Healers and Owners/Custodians of Initiation Schools. As is the case with all other institutions in the country, the institution of Traditional Leadership has been through some rough times, largely due to Lesotho's turbulent political past. However, given that the May 2002 General Elections ushered in a new dawn on the basis of a multi-party democratic dispensation, and as the political leaders continue to find ways for a win-win pluralistic future for the country, Traditional Leaders must also be afforded the chance to find and put their individual and collective best foot forward in transcending the past and working towards a unified nation. There is no better opportunity for doing this than that of all Basotho uniting to scale up the fight against the scourge of HIV/AIDS. The challenge—and the opportunity—is for Traditional Leaders to spearhead the fight against the pandemic in a non-partisan manner. After all, the virus afflicts human beings regardless of their race, gender, ethnicity, religion, socio-economic class or political affiliation. Hence the need to have a universal approach in tackling the pandemic.

Traditional Leaders can play a catalytic role in making sure that every Mosotho is HIV/AIDS-competent, that is, ensuring that all citizens living under their jurisdiction know what HIV is, how it is contracted, how it evolves to AIDS, how one can prevent oneself and others from getting it, what one should do if one or one's loved ones or others contract it, as well as knowing that, with proper care, treatment and support, an HIV/AIDS-infected person can live a long and productive life. In addition, Traditional Chiefs can play a key role in community-level initiatives for caring for orphans and other vulnerable children as well as People Living with HIV/AIDS. In particular, Traditional Chiefs can take the lead in forging strong partnerships with the Government, the Church, as well as the business sector in making sure that available medical, financial or other assistance reaches the people through the fastest and most accountable means possible. For instance, as Traditional Chiefs go about their civic duties—including teaching people about the pandemic—they would be able to also serve as the channel for the distribution of condoms and first-aid kits for home-based care, instead of people so often waiting for these supplies to be delivered to every community either by the Ministry of Health and Social Welfare or by LAPCA. These things are already beginning to happen and every effort must be made to ensure that this kind of collaboration becomes the norm rather than the exception.

Traditional Healers

Furthermore, as is the usual custom, most Basotho do have several encounters with Traditional Healers for one reason or another. In many cases, by the time most Basotho visit the health clinic or hospital, they would have already been to their Traditional Healer. Thus, they are very important agents for improved health and well-being. Establishing partnerships with them in the fight against the pandemic, therefore, makes a lot of sense. In fact, they are more likely to be believed than conventional health educators. In addition, it is now widely believed that some of the medicinal plants used by Traditional Healers—like the African potato, garlic and others—do have anti-fungal or immune-promoting qualities, which can be of benefit to their patients. What is important is to engage in a dialogue with Traditional Healers to ensure their patients know that there is no cure—as yet—for HIV/AIDS, so that infected and affected people do NOT live with false hopes.

Initiation Schools

Another very important component of Traditional Institutions is the Initiation School. This is where young boys "Go to the Mountains" for instruction on traditional norms and ethics, as part of their initiation from childhood to adulthood (*See chapter 7*). These teachings also include the subject of sexuality and responsible manhood. It goes without saying that the Initiation Schools are an excellent opportunity for teaching young men about responsible sexual behaviour, about safe sex, about the value of introducing and observing the practice of 'one man, one blade,' and about HIV/AIDS competency. If this happens, and as more Basotho men receive this kind of training from Initiation Schools, it will be less and less necessary for

Basotho women to worry about having to negotiate safe sex since their men would already be in the forefront promoting safe sex and responsible sexual behaviour. This is as it should be, because HIV/AIDS is a societal scourge, which afflicts both men and women, young or old. Fighting the pandemic should, therefore, be the responsibility of both. Most importantly, Initiation Schools tend to operate somehow on similar principles as those of an exclusive club or secret society: whatever is taught and learnt there is usually observed as long as one shall live. So, successfully promoting HIV/AIDS competence through Initiation Schools is the best way to ensure adherence as well as sustainability.

The Church

The Church has a crucial role to play in the fight against the pandemic. Like the traditional leadership, the Church has extensive networks of leaders, people and institutions with an estimated 3,000 churches throughout the country. Moreover, the Churches are responsible for the provision of some 40% of the health services in the country and 80% of the educational services. Leibowitz[2] identifies a number of strengths of these organisations, including the proximity to local communities and their jurisdiction over such areas as morality, rules of family life and sexual activity. It is clear that the Church has a major role in reducing stigma associated with HIV/AIDS along with taking a lead role in the fight against the pandemic itself. With 90% of the population claiming adherence to the Church, this is a massive resource that is waiting to be tapped.

Already, the church has been active in some areas, in particular in the care of orphans and vulnerable children. The Christian Health Association of Lesotho (CHAL) is the second biggest provider of health services after the Ministry of Health, and focuses on HIV/AIDS awareness programmes, prevention efforts, home-based care and stigma reduction in communities. The Christian Council of Lesotho trains youth as peer educators and offers training for women and men to care for the sick and for orphans. Other religions present in Lesotho are also initiating HIV/AIDS-related activities, yet they work mostly in isolation at this time. Despite these positive examples, religious organisations and religious leaders in general have been slow to take an active part in the national response to HIV/AIDS. Because the Church can be instrumental in promoting an ethic of care and altering prejudicial behaviour, their greater active involvement in the national response to HIV/AIDS is crucial.

GIPA

The principle of the Greater Involvement of People Living with HIV/AIDS (GIPA) is a cornerstone of a national, multi-sectoral response to HIV/AIDS. Evidence from other countries shows that people living with HIV/AIDS and their networks are probably the greatest resource in efforts to mobilise individuals and communities in the national response to the epidemic. In the first instance, many of these groups are the result of individuals coming together to share common experiences and give mutual support, but over time, many have evolved into service providers.

Civil Society

Furthermore, adherence to the GIPA principle also means that civil society organisations (like leadership structures, government sectors, the private sector, trade unions and international partners) need to actively encourage the involvement of those infected and affected by HIV/AIDS in their own HIV/AIDS programming and service provision.

A recent review of HIV/AIDS-related activities commissioned by LAPCA (2002) identified over 90 civil society organisations that are involved in HIV/AIDS activities in Lesotho. These, combined with the outreach of traditional leaders and their institutions and the church, can contribute to the capacity required to break the back of the pandemic.

Key Actions

The involvement of individuals, organisations and communities as active participants in the national response, rather than as passive recipients of particular projects or services, is a cornerstone of a comprehensive national response to HIV/AIDS. In Lesotho, there is a need to widen the scope for such involvement and strengthen the contributions of a wide variety of civil society organisations. Key to this is ensuring cohesion across all actors involved in the fight against HIV/AIDS. We must move towards a situation where every household in the country is involved in some way or other in the national response to the pandemic. If, as the Government of Lesotho has said, this is a war, then it should be treated as such, with all sections of society clear about their role.

Along with the Government, Traditional Leadership and Churches are perhaps the key actors to lead the process of scaling up the fight against HIV/AIDS. The challenge is there for these institutions to immediately begin the process of moving towards an HIV/AIDS-Competent Society. This will demand considerable change in the way the Traditional Leadership sees its role and how the Church begins to scale up the national response to the pandemic. The first step is for the leadership of these organisations (traditional, political and religious) to inform themselves about what the epidemic is, its causes, manifestations and impacts. The next step then is to involve their constituents to facilitate a full and comprehensive response to the crisis across the country. For example, the Traditional Leadership should engage with Traditional Healers, who run the Initiation Schools for young boys, and with the Chiefs down to the village levels.

Table 8 includes proposed actions for various civil society organisations in relation to the four domains of the national response to HIV/AIDS. In addition to these specific suggestions, some common actions should be pursued by all civil society organisations. These include the following:

- Adopt the Greater Involvement of People Living with HIV/AIDS (GIPA) Principle and advocate for its adoption among all stakeholders in Lesotho;
- Establish appropriate national forums or networks of civil society organisations on HIV/AIDS (for example, a National Network of Women's Organisations on HIV/AIDS, and more); and
- Actively participate in *community mobilisation* responses to HIV/AIDS with the Government and other stakeholders at national and community level to facilitate cooperation and avoid duplication or gaps/oversights in civil society action on HIV/AIDS, while adopting the motto: *Together We Can Build An HIV/AIDS Competent Community!*

Table 8.Pragmatic Actions for Mobilising Civil Society Organisations for an HIV/AIDS Competent Society

Prevention	Treatment & Care	Impact Mitigation	Addressing Systemic Development Factors*
Leadership structure: Traditional Leaders			
Pioneer community-mapping exercises at the village level to understand the particular dynamics and prevalence of HIV. Initiate, or participate in, community-based and nation-wide debates on those aspects of customary law, cultural values and practices, which may be facilitating the spread of HIV. Develop, or participate in, prevention programmes at community level. Review customary/cultural practices at the Village level with a view to reducing vulnerability. Promote new sexual behaviour patterns that can reduce the risk of HIV infection. Promote UVT	Promote an ethic of care and mobilise community caregivers to care for people suffering from HIV/AIDS-related illnesses. Involve Traditional Healers, who have participated in HIV/AIDS workshops, in the care and treatment of PLWHA.	Publicly support PLWHA and their relatives, including orphans. Establish a practice at community level that encourages families and friends to acknowledge an AIDS-related death to help reduce stigma. Establish and monitor village support services for Orphans and Vulnerable Children. Convene regular *pitsos* to discuss and review the impacts of HIV/AIDS on the local community.	Advocate on behalf of the local community for the provision of public services and employment opportunities to the government. Ensure equitable access to, and distribution of, resources at community level. Support, or participate in, rapid HIV-Vulnerability Assessments at community level to establish which households and social groups require targeted support to reduce their vulnerability to HIV infection. Ensure equitable access to land and property for women.

*(Vulnerability/risk reduction & enhancement of capabilities)

Table 8.Pragmatic Actions for Mobilising Civil Society Organisations for an HIV/AIDS Competent Society			
Prevention	**Treatment & Care**	**Impact Mitigation**	**Addressing Systemic Development Factors***
Leadership structure: The Church			
Initiate, or participate in, community-based and nation-wide debates on those cultural values and practices, which may be facilitating the spread of HIV. Initiate church-led prevention campaigns at the village level involving face-to-face counselling. Develop, or participate in, prevention programmes at community level. Promote new sexual behaviour patterns that can reduce the risk of HIV infection. Promote UVT	Promote an ethic of care and mobilise community caregivers to care for people suffering from HIV/AIDS-related illnesses. Train and utilise lay-counsellors and caregivers using the broad network of congregants. Utilise the church's network of health practitioners to offer care and monitor treatment to complement government health workers.	Publicly support PLWHA and their relatives, including orphans. Establish a practice at community level that encourages families and friends to acknowledge an AIDS-related death to help reduce stigma. Use weekly services to monitor initiatives that mitigate impact.	Advocate on behalf of the local community for the provision of public services and employment opportunities to the government. Actively participate in policy dialogue on matters related to poverty and food insecurity and advocate for appropriate policy interventions to address these development challenges.
*(Vulnerability/risk reduction & enhancement of capabilities)			

Table 8.Pragmatic Actions for Mobilising Civil Society Organisations for an HIV/AIDS Competent Society			
Prevention	**Treatment & Care**	**Impact Mitigation**	**Addressing Systemic Development Factors***
Organisation: Organisations of People Living with HIV/AIDS (PLWHA) and AIDS Service Organisations.			
Develop, or participate in, prevention programmes using a variety of media. Promote VCT programmes. Raise awareness of PMTCT programmes and advocate for the broad-based establishment of PMTCT programmes. Promote UVT	Advocate for affordable life-enhancing (treatment of opportunistic diseases) and life-prolonging (i.e. ARV treatment) interventions to be made available to all those infected. Develop, or participate in, peer support programmes for PLWHA. Provide referral services to PLWHA, for example, on Home-Based Care (HBC) programmes from government and non-government organisations. Participate in the design and implementation of capacity-building programmes for HBC.Raise awareness about the dietary dimension of care and support nutritional programmes. Raise awareness about the situation of women living with HIV/AIDS, who continue to fulfill a role as caregivers.	Advocate for special initiatives on AIDS orphans by government and NGOs, such as an income grant for orphans. Advocate for the urgent adoption and implementation of legislation safeguarding the human rights of PLWHA and their relatives. Initiate, or participate in, media campaigns aimed at breaking the cycle of stigma and discrimination related to HIV/AIDS. Support networks of community structures, which assist those living with HIV/AIDS at household level. Provide income-generating projects for households affected by HIV/AIDS.	Engage in advocacy on human rights and other core determinants of vulnerability, risk and reduced coping capability. Advocate for the participation of PLWHA in policy development & implementation, in particular in relation to poverty, gender, human rights and HIV/AIDS. Advocate for resources to be committed to organisations of PLWHA.
*(Vulnerability/risk reduction & enhancement of capabilities)			

Table 8. Pragmatic Actions for Mobilising Civil Society Organisations for an HIV/AIDS Competent Society			
Prevention	**Treatment & Care**	**Impact Mitigation**	**Addressing Systemic Development Factors***
Organisation: Youth Organisations			
Develop, or participate in, peer education programmes targeting youth (e.g. at football tournaments or other places where youth congregate). Provide targeted IEC and referral services to encourage youth to seek STD treatment. Design and implement a 100% VCT programme for all young people considering marriage. Design and implement a 100% condom-use programme for young people at the National University of Lesotho and other institutions of higher education. Encourage the active participation of youth in IEC programmes, including those already living with HIV/AIDS. Promote UVT	Develop, or participate in, peer-support programmes for youth infected and affected by HIV/AIDS. Provide targeted referral services for youth regarding care and support. Actively participate in, and generate awareness of, HBC facilities, specifically with the intention to reach youth living with HIV/AIDS.	Advocate for an Education Policy protecting the right to education for youth living with HIV/AIDS and for orphans. Identify child-headed households and advocate on their behalf for appropriate support. Constitute peer support groups of youth, supporting both in- and out-of-school youth affected by HIV/AIDS.	Advocate for the active participation of youth in all policy development and policy implementation. Advocate for a comprehensive Youth Development Policy and its effective implementation (including adequate resource allocation). Identify youth-specific barriers affecting the status of youth and their quality of life and advocate for the removal of such barriers. Advocate for policy development and policy implementation to minimise the socio-cultural, economic and political vulnerability of young girls to HIV infection.
*(Vulnerability/risk reduction & enhancement of capabilities)			

Table 8.Pragmatic Actions for Mobilising Civil Society Organisations for an HIV/AIDS Competent Society			
Prevention	**Treatment & Care**	**Impact Mitigation**	**Addressing Systemic Development Factors***
Organisation: Women's Organisations			
Develop, or participate in, peer-education programmes targeting women. Provide targeted IEC and referral services to encourage women to seek STI treatment. Encourage women, including married women, to seek VCT. Design life-skills programmes for women to enable them to better negotiate safe sex. Actively participate in a mapping exercise of sexual networks in communities that might enhance the spread of HIV-infection and design appropriate prevention strategies based on the findings.	Develop, or participate in, peer-support programmes for women infected and affected by HIV/AIDS. Provide HBC and counselling services. Provide training for community members on HBC and establish a support network for these caregivers. Provide targeted referral services regarding care and treatment of women with HIV/AIDS.	Highlight the burden of care that women, in particular, experience in the care of relatives with HIV/AIDS and advocate for appropriate support measures to alleviate this burden. Constitute peer-support groups of women and highlight their plight in the wider community to elicit more support for their work. Provide income-generating projects for women infected and affected by HIV/AIDS.	Advocate for the active participation of women in all policy development and policy implementation. Advocate for the adoption and effective implementation of legislation that entrenches gender equality, such as the Sexual Offences Bill or legislation on the status of women in customary marriages. Advocate for the adoption of a national affirmative action policy and programme in relation to women and employment. Advocate for access to credit and land for women. Conduct *Pitsos* to review cultural and other social barriers that might contribute to the increased vulnerability of girls and women to HIV infection. Design and implement leadership programmes for women.
*(Vulnerability/risk reduction & enhancement of capabilities)			

Table 8.Pragmatic Actions for Mobilising Civil Society Organisations for an HIV/AIDS Competent Society			
Prevention	**Treatment & Care**	**Impact Mitigation**	**Addressing Systemic Development Factors***
Organisation: Khotla[3]			
Develop, or participate in, IEC programmes, especially those targeting boys and men. Encourage men, including married men, to seek VCT. Encourage men to seek STI treatment. Provide marital counselling to married couples and those intending to get married on the risk of contracting or transmitting HIV within the context of marriage and the need for safe-sex relationships. Promote a culture of "*responsible men*" within the context of HIV/AIDS.	Provide an ethic of care for those infected and affected by HIV/AIDS. Develop, or participate in, peer-support programmes at community level, particularly for men and boys. Provide referral services regarding treatment and care, particularly for men and boys. Promote a culture of men as caregivers and provide workshops for men on HBC.	Mobilise men through traditional organisations (e.g. burial societies) in communities to provide support to overburdened caregivers. Publicly support PLWHA and their relatives and ensure their active involvement in community matters.	Promote a culture of human rights based on respect of everyone's basic rights, with particular emphasis on the rights of women. Actively participate in policy dialogue on matters related to poverty and food insecurity and advocate for appropriate policy interventions to address these development challenges. Speak out against gender-based violence and sexual abuse (both within and outside the context of marriage). Promote equitable access to land and property for women. Since women are legally minors in Lesotho, equal rights to property is the key to securing the livelihoods of female-headed households in the case of husband's death fom AIDS.
*(Vulnerability/risk reduction & enhancement of capabilities)			

NOTES *for Chapter 10*

1. Based on a discussion with the President of the Senate (the Upper House of Parliament in Lesotho), Mr. Sampe Lejaha, Principal Chief, at a workshop on 28/29 July 2003, in Mohale, Lesotho.

2. Leibowitz (2002).

3. A meeting place where men discuss village business.

11

The Role of the Private Sector in Scaling up the National Response to the HIV/AIDS Pandemic

Global Lessons

UNGASS Declaration on the World of Work

- By 2003, develop a national legal and policy framework that protects in the workplace the rights and dignity of persons living with and affected by HIV/AIDS and those at the greatest risk of HIV/AIDS, in consultation with representatives of employers and workers, taking account of established international guidelines on HIV/AIDS in the workplace (paragraph 69);

- By 2005, strengthen the response to HIV/AIDS in the world of work by establishing and implementing prevention and care programmes in public, private and informal work sectors, and take measures to provide a supportive workplace environment for people living with HIV/AIDS (paragraph 49);

- By 2005, develop and begin to implement national, regional and international strategies that facilitate access to HIV/AIDS prevention programmes for migrants and mobile workers, including the provision of information on health and social services (paragraph 50).

As the UNAIDS Global Report on the HIV/AIDS Epidemic 2002 notes, HIV/AIDS dramatically affects labour, setting back economic activity and social progress. The vast majority of people living with HIV/AIDS worldwide are between the ages of

15-49, people who are in the prime of their working lives. Increased absenteeism, organisational disruption, and the loss of skills and institutional memory have negative impacts on productivity and staff morale. At the same time, company costs for health-care, funeral benefits and pension fund commitments are likely to rise significantly as early retirement and deaths mount. For example, a study of a commercial agricultural estate in Kenya showed that AIDS-related medical expenditure surpassed projected expenses by 400 per cent. Another study covering several southern African countries has estimated that the combined financial impact of AIDS-related absenteeism, productivity decline, health-care expenditures, and recruitment and training expenses could cut profits by at least 6-8%.[1] Less easy to quantify is the loss of experience, skills and organisational memory, which can result in a strategic deficit for private corporations and public sector institutions alike. *Figure 19* shows how HIV/AIDS impacts on organisations and companies.

Of particular concern is the devastating impact of HIV/AIDS on small-scale and informal enterprises. HIV/AIDS-related illness and death of a lead entrepreneur is likely to result in the collapse of the enterprise, which will have far reaching implications for the household of that individual, for other employees in the enterprise and for the local economy. Unlike formal businesses, small and informal enterprises have no resources for medical and life insurance, for pension schemes or even for funeral costs. The illness and death of an entrepreneur can therefore impact severely on the resources and savings of affected families, who are then forced to sell off their assets or to borrow money to care for their loved ones or even to bury them.

Given these devastating impacts on labour, productivity and profitability, it is imperative that the world of work (that is, employers in the public, private and non-profit sector in partnership with trade unions) takes an active part in the national response to HIV/AIDS.

In 1999, the Government of Lesotho produced a policy document on HIV/AIDS in the workplace, in line with the SADC Code of Conduct, focusing on prevention and control of HIV/AIDS in workplaces. It is also a non-discrimination policy that is aimed at people living with HIV/AIDS so that they are properly treated by management, co-workers and clients. The document recognises the devastating impact of HIV/AIDS on the world of work:

"HIV/AIDS not only causes illness disability and death to employees and severe economic and emotional disruptions of their families, it also increases

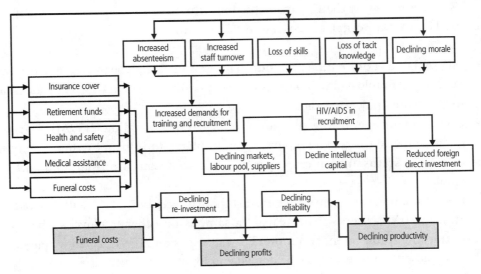

Source: UNAIDS (2002)

Figure 19. The impact of HIV/AIDS on the private sector, industries, small and informal enterprises: an overview

the cost of doing business. Employers face a great burden of health care, death benefits, pension and other costs. AIDS causes decreased productivity as workers are absent or away from work to care for the sick relatives. Costs rise, as expected workers with valuable skills become ill and unable to work; this causes disruptions in production and increases training and labour costs."[2]

Employers in Lesotho are beginning to respond to the pandemic. Recently, a Business Coalition against HIV/AIDS was established. Some employers have initiated HIV/AIDS workplace programmes for their workforce. During a visit of the UN Special Envoy to the Secretary General for HIV/AIDS, Mr. Stephen Lewis, the CGM Factory, which employs close to 7,000 Basotho (mainly women), shared its experience of a HIV/AIDS workplace programme. This programme involves primarily an IEC and peer-education programme, which includes the use of drama and the provision of health services through a local clinic. Based on global lessons on HIV/AIDS in the workplace, CGM is really only in the early phase of a comprehensive workplace programme.

A recent review by the ILO made the following recommendations for comprehensive HIV/AIDS workplace programmes in Lesotho:

- HIV/AIDS/STI prevention and control programmes shall be implemented at the workplace. Employers will be encouraged to provide HIV/AIDS/STI education to all their employees at their workplace.
- Confidentiality regarding all medical information, including HIV/AIDS status, must be maintained. An employee is not obliged to inform his/her employer of his/her status and an employer may not seek such information about an employee.
- Discrimination in the workplace against those infected with HIV will be avoided. Healthy HIV-carriers will be treated the same as any other employee with regard to training, promotion, and more. For as long as an HIV-infected employee is medically fit, he/she will not be denied employment opportunities.
- Counselling services at the workplace should be mandatory.[3]

Two other areas of concern require careful attention. The first is the impact of HIV/AIDS on small and informal enterprises and the need to develop appropriate measures to support these enterprises. The second area of concern relates to the large number of migrants in search of immediate, short-term, seasonal or longer-term employment. Appropriate policy and programmatic interventions targeting both areas are required.

Key Actions

Table 9 reflects suggested actions for business that will set it on the path to an HIV/AIDS-Competent Society. It includes key actions for the private sector (including the textile industry, which is a key industrial sector and employer in the national economy of Lesotho), small-scale enterprises (mainly in the informal economy) and trade unions.

In addition, the following basic or foundation-building actions should be pursued by the private sector:

- Adopt the Greater Involvement of People Living with HIV/AIDS (GIPA) Principle;
- Participate in, and support the work of, the Business Coalition Against HIV/AIDS;
- Adopt a Corporate Social Responsibility Policy;
- Adopt a comprehensive HIV/AIDS Workplace Policy and Programme in accordance with the ILO Code of Practice on HIV/AIDS and the World of Work;
- Participate in a negotiating forum between Government, the private sector and labour to ensure the rights of employees living with HIV/AIDS; and
- Develop an information-management system that provides regular data on the impact of HIV/AIDS on the workforce, the company's operations and product markets and the company's response to HIV/AIDS, which can be used for monitoring purposes.

Small-scale enterprises (mainly in the informal sector) may want to consider the following basic and foundation-building actions:
- Establish an association of small-scale enterprises, which also focuses on the impacts of HIV/AIDS on the sector and plays an advocacy role on behalf of the sector with government. This association should adopt the Greater Involvement of People Living with HIV/AIDS (GIPA) Principle.

For trade unions, the basic and foundation-building actions include the following:
- Adopt the Greater Involvement of People Living with HIV/AIDS (GIPA) Principle;
- Participate in, and support the work of, a forum for Trade Unions on HIV/AIDS;
- Participate in a negotiating forum between Government, the private sector and labour to ensure the rights of employees living with HIV/AIDS; and
- Adopt a comprehensive HIV/AIDS Workplace Policy and Programme in accordance with the ILO Code of Practice on HIV/AIDS and the World of Work for trade union officials.

Table 9. Pragmatic Actions for Mobilising the World of Work for an HIV/AIDS Competent Society			
Prevention	**Treatment & Care**	**Impact Mitigation**	**Addressing Systemic Development Factors***
Sector: The Private Sector			
Provide lifestyle-training for employees to create a culture of communication on sexual relations. Encourage employees to seek VCT and STI treatment. Provide access to VCT, STI treatment, IEC, condoms and other prevention services through a referral service or internal facility. Design and implement a 100% condom-use programme, particularly for companies or industrial sectors with highly mobile employees.[4] Support prevention programmes in particular communities or for particular target groups (e.g. youth) as part of a Corporate Social Responsibility programme.	Conduct an organisational assessment to ascertain the need for treatment and care and the financial implications of providing comprehensive employee benefits (for example, medical insurance, sick leave, etc.). Provide appropriate treatment and care for employees and, where possible, for their spouses (for example, ARV treatment). Develop gender-sensitive workplace programmes that recognise the particular burden of care on women workers in response to the HIV/AIDS epidemic. Support HBC programmes in particular communities or for particular target groups (e.g. youth) as part of a Corporate Social Responsibility programme.	Adopt a policy of non-discrimination of PLWHA in the workplace. Develop a comprehensive human resources plan, which takes into account the impacts of HIV/AIDS on the workforce (for example, compassionate leave for funeral attendance, financial support for funerals of employees, etc.). Adopt a policy on flexible working arrangements for infected/affected employees. Develop partnerships with government on social responsibility initiatives aimed at mitigating the impact of HIV/AIDS on the workforce, their areas of residence or society at large. Conduct institutional audit of the impact of HIV/AIDS on the operations of a company/industrial sector, including impact on (potential) customer base and implications for product markets.	Adopt an Affirmative Action policy to target women for employment in the context of the national employment-creation strategy. Adopt and enforce a Sexual Harassment Policy and Programme in the workplace. Ensure compliance with minimum wage to support sustainable livelihoods of employees. Promote formal and on-the-job training programmes for Basotho workers. Support community initiatives aimed at addressing food insecurity, poverty, violence against women and children, and lack of access to basic services as part of a Corporate Social Responsibility Programme.
*(Vulnerability/risk reduction & enhancement of capabilities)			

Table 9. Pragmatic Actions for Mobilising the World of Work for an HIV/AIDS Competent Society			
Prevention	**Treatment & Care**	**Impact Mitigation**	**Addressing Systemic Development Factors***
Sector: Small-scale Enterprises and the Informal Economy			
In partnership with local NGOs, participate in prevention activities targeting local entrepreneurs that encourage them to access VCT, STI treatment, IEC, condoms and other prevention services. Participate in an assessment of the vulnerability of women and men in this sector to the spread of HIV, focusing on sexual networks that involve transactional sex. Disseminate relevant information and condoms to local community members (i.e. customers).	In collaboration with NGOs, offer appropriate referral services to employees, other entrepreneurs and to community members ('customers') regarding treatment and care. Establish, and participate in, peer-support groups for small-scale entrepreneurs living with HIV/AIDS.	Advocate for government support to small-scale enterprises and entrepreneurs (and their families) infected/affected by HIV/AIDS. Constitute peer-support groups for small-scale entrepreneurs and/or their dependents to identify the main impacts of HIV/AIDS on the sector and on entrepreneurs and their families. Expand training of SMMEs to groups rather than individuals to ensure that there is additional capacity to run the enterprise in the event of illness or death. Participate in media campaigns aimed at breaking the cycle of stigma and discrimination related to HIV/AIDS by highlighting the plight of small-scale entrepreneurs living with HIV/AIDS.	Where applicable, ensure compliance with a minimum wage to support sustainable livelihoods of employees. Advocate for job security and improved working conditions for small-scale enterprises (for example, through the provision of public services and infrastructure).
*(Vulnerability/risk reduction & enhancement of capabilities)			

Table 9. Pragmatic Actions for Mobilising the World of Work for an HIV/AIDS Competent Society			
Prevention	**Treatment & Care**	**Impact Mitigation**	**Addressing Systemic Development Factors***
Sector: Trade Unions			
Develop, or participate in, peer-education programmes targeting trade union members (through shop stewards, for example). Provide targeted IEC and referral services to encourage trade union members to seek STI treatment. Design and implement a 100% VCT programme for trade union members. Design and implement a 100% condom-use programme for trade union members. Advocate for the provision of VCT services and STI treatment at all workplaces. Identify workplace conditions that put certain groups of employees at risk of contracting HIV and advocate for the necessary changes in those conditions (for example, the placement of teachers in rural areas, without provision for their families to join them).	Engage with employers to provide treatment, care and counselling services at the workplace. Advocate for comprehensive employee benefits (e.g. medical insurance, sick leave, and more). Advocate for the development of gender-sensitive workplace programmes that recognise the particular burden of care on women workers in response to the HIV/AIDS epidemic. Establish peer-support groups for trade union members living with HIV/AIDS. Provide, or participate in, training for trade union members on HBC and establish a support network for these caregivers. Provide targeted referral services regarding care and treatment for trade union members living with HIV/AIDS.	Adopt a policy of non-discrimination of PLWHA for trade unions. Advocate for a policy of non-discrimination of PLWHA in the workplace. Advocate for comprehensive workplace programmes protecting the rights of infected employees. Advocate for a policy on flexible working arrangements for infected/affected employees. Establish peer support groups for trade union members living with HIV/AIDS and/or their relatives to identify what support they require.	Advocate for the adoption and effective implementation of a national Labour Policy that protects the rights of employees. Adopt a Sexual Harassment Policy for trade unions. Monitor the implementation of Sexual Harassment Policies and Programmes in the workplace. Advocate for the effective implementation of a national employment creation strategy and monitor its implementation.
*(Vulnerability/risk reduction & enhancement of capabilities)			

NOTES *for Chapter 11*

1. UNAIDS Report on the Global HIV/AIDS Epidemic 2002, UNAIDS, Geneva, Switzerland, 2002: 54-55.

2. Government of Lesotho, *Policy Document on HIV/AIDS in the Workplace*, Government of Lesotho, Maseru, 1999: 13.

3. Quoted in A. J. Mturi, *HIV/AIDS and the World of Work in Lesotho*. Report prepared for the ILO Area Office, Lesotho, 2002.

4. This could be similar to the 100% condom-use programme in the commercial sex industry pioneered by Thailand. The programme targets sex workers and their clients and monitors condom use on a regular basis (UNAIDS, 2002).

12

The Role of International Partners in Scaling up the National Response to the HIV/AIDS Pandemic

Global Commitments

With HIV/AIDS as one of the biggest threats to human development in many countries on the African continent, the international community has a critical role to play in supporting national efforts and leveraging all available resources to combat the epidemic. This was emphasised in the Millennium Declaration, in which the international community has committed itself to: "help Africa *build up its capacity to tackle the spread of the HIV/AIDS epidemic.*"[1]

Since the Millennium Summit in September 2000, HIV/AIDS has been on the agenda of various global gatherings under the auspices of the United Nations, the G8 and G77 Nations, the European Union, the Commonwealth of Nations, the Organisation of African Unity (now the African Union) and equivalent structures in other regions.

Of particular significance is the Special Session on HIV/AIDS of the General Assembly of the United Nations, which took place in June 2001. The outcome of this meeting is the UNGASS Declaration of Commitment on HIV/AIDS, which includes

UNGASS Declaration on International Partnership:

There are numerous references in the UNGASS Declaration related to the role and responsibilities of the international community in addressing the HIV/AIDS pandemic. These include the following targets and appeals:

- By 2005, ... reach an overall target of annual expenditure on the pandemic of between 7 and 10 billion United States dollars in low and middle-income countries and those countries experiencing or at risk of experiencing rapid expansion for prevention, care, treatment, support and mitigation of the impact of HIV/AIDS, and take measures to ensure that the resources needed are made available, particularly from donor countries ... (paragraph 80);

- Call on the international community, where possible, to provide assistance for HIV/AIDS prevention, care and treatment in developing countries on a grant basis (paragraph 81);

- Urge the developed countries that have not done so to strive to meet the targets of 0.7 per cent of their gross national product for overall official development assistance and the targets of earmarking 0.15 per cent to 0.20 per cent of gross national product as official development assistance for least developed countries as agreed ... taking into account the urgency and gravity of the HIV/AIDS pandemic (paragraph 83);

- Urge the international community to complement and supplement efforts of developing countries that commit increased national funds to fight the HIV/AIDS pandemic through increased international development assistance ... (paragraph 84);

- Integrate HIV/AIDS actions in development assistance programmes and poverty eradication strategies as appropriate, and encourage the most effective and transparent use of all resources allocated (paragraph 85);

- Call on the international community ... to take appropriate measures to help to alleviate the social and economic impact of HIV/AIDS in the most affected developing countries (paragraph 86);

- Without further delay, implement the enhanced Heavily Indebted Poor Country (HIPC) Initiative and agree to cancel all bilateral official debts of HIPC countries as soon as possible, especially those most affected by HIV/AIDS ... and urge the use of debt service savings to finance poverty eradication programmes, particularly for prevention, treatment, care and support for HIV/AIDS and other infections (paragraph 87).

specific targets and actions to reverse the spread of HIV/AIDS and address its devastating impacts within the next decade. The Declaration of Commitment was adopted unanimously, binding all states to its targets and actions. Of particular interest are those clauses that implore the international community to allocate resources for HIV/AIDS on a grant basis, to reduce the external debt of countries most affected by HIV/AIDS, and to increase international development assistance.

To make the Declaration a live reality where it matters most (that is, in those countries and communities worst affected by HIV/AIDS), rather than a beautifully worded document with little impact, all nations have to accept their global responsibility to bring about HIV/AIDS-Competent Societies—in other words, to become an HIV/AIDS-Competent Global Community. As a UNAIDS Report notes: "... *success in the struggle against the epidemic requires a global community that acts on the basis of human concern and humane values.*"[2]

The involvement of development partners in the Lesotho national response to the HIV/AIDS pandemic varies from limited to extensive support. Ireland's aid package devotes up to seven percent of its total bilateral assistance to a variety of HIV/AIDS programmes in relation to prevention, treatment and care, and impact mitigation (care for orphans and vulnerable children). The Department for International Development (DfID) funds an IEC programme (*Soul City*) and the Nutrition, Agriculture and HIV/AIDS Programme in the Department of Agriculture. USAID supports three cross-border HIV awareness initiatives coordinated by the international NGO, CARE. UN agencies also offer significant technical and financial assistance for the national response to HIV/AIDS.

Development partners in Lesotho work together under the mechanism of the Expanded UN Theme Group on HIV/AIDS. Also, UN agencies and other partners have reaffirmed their commitment to work in partnership with the Government of Lesotho and to offer coherent and complementary support.

Development partners have played an important role in the development of a national proposal to the GFATM, which outlines a number of envisaged activities aimed at effectively reducing HIV/AIDS and TB through a series of community programmes. Financial and technical assistance from development partners in realising the objectives of this proposal remains critical. In addition, the Government will need support from development partners related to the integration of HIV/AIDS into the ongoing PRSP and Vision processes; the integration of HIV/AIDS into sectoral policies; budgeting and the development of action plans; reviews of macro-economic planning; and capacity development throughout sectors and within local government.

The pandemic has reached unacceptably high proportions in Lesotho, which is compounded by the food crisis that has threatened the country and its neighbours. Although the international community is involved at a number of levels of the pandemic and provides significant financial support, in many instances this support is for pilot initiatives in select communities and districts—often those most accessible and capacitated. There is a danger that this approach will create 'islands of excellence' with apparently effective projects and programmes that are difficult to replicate. The challenge of scaling up the national response to the HIV/AIDS pandemic in Lesotho is as much with the international partners as it is with the Government. In essence, the effect of international support to the national response in Lesotho is disparate and watered down. Thus, a strategic position is required for the International Partnership.

It is important that the International Partnership step back and consider the following questions:

- Where is the most useful place to target resources in a coordinated and upscale manner?
- How can development partners support HIV/AIDS core streaming in all activities?
- How can development partners use their comparative advantage in an effective way to fight HIV/AIDS?
- Can development partners take examples of good practices in other countries and share these with Basotho partners?
- Do development partners have (and implement) a workplace policy on HIV/AIDS?

Key Actions

Table 10 incorporates examples of pragmatic actions for various international partners to support Lesotho in becoming an HIV/AIDS-Competent Society. In addition to bilateral and multilateral donor agencies (UN agencies), attention is given to international financial institutions and to international NGOs.

General actions for International Partners (particularly donors) include the following:

- Adopting the Greater Involvement of People Living with HIV/AIDS (GIPA) Principle as a cornerstone of all donor programmes on HIV/AIDS;
- Participating in, and supporting the work of, the International Partnership on HIV/AIDS and ensuring it has sufficient capacity and resources to fulfill its tasks effectively;
- Adopting a comprehensive HIV/AIDS Workplace Policy and Programme for parliamentary staff in accordance with the ILO Code of Practice on HIV/AIDS and the World of Work;
- Providing support for the establishment and proper functioning of key structures on HIV/AIDS across all sectors in Lesotho;

- Providing assistance for HIV/AIDS prevention, treatment and care, and impact mitigation on a grant basis, in accordance with the UNGASS Declaration of Commitment on HIV/AIDS;
- Ensuring that annually between US$7-10 billion is made available for a comprehensive response to HIV/AIDS in developing countries (through the GFATM), in accordance with the UNGASS Declaration of Commitment on HIV/AIDS.

Table 10. Actions for Mobilising International Partnership for an HIV/AIDS Competent Society

Prevention	Treatment & Care	Impact Mitigation	Addressing Systemic Development Factors*
Organisations: Bilateral Donors			
Support awareness-raising and IEC programmes at national and community-based level. Support the establishment of VCT services throughout the country. Provide support for the effective roll-out of PMTCT programmes across the country. Support capacity-building programmes for government and civil society representatives in VCT, IEC and other prevention activities. Share global best practices on prevention. Document lessons from prevention in Lesotho to share globally. Promote UVT.	Support national treatment and care, and counselling programmes. Consider the feasibility of sponsoring ARV treatment. Support programmes aimed at strengthening the health system and its infrastructure. Support capacity-building programmes for local communities in HBC. Share global best practices on treatment and care. Document lessons from treatment and care in Lesotho to share globally.	Prioritise support for initiatives related to impact mitigation, in particular of orphans, girls and women burdened by care. Support an assessment of public-sector capacity to cope with HIV/AIDS and/or how HIV/AIDS impacts on public sector capacity to deliver on its development mandate. Support interventions aimed at strengthening institutional systems and mechanisms to cope better with the envisaged impact of HIV/AIDS (especially in the public sector). Provide the necessary support to scale up pilot programmes. Initiate, or participate in, policy dialogue on the link between poverty, food insecurity and HIV/AIDS. Share global best practices on impact mitigation and document lessons from Lesotho to share globally. Support, and participate in, campaigns aimed at reducing stigma and discrimination.	Ensure sustained and unconditional development assistance to Lesotho (based on an overall contribution of 0.7% of GNP to official development assistance). Review terms of trade and trade conditionalities imposed on Lesotho. Support government and civil society programmes on food security and poverty reduction. Support government and civil society programmes on women's empowerment and gender equity (including those addressing violence against women). Support community-based initiatives that strengthen social networks and instill a sense of social cohesion.
*(Vulnerability/risk reduction & enhancement of capabilities)			

Table 10. Actions for Mobilising International Partnership for an HIV/AIDS Competent Society

Prevention	Treatment & Care	Impact Mitigation	Addressing Systemic Development Factors*
Organisations: The United Nations			
Support national prevention programmes. Share global best practices on prevention. Support the review of national policies and projects that might fuel the spread of HIV. Establish HIV-Prevention programmes in the UN workplace as part of a comprehensive UN Workplace programme.	Support national treatment and care programmes. Share global best practices on treatment and care. Support HBC programmes that can alleviate the burden of care on women.	Support national efforts to mitigate the impact of HIV/AIDS on poverty and food security. Support programmes targeting orphans and child-headed households. Support, and participate in, campaigns aimed at reducing stigma and discrimination. Share global best practices on impact mitigation.	Review UN instruments for support to Lesotho to ensure that priority consideration is given to poverty reduction, food security and gender equity. Support the implementation of Lesotho's Gender Policy and advocate for the review of the UN Convention on the Elimination of All Forms of Discrimination Against Women (CEDAW) commitments. Support government policy and programmes aimed at addressing the determinants of risk and vulnerability, e.g. creation of employment and other income-generating opportunities; social security arrangements; provision of effective, accessible and affordable public services; and more. Provide technical and financial support to ensure the effective capacitation of government sectors to deliver on their development mandate.
*(Vulnerability/risk reduction & enhancement of capabilities)			

Table 10. Actions for Mobilising International Partnership for an HIV/AIDS Competent Society			
Prevention	**Treatment & Care**	**Impact Mitigation**	**Addressing Systemic Development Factors***
Organisations: International Financial Institutions			
Support (on a concession basis, if possible) national HIV-prevention programmes. Provide financial support for the establishment of VCT and STI control centres country-wide.	Support (on a concession basis, if possible) national programmes for treatment and care. Support government programmes aimed at strengthening the health system and its infrastructure.	Analyse the macro-economic impacts of HIV/AIDS in Lesotho and advise the government on appropriate forward-looking measures to pre-empt future impacts. Conduct, or support, an assessment of public-sector capacity to cope with HIV/AIDS, including how HIV/AIDS impacts on public-sector capacity to deliver on its development mandate. Support appropriate interventions aimed at strengthening institutional systems and mechanisms to cope better with the envisaged impacts of HIV/AIDS in the public sector. Initiate, or participate in, policy dialogue on the link between poverty, food insecurity and HIV/AIDS.	Review all loan agreements for development and consider changing these into concession agreements in light of high levels of poverty and food insecurity. Review the Options for Growth in Lesotho to ascertain whether the proposed strategies will help diminish the determinants of risk and reduced coping capabilities or are likely to worsen these factors.
*(Vulnerability/risk reduction & enhancement of capabilities)			

NOTES *for Chapter 12*

1. UN General Assembly Special Session (UNGASS) on HIV/AIDS Declaration of Commitment. Goals set to be achieved by 2003 and 2005, June 2001 (paragraph 58).

2. UNAIDS Report on the Global HIV/AIDS Epidemic 2002, UNAIDS, Geneva, Switzerland, 2002: 20.

CHAPTER

13

Children Rearing Children
A Challenge at the Heart of the Pandemic

Perhaps the most heartbreaking part of the HIV/AIDS saga is that of the plight of "children rearing children" or "orphans and vulnerable children", as they are formally referred to. The HIV/AIDS pandemic has dramatically changed the way in which many children live; it is gnawing away at the very core of society. In a country such as Lesotho where the traditional coping mechanisms have always provided safety nets for those who lost their parents, the HIV/AIDS pandemic has undermined the capacity of society to provide care and security to those who are most vulnerable. With an infection rate of over 30%, the capacity of these coping mechanisms to support the most vulnerable is totally undermined. As Alex de Waal states in his paper titled *New Variant Famine in Southern Africa*,[1] "just as HIV/AIDS destroys the body's immune system rendering it susceptible to a range of familiar pathological diseases that would otherwise be harmless, so too does the HIV/AIDS pandemic render society susceptible to familiar social and economic problems—and makes them more virulent and harder to treat". As in other African countries, the old, whenever they can, face the burden of looking after the children of their children and, where this is not an option, young children are faced with looking after siblings in an environment often characterised by fear, stigma and discrimination.

The United Nations World Food Programme (WFP), the Ministry of Health and Social Welfare and the Disaster Management Authority are in the process of finalising a national list of orphans, which is expected to number over 95,000. This will be completed in early 2004. This is higher than the findings of a recent study by the Ministry of Health and Social Welfare,[2] which estimates that 68,000 children in the 10 districts of the country have lost one or both parents. There is as yet no systematic registration of orphans, and birth registration is only 51%, with only 25% having birth certificates. There are increasing reports of the abandonment of infants and newborns from institutions, such as the Social Welfare Department, district hospitals and the police. Most of the abandoned children are not tested for HIV. However, given that HIV prevalence among pregnant women is high, the working assumption is that a significant percentage of abandoned children will require care that includes treatment for AIDS.

The issue of definition is pertinent in regard to orphans in the country. In Lesotho, as elsewhere in Africa, communities often define orphans as vulnerable children, including children who are disabled, or destitute children who may not necessarily be biological orphans, but may be termed as social orphans. In Sesotho culture, the term *khutsana* is a person who has lost both parents. This does not relate to age, but to the extent that anyone of any age can be khutsana. In some parts of the country, children who lose just one parent are known as orphans and must go through a cleansing ceremony, known as the *ho tosa khitsana*.

Not all orphans are left on their own, as there are many cases throughout the country where orphans are assisted by relatives and even by non-relatives in the community. However, this can often put considerable burden on the household, which is largely struggling with poverty and, in many cases, can actually pull households below the poverty line. In a report by the Ministry of Health and Social Welfare,[3] a woman from a rural area said:

> *I have four children of my own. On top of this, I have taken in others who are not even my relatives. Education is quite costly, especially school fees. If only government could meet us halfway and pay part of the fee for these orphans.*

Another woman in the town of Mafeteng said:

> *I have in my place four orphans from my son and four others belonging to my daughter. I have a problem feeding them and they are always complaining.*

These children suffer profoundly as their parents fall sick or die, with their experience characterised by psychosocial distress from their parents' illness or death, which is worsened by the stigma and shame associated with HIV/AIDS. The psychosocial impact of caring for ill and dying parents cannot be overestimated. It can affect schoolwork and the ability to keep up in class. There is also the obvious hardship in relation to the inability of parents to work, resulting in children often being forced to take on frightening adult responsibilities. Withdrawal from school is also a characteristic of these vulnerable children even before the death of their parents, with the pressure to abandon schools when their parents die. Malnutrition and illness are also associated with children who are alone after the death of their parents. This process of decline begins before the parents' death as they cease work in the fields or elsewhere, and have used up family reserves in medical costs for the opportunistic diseases that are characteristic of AIDS. In this environment, young children lose their sense of direction, security and well-being even before they become orphans.

In addition to this trauma, there are numerous cases of orphans who lose inheritance rights as they are forced out of the family property due to relatives taking over the land. Neither existing legislation nor customary law is effectively enforcing the basic rights of children to inherit their parents' property. The Report from the Ministry of Health and Social Welfare refers to cases where deceased parents leave property, which is then taken by relatives, leaving the children with nothing. As one person interviewed for the report said:

People take property. They start misappropriating it from the time the parents are still ill: before they are even dead or buried. But this is not fair or just because they take what is not rightly theirs; but this is common practice.[4]

The Impact of the Orphan Crisis

The impact of the pandemic, combined with chronic poverty and food insecurity, has created a new crisis of vulnerability, which poses a different challenge to the government and all those involved in the development process in Lesotho. There is evidence that young girls are dropping out of school to look after ailing parents and younger siblings and are seeking employment—even in hazardous work, such as commercial sex and domestic labour. This places them at high risk and can lead to situations of orphans being infected with HIV/AIDS often as a result of sexual abuse and exploitation.

Lesotho has ratified the UN Convention on the Rights of the Child. It has committed itself to the outcomes of UNGASS on HIV/AIDS (May 2001) and UNGASS on Children (2002). These oblige Lesotho to recognise that the care and protection of orphans and vulnerable children should form an integral part of national development strategies, policies and the legal framework, in order to ensure that adequate resources are allocated to address the needs of these children. At the July 2000 International AIDS Conference in Durban, South Africa, a consensus was developed through consultations involving governments, international agencies, non-governmental agencies and community organisations. These principles are a crucial point of reference for all governments and stakeholders involved in protecting the rights of children, especially those affected by the HIV/AIDS pandemic. Key among these are the following:

- Strengthen the protection and care of orphans and other vulnerable children with their extended families and communities;
- Strengthen the economic coping capacities of families and communities;
- Enhance the capacity of families and communities to respond to the psychosocial needs of orphans, vulnerable children and their caregivers;
- Link HIV/AIDS prevention activities to care and support for people living with HIV/AIDS and efforts to support orphans and other vulnerable children;
- Focus on the most vulnerable children and communities, not only on those orphaned by AIDS;
- Strengthen schools and ensure access to education for all;
- Reduce stigma and discrimination; and
- Accelerate learning and information exchange.

As yet, there is no national programme for orphans and vulnerable children in Lesotho. The Ministry of Health and Social Welfare Report states that there is heavy reliance on privately owned homes and community centres run by churches and NGOs. According to the report, these do not address the growing needs of the large number of orphans in the country. There is a clear need for synergy between community response and government and international partners. The key to the success of any intervention in this regard is a focus on children's rights as well as on psychological welfare.

Such an appointment is underpinned by key principles, which include:

1. The right to survival, development and protection from abuse and neglect;
2. The right to have a voice and to be listened to;
3. That the best interests of the child should be of primary consideration; and
4. The right to freedom from discrimination.[5]

It is clear that the rights of children infected or affected by HIV/AIDS are being compromised and that they may often experience discrimination and exclusion from

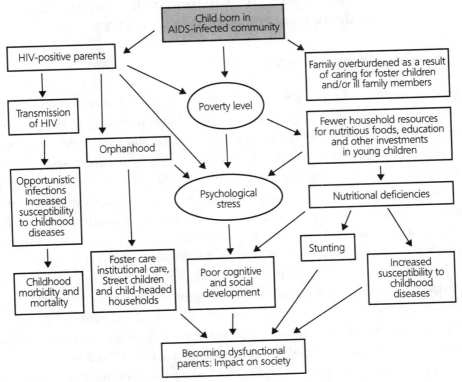

Source: Operational Guidelines for supporting Early Childhood Development (ECD) in multi-sectoral HIV/AIDS programs in Africa, 2003 UNAIDS, UNICEF, World Bank.

Figure 20. Young Children Born into AIDS-affected Communities

the community. Stigma is one of the greatest barriers to the effective implementation of programmes to mitigate the impact of HIV/AIDS. An inclusive approach is called for, which emphasises all children. Ideally, before any interventions take place, it is important to determine the scale of the problem, including distribution, the existing coping mechanisms, the capacity of community structures and the levels of vulnerability. However, the approach must be holistic in dealing with all aspects of prevention, care and impact mitigation, while also addressing the environment within which the children live. This is fundamentally based on the rights of the child and the obligation and duty of individuals, communities, government and society in general to deliver on, protect and strengthen these rights.

The Way Forward in Managing the Crisis of Orphans and Vulnerable Children

The Millennium Development Goals and Children

In September 2000, all the leaders of the United Nations member states, including Lesotho, adopted the Millennium Declaration. This mainstreamed a set of time-bound and measurable goals and targets for combating poverty, hunger, disease, illiteracy, environmental degradation and discrimination against women. Now placed at the heart of the global agenda, these are called the Millennium Development Goals (MDGs). A series of targets have been set for each goal, which are to be achieved by the year 2015, with indicators selected to monitor progress for each. The Government of Lesotho is committed to achieving these goals and implementing the necessary structures and systems. The MDGs are at the core of the development process in Lesotho today and are particularly relevant to the rights, protection and well-being of children. They provide the basic signposts on a road map for all duty bearers who are concerned with the protection of children in Lesotho. The goal to eradicate poverty and hunger directly affects the child, as does the goal to achieve universal primary education and the goal to combat HIV/AIDS. But also the goal to reduce infant mortality by one third and the goal to increase maternal health are key objectives in providing children with safe, healthy and secure livelihoods. The MDGs, if implemented from the perspective of the most vulnerable, put the child at the centre of the development process, providing a framework for a broad and comprehensive response to the HIV/AIDS crisis in Lesotho. Key elements of this framework must include:

- fostering links with all prevention activities in government, non-government and community sectors (including traditional leadership and churches);
- identifying the gaps in prevention and taking swift action to address these through synergy between the government and non government sectors;
- supporting treatment and care activities through government and community-based organisations, identifying gaps in the treatment and care cycle and addressing these gaps;
- establishing a targeting system that will touch the lives of those most vulnerable in a long-term and sustainable manner;
- strengthening the role of schools in the community, creating a secure environment for children;
- creating awareness of HIV and AIDS and reducing stigma and discrimination; and
- creating HIV/AIDS-competent communities.

This approach is about ensuring that an HIV/AIDS-Competent Community exists everywhere in the country. These are communities that take responsibility for fighting the pandemic and provide a support network for those infected and affected by HIV/AIDS. Each community must be aware of the vulnerable, support the coping mechanisms, and link up with the health and social services to ensure that their children are protected. Schools and other institutions, such as churches, are crucial in developing an environment that protects and provides security to the vulnerable.

In this regard, it is now clear that the role of teachers is changing, as they must learn to deal with large numbers of orphans in their classes. In a verbal presentation to the United Nations Country Team in Maseru by consultants from the UN Secretary General's Task Force on Women, Girls and HIV/AIDS, one team member spoke of the increased pressure and stress on teachers as they deal with vulnerable children with no support structures in the home. Teachers, often faced with a lack of concrete support and limited understanding of the dynamics of the virus and how it is transmitted, are fearful and feel vulnerable themselves. This can result in teachers not knowing how to deal with children who face injury. For example, at the meeting in the United Nations House, it was reported that one teacher had said that he would not assist a child with an injury because he may get infected. This clearly shows the need for a massive awareness campaign for the whole country.[6]

The Government, through the Ministry of Education, has commenced a Free Primary Education Scheme. This was introduced on a one-year rollout basis in the year 2000 and completing all primary grades by the year 2007. Currently, the Government also offers bursaries for orphans and other vulnerable children in grades five to seven. The funds available target 30,000 children, but only 17,000 children have so far benefited from the scheme. The Ministry of Education is currently contemplating rolling out Free Primary Education in the remaining three grades by the year 2004. This would involve a considerable change in the role of the school within the community by providing a secure appropriate location for addressing the needs of vulnerable children, and is particularly important, as evidence exists from Lesotho and elsewhere that orphans are less likely to be in school. The United Nations World Food Programme (WFP) is working closely with the Government to assist with the provision of school food. In investigating ways to review this, WFP is tailoring the scheme to meet the needs of vulnerable children. The contents of the food basket need to be addressed, along with the need to provide food to children not only during school days but also throughout the year. This school-feeding programme should be seen as akin to a family support programme. With the involvement of local community structures, there is real potential to develop community structures involving all duty bearers taking responsibility for vulnerable children at the village level.

The district AIDS Task Forces, which exist in all districts of the country, are positioned to play a growing and crucial role in the protection of vulnerable children. These need to be strengthened. Considerable progress has already been made in this regard with the involvement of different stakeholders in all Task Forces. However, they require assistance with developing plans and supporting basic responses, using community structures. The upcoming local elections, expected in 2004, and the establishment of new local government structures, provide a unique opportunity to achieve greater levels of accountability at the local level. New Local Government structures will also open the way for appropriate structures and responses to be established, as part of a comprehensive regional response to the HIV/AIDS pandemic.

In this regard, there is a need on the part of the international community to strengthen the Ministry of Local Government, which is driving the present decentralisation process and which would, therefore, be responsible for ensuring the convergence and delivery of services at the district level and below. This will only be successful if government and all stakeholders can build on the opportunities, which are clearly evident. There is a need to come up with operational programmes of transformational leadership to enable communities to move towards HIV/AIDS competence, with particular emphasis on generating community accountability for fighting the pandemic.

An additional strategy to explore may be, ironically, that of children teaching children. Children should be encouraged through support and guidance to raise awareness by speaking out about the impact of HIV/AIDS on their lives. Institutions or programmes can be identified to facilitate and promote the participation of children as peer educators both within and outside of schools. Also of interest is the idea of encouraging, where appropriate, children living with HIV/AIDS to share their experiences with peers and community members. Raising awareness in this manner is invaluable for effective prevention as well as efforts to minimise the stigma and discrimination surrounding HIV/AIDS. But this option is delicate and will need to be carefully thought through, with the advice of appropriate child psychologists.

Legislation for the Protection of OVC, Inheritance and Property Rights

The existing Child Protection Act (1980) is outdated and is being revised to bring it in line with the United Nations Committee on the Rights of the Child (CRC) principles, under the auspices of the Lesotho Law Reform Commission (LLRC) and the Ministry of Justice and Human Rights, with support from UNICEF. The draft already incorporates explicit recognition of the rights of children affected and infected by HIV/AIDS, including non-discrimination and the need for additional protection measures, such as legal safeguards to claims of inheritance. It is also being cross-referenced with the recently approved Sexual Offences Act for optimal effect. The recently approved Social Welfare Policy explicitly recognises orphans as a vulnerable category/disadvantaged group—thus creating a useful entry point for services to them.

A key issue is the registration of orphans and vulnerable children under 18 throughout the country. The format is being piloted in a selected district in collaboration with district staff, social welfare and chiefs who are responsible for compiling and updating lists of vulnerable households. Once approved by the Civil Registrar's Office of the Ministry of Local Government, it will be used nationwide and incorporated in the computerised vital registration system. The revised Child Protection Act is expected to give responsibility to the Ministry of Social Welfare to register these children.

Key issues in dealing with orphans and vulnerable children

Adoption and Implementation of the National Policy for Social Welfare and the Child Protection Act.

- A national work plan finalised and adopted.
- Community sensitisation on the Social Welfare Policy, Sexual Offences Act and Children's Act.
- Translation and dissemination of the Social Welfare Policy, Sexual Offences Act and Child Protection Act.
- Equipment and development of the capacity of the Child Gender Protection Unit.

Advocacy for stronger leadership and commitment at the highest level

- Print and distribute toolkits and IEC materials.
- Train parliamentarians, chiefs, religious leaders, NGOs, CBOs and FBOs on issues relating to the support and protection of OVCs.
- Establish HIV/AIDS competent communities

Mitigation

- Support school feeding programmes for all vulnerable children seven days a week throughout the year.
- Encourage support groups to use the school as a support centre, especially where no community structure exists.

Bringing together the lessons learnt from efforts to mitigate the impact of HIV/AIDS on children, a number of conclusions can be drawn to guide policy makers and other stakeholders. These include the following:

- The number of orphans and vulnerable children is already so large that traditional coping mechanisms are barely enough, thus strengthening the case for active public intervention supported by all sections of society. However, interventions need to focus on keeping the children within the community.
- There is a need to strengthen the existing mechanisms rather than supplant them. This includes aiding families that take in children, supporting the schools

and church structures that provide assistance to orphans, and supporting and strengthening community networks that focus on providing a secure and safe environment for orphans and vulnerable children at the community or village level.

- There is no single best practice but many examples of local communities, with little or no support from outside, taking responsibility for helping orphans and vulnerable children. This needs to be supported in the long run.

- There is a need to examine ways in which fostering can be encouraged with assistance provided to the host families. Often families are prepared to take in children from the locality if they get support from the local government. This can be limited to assistance with school fees and medical expenses along with a small annual grant as a contribution to the additional family costs. However, evidence from other countries would suggest that cash payments are difficult to monitor. A community response driven by targeting and monitoring approaches involving the local traditional leaders, the Church and NGOs is thus necessary.

- Orphanages are expensive and should be a last resort. Other halfway options, such as community-run children's villages or safe houses, with grant support from government, should be investigated. The challenge is to provide a nurturing environment that does not encourage stigma and discrimination.

- Each community at the rural and urban level must strive to become HIV/AIDS Competent. They should have a full list of all children in the village or community, with special regard to all aspects of vulnerability, along with a plan to address their special needs. This should be agreed upon with the appropriate government institutions, and overseen by both the community and government. The community should thus be accountable for those who are vulnerable and need community support.

NOTES *for Chapter 13*

1. A. De Waal, *New Variant Famine in Southern Africa.* Presentation for SADC VAC Meeting, Victoria Falls, 2002.

2. Government of Lesotho, Ministry of Health and Social Welfare, *The Problems of Orphans in Lesotho.* Final Report. October 2001, p35.

3. Ibid.

4. Ibid: p 45

5. World Bank. *Social Protection of Africa's Orphans and Vulnerable Children: Issues and Good Proactive and Practice Program Options.* Africa Human Development Paper Series, World Bank, 2002.

6. Meeting of the United Nations Country Team with Consultants from the UN Secretary General's Task Force on Women, Girls and HIVAIDS, 16 October 2003.

Mechanisms for an Appropriate National Response to the HIV/AIDS Pandemic

In his *Foreword* to this manual, The Right Honourable Prime Minister, Mr. Pakalitha Mosisili, called on ALL Basotho and their international partners to commit to
A New Resolve to Fight the Pandemic, given the stark reality that the national infection rate is already around one third of the adult population—and still rising—and
that the number of Basotho dying every day due to HIV/AIDS-related illnesses is
estimated at 70, a very high figure for a country of only about 2.2 million people.
The Prime Minister also laid out the commitment of His Majesty's Government to
leave no stone unturned in fighting this scourge and urged all other duty bearers to
do the same. Responding to this clarion call requires fundamental change in the way
we all do business.

An attempt has been made in the preceding chapters to reflect on how things
could be done differently, not only to beat the pandemic, but also to use this crisis to
catapult the country to a completely new level of efficiency, effectiveness and global
competitiveness. The purpose of this short chapter, therefore, is to recap the implications for the different mechanisms for appropriate development policies, planning,

implementation, oversight, accountability, monitoring of progress and evaluation. In this regard, every effort has been made to vigorously promote a systems-thinking approach to the forging of partnerships based on the principles of decentralisation, interdependence and synergy.

This approach requires an attitude change, a paradigm shift in the way we look at institutions and the people who work in them. First, it requires that all of us engaged in, and committed to, operationalising the new resolve to fight the pandemic must be prepared to think *win-win*. The concept of win-win can be defined as a frame of mind and heart that constantly seeks mutual benefit in all human interactions. Win-win means that agreements or solutions to problems are mutually beneficial and mutually satisfying. With a win-win solution, all parties feel good about the decision and feel committed to the action plan. Win-win sees life as a co-operative, not a competitive arena. Most people tend to think in terms of dichotomies: strong or weak, hardball or softball, win or lose. But that kind of thinking is fundamentally flawed, because it is based on power and position rather than on principle. Win-win is based on the paradigm that there is plenty for everybody, that one person's success is not achieved at the expense or exclusion of the success of others. In other words, win-win is a belief in the *Third Alternative*. It is not your way, or my way; it is a *better* way, a higher way.

Furthermore, most life situations—and definitely the process of scaling up the national response to the HIV/AIDS pandemic—are part of an interdependent reality. *Interdependence* is a recognition that although one may be an independent person or institution, one's ability to achieve maximum effectiveness in any undertaking is largely dependent on one's willingness to work in true partnership with others. This makes a win-win approach by all duty bearers in the fight against the pandemic—or in any other undertaking—the only viable delivery approach that is likely to generate *synergy* for lasting success. Simply defined, synergy means that the sum total of the whole is greater than its constituent parts. It means that the relationship that the parts have to each other is a part in and of itself. It is not only a part, but is also the most catalytic, the most empowering, the most unifying, and the most exciting part.[1] This is *how* each and every duty bearer, who will commit to the new resolve to fight the pandemic, must view his or her contribution and co-operation, be it in material, financial or structural terms.

Governmental Mechanisms

As already stated in previous chapters, there are many things that the Government is already doing to fight the pandemic. However, the Government can do more even with existing levels of human, financial and organisational resources, primarily by making sure that the system and existing governmental structures work better (*see also Figure 1 in Chapter 2*).

Parliamentary Select Committee(s) on HIV/AIDS

The appointment and deployment of a Senate Committee on HIV/AIDS as well as a National Assembly Committee on HIV/AIDS, is an excellent step in the right direction. Firstly, these two Committees afford the different political parties an opportunity to work together on an issue of critical national importance, beyond petty partisan interests. Secondly, the establishment of a Senate Committee on HIV/AIDS serves as both a challenge *and* an opportunity for the Principal Chiefs, who are Members of the Senate, to assert their leadership in galvanising the energy and commitment of all traditional leaders behind the "Scaling Up" initiative. In addition, not only do these actions contribute to the deepening of democracy, but they also make it easier for the 10 political parties that constitute the Sixth Parliament to deliver on a life-and-death concern for all Basotho, on the same platform. In other words, from now on, Parliamentarians have a unified agenda on the basis of which to go back to the people to help every Mosotho to become HIV/AIDS-competent, especially when Parliament is in recess.

Cabinet Committee on HIV/AIDS

The Lesotho Government has a tradition of establishing and working through intersectoral, thematic Cabinet Committees. This is as it should be as this promotes greater effectiveness. However, although it was the Government's original intention to establish a Cabinet Committee on HIV/AIDS (at about the same time as LAPCA was established), somehow these honourable intentions do not as yet seem to have been translated into action. One is, therefore, hereby arguing that the time has come for such a Committee to be established. If today, the Government was informed that there was an invading army at its borders, which would kill about one third of its adult population by the time the war was over, the Government would immediately set up a War Cabinet Committee. The same should be true for the national response to the HIV/AIDS pandemic in Lesotho (and any other country with similarly high infection rates). Understandably, one can argue that already, there are too many Cabinet Committees. Fair enough. Then maybe the Government should consider assigning this responsibility to the Food Security Cabinet Committee—which is already a very well functioning mechanism—not least because of the close inter-relationship between the pandemic, food insecurity and poverty. This is an important strategy for making sure that the Cabinet gets regular briefings on the status of the fight against the pandemic, as well as a planned opportunity to take necessary corrective action, as the situation demands.

Principal Secretaries/Senior Officials Committee on HIV/AIDS

The Principal Secretaries meet every Friday—in their capacity as Chief Executive Officers of each sector of Government—to review progress being made with implementing Government's priority development agenda and to recommend necessary course corrections to Cabinet. Again, from the time when the Government declared the pandemic a national disaster, it had planned to set up, among others, an HIV/AIDS Committee of Senior Officials in order to accord the matter the attention it deserves. However, this honourable intention is also yet to be translated into action. This is, indeed, the right time to correct this anomaly. And, as with the Cabinet Committee, it should be possible to task the Food Security Committee of Senior Officials—which has been meeting on a weekly basis since the onset of the current food crisis—with the responsibility to also meet and discuss weekly, progress and areas needing corrective action in order to ensure that the scaling up national effort against HIV/AIDS is successful. In particular, the Principal Secretaries must be tasked with the responsibility to ensure the core streaming of HIV/AIDS into their respective sectors.

District and Community Level AIDS Committees

Likewise, it is prudent for the Government to seriously consider which of the currently existing inter-disciplinary and inter-stakeholder development structures at District and Community levels should be tasked with the challenge of addressing the

HIV/AIDS pandemic. There may not be a need for new structures to be tasked with the responsibility of ensuring that each and every duty bearer at that level has the chance to play a catalytic role in the scaled up national response to the HIV/AIDS pandemic.

Civil Society Institutions

Here, it is prudent to state from the outset that the idea is NOT to centralise and thus strangulate the initiative of any, or all, civil society institutions. Rather, each civil society institution—be it the Church, the Youth, the Women, the Traditional Leadership institutions, Professional Associations, and more—must decide on how they are going to core stream the fight against the pandemic into their core mandates, programmes and delivery mechanisms. For instance, it is hereby assumed that consultations within the Church—through the leadership of the Lesotho Christian Council—are already at an advanced stage in its efforts to figure out how the Church can scale up its national response to the pandemic. In addition, the leadership of the Church and of other civil society institutions will have to take the initiative to seek ways of forging the kind of partnerships within civil society, with the Government as well as with the Business sector in order to obtain maximum synergy for the interdependence that is so inherent in the process of addressing the pandemic.

The Case for a Business Coalition Against HIV/AIDS

The Business sector is one of the most seriously affected by the pandemic, through the loss of labour, declining productivity, increasing human resource costs and possible erosion of markets. In addition, Business has a social responsibility to support the national response to the HIV/AIDS pandemic in this context of emergency. So, it is very possible that efforts by the Private Sector are already at an advanced stage, not only in figuring out how to effectively address the pandemic, but also the need to establish a Business Coalition Against HIV/AIDS to undertake, on a more structured basis, the following actions:

- Coordinate the involvement of the business sector in the national response;
- Develop and promote a corporate social responsibility programme on HIV/AIDS among the business community;
- Develop and promote comprehensive HIV/AIDS Workplace Policies and Programmes among the business community;
- Commission research on the impact of HIV/AIDS on the world of work and the economy; and
- Seek ways to forge strong Private/Public/Civil Society partnerships—at all levels of society—in order to enhance possibilities for improved efficiency and effectiveness in the fight against the pandemic.

Artists, Intellectuals, Folk and Mass Media Channels United Against HIV/AIDS

Lesotho is a country with a very strong tradition of using folk media—traditional song, dance, poetry, and drama—as channels for mass communication and social mobilisation. There is even an annual national event, *The Morija Festival*, where various artists get to show off their prowess and skill. This is why folk media has very high potential for playing the most critical—and enjoyable—role towards the creation of an HIV/AIDS-competent society in this country. Others include intellectuals, such as writers, novelists, journalists, literary scholars, and more. They should come together, possibly in conjunction with the Ministry of Tourism, Environment and Culture, to explore the most creative ways of core streaming the national response to the HIV/AIDS pandemic into their planned activities from now on, at least until the country manages to break the back of the pandemic.

International Partners

There are several mechanisms for regular co-operation between international partners, the Government and the people of Lesotho. Of critical importance with regard to the response to the HIV/AIDS pandemic in Lesotho is the Expanded Theme Group on HIV/AIDS, which is responsible for having spearheaded the consultative process that led to the publication of this manual, as part of its response to the Prime

Minister's call for a new resolve to fight the pandemic. The international partnership against HIV/AIDS stands ready to both core stream its existing programmes and resources towards the scaling up effort as well as to seek additional resources in favour of Basotho, should the absorptive rates improve sufficiently to warrant such a move. This commitment is in line with the September 2000 UN Millennium Summit Declaration, which committed Member States to halt and reverse the global spread of HIV/AIDS by the year 2015, as well as the June 2001 UN General Assembly Special Summit Declaration on HIV/AIDS.

The Case for a Semi-Autonomous National Commission on HIV/AIDS[2]

If all of the above institutions and mechanisms can be mobilised, encouraged and supported to give of their best in scaling up their efforts to fight the pandemic, it would release exponential capacity—human, financial and organisational resources—to fight the pandemic. At the moment, there is LAPCA, which undertook this mammoth task since the year 2001. And yet, LAPCA is only a small unit in a Government Ministry, albeit the Prime Minister's Office. What is required to help galvanise the totality of the various aspects of a scaled up national response is a semi-autonomous body with sufficient political and administrative clout and mandate to enable it to do a world-class job—much like the Independent Electoral Commission. In other words, it would be prudent to appoint a National AIDS Commission (NAC) as the most effective, win-win strategy to sufficiently strengthen LAPCA for it to be able to deliver on the mandate, with LAPCA's current staff being appointed to serve as the Secretariat of the Commission. Interestingly, this is not at all a new idea. It was Government's original intention—after establishing LAPCA—to actually appoint a National Commission on HIV/AIDS. Somehow, these noble intentions seem to have fallen in-between the cracks. However, it is correct to now say that the establishment of a National AIDS Commission is an idea whose time is long overdue.

Once a decision has been made by the Government to establish such a semi-autonomous body, then it would be prudent to appoint a small task force to draw up the terms of reference for such a Commission as well as the structure and a budget. Suffice it to say here, however, that membership of the National AIDS Commission must be seen to be representative of the country's key stakeholders and duty bearers.

It should have the clout to call to account, any component of society regarding its contribution to the struggle against HIV/AIDS. It should also be able to have direct access to both the Head of State and the Head of Government on matters concerning the pandemic. It is very important that the goals and objectives of the National AIDS Commission are kept at the *strategic, advocacy* and *policy levels,* thus leaving the responsibility for programme/project planning and implementation to all of the above stakeholders and duty bearers, because it makes perfect sense. To do otherwise is to fall into the same trap as LAPCA did which, in turn, made it near impossible to fulfill its strategic mandate.

NOTES *for Chapter 14*

1. Stephen R. Covey, *The Seven Habits of Highly Effective People. Powerful Lessons in Personal Change.* Free Press, New York, 1989.
2. At the time of going to press, the Cabinet approved this recommendation. A Bill is in the process of being prepared for deliberation by Parliament.

CHAPTER

15

Financing the National Response to the HIV/AIDS Pandemic

So, who will pay for all of the recommendations in this book? Yes, money is important, but first and foremost, it will demand a new kind of thinking so that—as indicated in the earlier chapters—the core streaming approach results in every Maluti that is spent contributes to the national response to the HIV/AIDS pandemic. This is not about requesting more funding from development partners—more money is certainly required—but it is about using the existing resources in a manner that supports the national response to the pandemic in a more effective and innovative approach.

As the Prime Minister stated in the forward to this document, this fight will be won. Lesotho will defeat HIV/AIDS. It is primarily a Basotho fight using the resources, which we all know exist here: human, financial, technical and material. Money does matter, but it must be allocated and spent within an appropriate policy environment, one that facilitates the scaled up national response to HIV/AIDS. The establishment of an HIV/AIDS Commission to coordinate the national response to the crisis will provide a unique opportunity to make things happen. This new body, when established, will have the opportunity to lead efforts in creating an HIV/AIDS-

Competent Society. In such an environment, every Mosotho will know his/her status, will know what to do if infected or a loved one is infected and will understand that HIV is not an automatic death sentence. At a meeting of the Government of Lesotho/UN Task Force on HIV/AIDS on 30 October, 2003,[1] the issue of scaling up the national response to the crisis was discussed in detail, and in a report prepared for the Government Secretary, Mr. Sekhamane, it was agreed that Government should focus on two key objectives in order to create an HIV/AIDS-Competent Society:

1. Extend the lives of all people living with HIV/AIDS; and
2. Ensure that all people who are HIV/AIDS-negative remain so.

Another more overarching objective was chosen around the issue of sustainable development which, while important, does not directly relate to the urgency of the need for a response to the HIV/AIDS crisis.

Already, the Government has allocated 2% of the budget in each sector to the national response to the HIV/AIDS pandemic in Lesotho. Each Government Ministry has, after a slow start, initiated projects/activities to core stream the fight against HIV/AIDS. Other initiatives, such as those by the National Assembly and the Senate, have also commenced. The Senate has organised a series of public meetings with traditional leaders across the country to raise awareness of the role of the traditional leadership in creating HIV/AIDS-Competent Communities. With over 2,700 registered chiefs, these leaders play a crucial role in the national response. However, this is only part of the solution. In the longer term, there is a need for Ministries to see the total budget as part of the fight against HIV/AIDS. As core streaming activities commence in earnest, all activities within communities (at all levels) should be seen in the context of the national response to HIV/AIDS. This book has brought the message of change, suggesting that HIV/AIDS represents an opportunity for Basotho to transcend the past and unite behind this nationwide imperative—a strategic imperative—to defeat the pandemic.

The Global Fund/International Donors

The Global Fund approved a payment of some US$12.5 million for HIV/AIDS and TB Programmes in Lesotho. This was signed by the Minister of Finance on

October 7, 2003, and includes US$10 million for the HIV/AIDS component. A key donor is the Irish Government, which is one of the leading international partners of Lesotho. The Irish have put the fight against HIV/AIDS at the centre of their agenda. Development Cooperation Ireland (DCI) is contributing approximately US$1 million per annum to Government and non-government organisations in support of anti HIV/AIDS activities. The UK Department for International Development (DfID) is also working closely with the government and community-based organisations with the view to strengthening the local responses and supporting national mechanisms involved in HIV/AIDS work. Besides supporting community groups and the Lesotho AIDS Coordinating Authority (LAPCA), DfID is working closely with UNDP to develop a programme of support to Government, which will focus on support to the new Commission, transformational change and core streaming.

The US Embassy, as part of its programme of support to Lesotho, works closely with the Ministry of Defence and LAPCA, while the Ambassador acts as Co-Chairperson of the Expanded Theme Group on HIV/AIDS, which has been leading the international partnership in the fight against the pandemic. Other bilateral support comes from France, Germany, Japan and Sweden, among others. The UN Agencies, as members of the Expanded Theme Group and the joint Government of Lesotho/UN Task Force on HIV/AIDS, play a major role in the fight against the pandemic in accordance with their mandates.

Yet while the support from development partners is important, it can only complement ongoing government and civil society strategies in the scaled up response to HIV/AIDS. This is not about who pays the bills or how much a Mosotho life is worth. Rather, it is about mobilising all resources of the nation in the response to the pandemic.

In the same way as we cannot put a price on the life of a Mosotho, so too we cannot put a value on the countless community-based efforts throughout the country, which are led by people who, day-in, day-out, believe they have an obligation to their fellow Basotho. This comes from a sense of solidarity among those who are less well off and affected by the pandemic. People from all walks of life are giving time, energy and resources to support those families affected by the virus, whether they are child-headed households or households with sick adults. They represent the front line in the response to the pandemic and often get little recognition. They need support urgently, which must be provided in a structured and dependable manner and become part of normal government activities. If core streaming is to be truly successful, then all Government expenditure and that of international partners should be seen as part of the response to the pandemic.

Due to the extensive nature of the HIV/AIDS crisis, it is important to recognise the difficulties in trying to cost the response to the pandemic. The question should be: What is the cost of doing nothing and continuing business as usual? In a country with an infection rate of over 30%, the reality is that the cost of continuing business as usual is unimaginable and includes an increased number of orphans, a further reduction in life expectancy, higher levels of mobility and mortality, reduced institutional capacity, increased demands on public service and decreased capacity to delivery. In addition, the impact of a death on household food security is well documented: food consumption drops by 15% in the poorest households after the death of the adult.[2] The infection rate will continue to increase; life expectancy will decrease and community coping mechanisms will be undermined. The issue here is about forging synergies among all actors and stakeholders, with multi stakeholder partnerships aimed at encouraging a level of personal, community and institutional accountability. Most of the activities that will help mitigate the impact of HIV/AIDS should not be considered as "HIV/AIDS Projects", but rather as part of the normal day-to-day activities of Government: every government sector should be considered to be in the front lines of the battle to win this war.

There are many examples of areas where sectors can increase and deepen their roles in the fight against the pandemic, which have been outlined in earlier chapters of this document. They include, for example, increasing public works with an emphasis on labour intensive activities and ensuring that they are targeted for useful outcomes, for example developing rural footbridges and pathways, terracing and water shed management; and community initiatives. Urban areas (including peri-urban areas) should also be targeted, recognising that there are large numbers of unemployed young people who are vulnerable to HIV/AIDS and are affected by the spread of the virus. This population must be provided with opportunities to engage in activities that help to ease the poverty trap within which most find themselves.

Obviously, there are specific actions that need to be implemented in response to the crisis. These include the following:

- The implementation of a Universal Voluntary Testing Plan so that adults can have access to testing throughout the country;
- Supporting community-based groups with a view towards establishing HIV/AIDS-Competent Communities;
- Training community counsellors, providing for a national rollout of ARVs, and building community support groups; and
- Providing for sector-specific strategies.

Funding should not only be seen in the context of the government budget, as the churches, traditional leaders, private sector and other stakeholders have access to funds and are engaged in activities to combat the pandemic.

Thus, this is not about how much the fight against HIV/AIDS will cost, but this is about the cost of doing nothing, or continuing business as usual. At the opening of the SADC Summit on HIV/AIDS, hosted by the Government of Lesotho in July 2003, the Prime Minister captured the extent of the pandemic in this country when he stated that a child who turned 15 years in 2000 has a 74% chance of becoming HIV-positive by the time he/she reaches 50 years of age. Perhaps this, more than anything else, serves to demonstrate the need for mobilisation of all sectors and resources within the country.

Key Catalytic Actions

While this book has recommended a number of key actions that need to be taken to scale up the national response to HIV/AIDS, short of a process of transformation, Lesotho will find it very difficult to achieve the profound change necessary to succeed in reaching the goal of an HIV/AIDS-Competent Society. It may slowly manage to push back the pandemic, but without transformation, it is in danger of limping along with low growth rates, high levels of poverty, food insecurity and declining capacity within the public service. The premise made throughout this book is that the HIV/AIDS crisis is systemic, which expands and deepens weaknesses, gnawing away at the existing capacity and the development achievements built up over decades in all sectors of society. Transformational leadership is a process, which commences in action. According to Jonathan Love,[3] such leadership demands the empowerment of all people in a society at every level. No number of instructions given and followed can produce transformation.

The need for social mobilisation has been clearly outlined in this book, putting it at the core of the national response to the pandemic. Without this, it will be impossible to achieve an HIV/AIDS-Competent Society. To get transformation underway, it is essential to have an agreed upon goal into which the majority of people can buy. This should be seen as a key element in the national response to HIV/AIDS and will be difficult, but not impossible, to achieve if fundamental change is not made. Such a goal would galvanise the imagination of the majority of the people and will be achieved only with the active participation of all.

What goal would fit this description? This is a crisis. Decisions made now in response to this will influence the nature, quality and capacity of this society for decades to come. Such a goal could be universal testing for adults throughout the country within a year, starting with planning a national voluntary testing month, with the aim of establishing testing facilities within walking distance of every household in the country and supported with testing kits and community counsellors. Such a goal would demand mobilising up to 7,000 volunteers to be trained in community counselling and in using the rapid tests. A system, which is confidential and reliable, would be established to ensure that people have trust in the programme. It would be accompanied by a massive information campaign based around people understanding that knowing their status is essential to creating an HIV/AIDS-Competent Society. Testing would then become the norm rather than the exception. People would come to understand that if they are HIV-positive, they can take action to extend their lives, and if they are negative, they must take action to ensure that they remain this way. The information campaign, then, would also focus on the preventive aspect of HIV/AIDS, by making free condoms (along with education on correct use) accessible to Basotho in even the most rural areas of Lesotho.

In 2002, the Independent Electoral Commission organised the nationwide registration of voters, with photographs of every voter. The General Elections (coordinated by 17,500 volunteers trained over a period of six weeks) took place using a totally new electoral system that demanded that all election personnel be trained. One million ballot papers were printed and distributed across 2,500 polling stations.

Set against this achievement, a national week of testing is not at all insurmountable. The polling stations could be used as testing centres, supported by trained counsellors coming, in part, from the cadre of election workers (most of whom are still in their villages), the community health workers, traditional and church leaders, and rural development officers from the Ministry of Local Government. As part of this process, each community would establish HIV/AIDS-Competent Committees, which would take responsibilities for planning the month of tests in their area and the activities for the post-testing phase. If one accepts that the two key elements of the national response to the HIV/AIDS crisis are prolonging the life of those with the virus and ensuring that those not infected remain so, then a key action is for everyone to know their status. This will demand new thinking, new models and, in short, a profound change in the way business is conducted in this country.

National Voluntary Testing for All: What Cost?

Estimated Cost (Year 1)[4]	US$
One million testing kits	
(US $1.50 per person)	1,500,000
Counselling: Training of trainers	
[2,500 X US $100]	250,000
Training community counsellors	1,500,000
Starter packs for HIV AIDS-Competent communities	
Locally made sheets, gloves and condoms,	
Information Booklets, Community Planning Charts, etc.	3,000,000
Stipends for community counsellors	
(M200 per month X 7,000)	2,400,000
Backup support/administration	1,000,000
Contingency	465,000
TOTAL	**10,115,000**

For the fight against HIV/AIDS to succeed, changing the terms of the debate, setting new agendas, and demanding and expecting a level of creativity, innovation and new thinking are essential. How much will all this cost? In terms of the potential for success, not much. The issue is the cost to the country of doing nothing, or continuing as usual.

While the level of income poverty is high at the household level, Lesotho is well off among African countries, when one uses human development measures. According to the United Nations Development Programme, only Mauritius, South

Africa and Namibia have higher adult literacy rates than Lesotho, which has a rate of 82%. Its illiteracy rate for women between 15 and 24 is the best in Africa at 2%. Only South Africa and Zimbabwe have a lower percentage of underweight children. Lesotho's Human Development Index, up until this year, was number 127 on the list, below only those of South Africa, Cape Verde, Swaziland, Botswana, Sao Tome et Principe, and Gabon, in sub-Saharan Africa, but above those of Kenya and Nigeria. Nowhere in Lesotho is there the kind of human destitution and despair that mark the slums of Johannesburg and Cape Town, not to mention most other major cities in tropical Africa.[5] Thus, the HIV/AIDS response cannot be seen in isolation of the response to poverty and inequality in the country.

The government is in the process of finalising the Poverty Reduction Strategy Paper (PRSP), which will represent a blueprint for addressing poverty in the coming three years. If implemented in an imaginative and structured manner, the PRSP will lay the groundwork for bringing forward targeted responses to the poorest sections of the community, which are already carrying a disproportionate burden of the HIV/AIDS infection rate. While the initial expenditure will be relatively easy to address, there is no doubt that there will be long-term costs associated with this operation. For example, as people learn of their status, there will be a demand for anti-retroviral (ARV) drugs. The generic versions of ARVs can cost less than US $ 300 per year, or less than one dollar per day, per patient.[6] The funds allocated by the international partners, combined with the commitment of the government to address this pandemic, leaves one to believe that this will not only be possible, but is necessary for real change.

NOTES *for Chapter 15*

1. Meeting at UN House with UN/Government Task Force on HIV/AIDS chaired by the Resident Coordinator of the UN System and the Principal Secretary, Cabinet (Economic Affairs).

2. UNAIDS Report on the Global HIV/AIDS Epidemic. UNAIDS, Geneva Switzerland, 2002, p 155.

3. Internal Report by Jonathan Love, UNDP Consultant on *Leadership Training for Results*. UNDP Lesotho, November 2003.

4. Costs in the subsequent years would be substantially reduced as the number of people who get regular testing would become increasingly lower. This does not include the cost of support in the post-testing period which should be incorporated into sector and civil society budget plans.

5. Sechaba Consultants. *Poverty and Livelihoods in Lesotho 2000: More Than a Mapping Exercise*, Sechaba Consultants, 2000.

6. WHO/UNAIDS. *Statement on Global AIDS Emergency Treatment: Emergency and 3X5 Strategy.* WHO/UNAIDS, 2003.

CHAPTER

16

Conclusion: Taking Ownership of the HIV/AIDS Challenge*

Put quite simply, the strategy and plan of action that have been presented in this document, and the vision and objective of the initiative that they detail, are bold and unprecedented. To say that the challenge of *Turning the Crisis of HIV/AIDS into an Opportunity* for completely transforming Lesotho into a new society, driven by the compulsion of self-preservation to discover, mobilise and deploy all its knowledge, resource, will and genius, is daunting, would be an understatement. To say that this is an option of one out of one, would be a gentle phraseology of a basic truth. To say that this is a task that must be done, and done well, because the alternative is unthinkable, begins to approach a proper representation of the reality we are dealing with. To say that we can do it, all of us, the leadership and people of Lesotho alike, and alongside them, the leadership and people of Africa, all in partnership with the international community, and with the support of concerned individuals and institutions around

---

* This chapter is culled from *The Right of Ownership of Problems*, a work-in-progress by Joseph O. Okpaku, Sr., copyright © 2004.

the world, for the sake of all humanity, would be to capture the essence of the commitment behind this effort, and this enabling document which details it.

A Marathon for Life

The Journey of *Turning a Crisis into an Opportunity: Scaling Up the National Response to the HIV/AIDS Pandemic,* is a long and arduous one. To state this bluntly upfront is not to cause alarm or encourage hesitation, fear and anxiety. Rather, by detailing the enormous but real dimensions of the challenge, it is intended to prepare all who engage in this struggle to clear their slate, so to speak, take a deep breath, and then hit the road running in full knowledge of the distance ahead. We must do as long-distance runners do, because ours is a marathon, a marathon for life. The development of this document and its swift adoption by the Government of Lesotho as its official policy and programme to guide its response to the challenge of a life-time, are just the starting points, critical starting points, which are together a *sine quanon* for the race we must run.

But as the long-distance runners of this marathon, we must borrow a leaf from the training regime of seasoned marathon runners. Like them, we must build our stamina, pace ourselves, take full cognisance of all that is happening around us as we traverse vast terrain and distances, and know just when to pause for a drink of water without losing ground. Like them, we must anticipate the nature and extent of the challenge and its ability to change course without warning. We must manage our limited energy and resources in measured steps so as to conserve our stamina to last the whole distance, because the race will be won only when we reach the finishing line. We will begin to approach that finishing line when we contain the scourge of this disease, drastically and irreversibly reduce its prevalence by preventing its further spread, fully care for those already infected, control the impact of such infection so as to reduce the attendant physiological, psychological, social and economic disability to more tolerable levels, and prevent the yet unaffected from becoming infected. We will be close to the finishing line when we have learned to fully protect the young and the most vulnerable, especially Orphans and Other Vulnerable Children, as well as young boys and girls, men and women, from any and all of the myriad of consequences of the pandemic. That is the objective of creating and sustaining an *HIV/AIDS-Competent Society.*

A Comprehensive Road Map

This document is essentially a Road Map for the comprehensive scaled-up national response by the Government and People of Lesotho, in collaboration with their international and other partners, to the HIV/AIDS pandemic. As such, it is a basic reference and action manual. It details the challenge from many angles in order to provide as rounded a perspective and as holistic a picture as possible, of the true (even if potentially scary) nature of the problem and why we must respond vigorously.

As a Road Map, it represents the vision of where Lesotho has decided to go, and the nation's strategies for doing so. In detailing the role of each of the key stake-holders (the Government and Public Sectors, Traditional Leaders, Individuals, Civil Society—Women, Youth, People Living with HIV/AIDS, the Church—the Private Sector and the International Community), it simply provides a frame-work for the scaled-up response. It does not attempt to stipulate what programmes each stakeholder should undertake. The specifics of such programmatic response will devolve to each stakeholder, extrapolating from the template of the overall Government response strategy as set out here. But because this document derives from best practices and lessons learned from tested, on-going strategies globally, such extrapolation should find facilitation from, and synergy with, the policies outlined here.

It is important to state that the deliberate avoidance, in crafting this document, of seeking to delineate or stipulate prescriptive solutions, is its very strength. In so doing, we avoid the appearance of having exclusive knowledge of, or wisdom with respect to, the best solutions. We also create, in the true African sense, a context large enough to mobilise the collective wisdom of the entire family of stakeholders, national and international. This inclusive approach is important if we are to succeed in this undertaking, which is our only option. Furthermore, the main purpose of the promulgation of these strategic policies in the first place was, indeed, to create consensus and to galvanise sufficient official support for a courageous decision regarding this common challenge.

Now that the decision has been taken by Government, the first step is for all of us—Government, Civil Society, business, donors, UN and other international partners—to go back to the drawing board, roll up our sleeves and to determine how best to re-focus our policies and programmes in conformity with the scaling up strategies, the ownership of which now devolves to the Government and people of Lesotho. This document does not attempt or pretend to be a panacea. The very notion of a panacea to the HIV/AIDS pandemic is an oxymoron.

A Compelling March into the Future Against Time

In crafting this initiative, we have strived to cover as many bases as we possibly could. So, one might be tempted to ask a series of questions: Have we covered all aspects of the challenge of the HIV/AIDS pandemic? No, we have tried to cover what we consider to be the most critical issues. Do we have a complete road map? No, we do not, but we know the destination, the direction, and at least one way to get there. We have raised many questions and tried to find best answers. Do we have all the answers? No, no one does. But we know that what this initiative proposes can and will provide an eminently sound result, which will carry us a long way on the road out of the present quagmire.

We have proposed many specific programmes and actions in this document. Can we achieve all of them? We need to, if we are to succeed. We will not know if we can achieve all of them unless we try. What we do know is that if we give it our best shot, all of us, and do so with genuine commitment and faith, we have a better than good chance of achieving most of our objectives, enough to make the rest of the way a little easier for those who come after us. Fortunately, we do have the advantage of hindsight in the examples of nations like Uganda, which have tried and succeeded. This gives us a precedent and a firm basis for optimism.

Above all, what is eminently true, and what must be said, as much to others as to ourselves, is the fact that even as progress continues to be made globally in responding to the challenge, there is much we still do not know. And even as we find answers to some questions, even if partially, other new questions arise. So, it is a complex undertaking in which we are forced to deploy our forces on all fronts at the same time, while trying to move rapidly forward against the pandemic. In undertaking this bold offensive against the HIV/AIDS pandemic, we are embarking on a compelling march into the future against time, with all the odds stacked up against us, and yet without the option of staying put in our present position and biding our time in the hope that time will take care of us.

The Nature of the Challenge: Managing Intangibles

As a march into the future, there are of necessity, many intangibles we must confront, comprehend, manage and overcome even as yet another intangible comes upon us. This is the nature of the challenge. This compels us to find the perspicacity, insight, intellectual fortitude and excellence to craft a new kind of strategic game plan, one which embodies the dynamics of these intangibles, and yet is able to manage them in a dynamic rolling process in which new insights and lessons learned are immediately recycled into the solution process in a self-reinforcing and up-scaling continuum.

Taking Ownership of the HIV/AIDS Challenge

In order to undertake this compelling march into the future against time, in order to mobilise all our resources (material, intellectual, cultural, emotional, strategic and even resources of faith), and to deploy them towards turning this crisis of the HIV/AIDS pandemic into an opportunity, we must first take full ownership of the HIV/AIDS pandemic. We must see it as our problem, whatever its pedigree and whatever the blame. We must own it in the same way we own our culture, heritage, land, our home and our future (for it is the very future of the people of Lesotho at stake), and strike out to conquer it with all we have, just as we would strike out against whatever threatens what all we own. It is the Basotho nation at stake. It is the African family at stake. This is the only path to succeed in this daunting challenge. To do otherwise, to believe that others will solve this problem for us, or that they have an obligation to solve it for us, or even to care, is to shirk our quintessential responsibility to ourselves. It is to sleepwalk through glaring and challenging reality, risking waking up from our stupor to discover that we have simply lost our chance. Should that happen, we will also discover that it is too late to do anything. That is when the true guilt, the mother of all guilt, will step in and fully traumatise a nation and a people.

There are compelling reasons for taking ownership of the HIV/AIDS challenge. One of the most important of these is the fact that, inherent in problem solving is the opportunity for innovation and creativity.[1] If one loses the ownership of one's problem, one simultaneously loses the right and opportunity for creativity and innovation inherent in solving one's problem. Unless the people of Lesotho own the

HIV/AIDS problem, therefore, they cannot find the inner wherewithal to rise up to the challenge of solving it. In such circumstances, the crisis will always remain some alien inexplicable phenomenon in front of which Basotho are cowered, helpless, numb and immobilised. But the Basotho Nation is renowned for its bravery and resilience, once it has made up its collective mind. It is, indeed, through these qualities that the Basotho people have overcome various daunting threats in the past. It is these same qualities that will stand the Basotho Nation in good stead this time around.

The Need to do Business Differently

What is promulgated in this document lays out precisely the plan of action by which Basotho can take ownership of the HIV/AIDS challenge and solutions thereto. First amongst the steps to be taken is the recognition of the need to do business differently:

- In the Public Sector arena, that is, the Legislative, the Executive, the Civil Service and the Judiciary, by core streaming HIV/AIDS into *all* policies, plans and budgets, on the one hand, and by also accepting the need to re-engineer public service, through personal and institutional transformation;
- In the civil society and private sector arenas, by creating the best possible political and administrative space, through the establishment of an autonomous National AIDS Commission, thereby avoiding the incessant turf battles that have been characteristic of National AIDS Commissions, Councils and/or other mechanisms that have inadvertently conflated the roles of Government, civil society and the private sector in fighting the pandemic in so many other countries;
- In the international community, by the international partners revisiting the manner in which they have in the past configured their support agenda and programmes, including the deployment of financial support, in order to both create a new assistance environment more conducive to achieving concrete and measurable impact on the scaling up agenda, as well as maximising if not multiplying the impact and effectiveness of their material and other resource contributions on the palpable success of fighting against the pandemic.

It is worthy of note that the international partners in Lesotho have consistently demonstrated strong leadership and unity of purpose—through the Expanded Theme Group on HIV/AIDS—in recognition of the need for harmonisation of dialogue, policies and programmes in response to the innovative scaling up initiative of, and by, the Government and people of Lesotho.

For everyone, the primacy of recognising the paradigm shift inherent in this scaling up process and document, and the compulsion to create a corresponding new mindset and *modus operandi*, cannot be over-emphasised. We must adopt the battle cry: Business As Usual Is No Longer Acceptable Or Viable In Lesotho.

The Duality of the Challenge: A Crisis and an Opportunity

There is a duality of intent and strategy in the crafting of this formula for scaling up the national response to the HIV/AIDS pandemic in Lesotho: We have designed to both solve the challenge of the pandemic on the one hand and, on the other, to simultaneously undertake the quantum development of Lesotho into a modern socio-economic nation. This is, therefore, a dual complex strategy of solving a national crisis, and undertaking national development, both in a single comprehensive context and strategy, which integrates the plans and programmes for both in such a manner that the priorities of one (the response to HIV/AIDS) are *core streamed* into the dynamics of the other (national development).

Hence, when we talk about *Turning A Crisis into An Opportunity*, we squarely mean that our planned and expected outcome at the end of the aggressive phase of this national response is a Lesotho emerging at a much higher level of development than it is today. The boldness of this strategy can be best put in relief if viewed in contradistinction to a more common alternative, which would be to suspend all development programmes until the HIV/AIDS pandemic is "licked", and then resume the development process. In our strategy, we are taking on *both* challenges simultaneously. We do this from the bold strategic standpoint that since we cannot separate the dilemma of HIV/AIDS from the problems of development (poverty eradication, health, education, participatory and representative governance, equity, freedom, political and social stability, rural and urban development, industrialisation, socio-economic development, cultural development and self-awareness, global competitiveness and the overall drive for self-development and the attainment of a higher quality of life in the pursuit of self-actualisation), we must combine both. This approach is further compelled by the reality of limited resources that cannot be sustained if we separate both struggles and in so doing, find ourselves undesirably compelled to divide up such limited resources.

Fortunately for us, the two pursuits are inherently mutually reinforcing, making our strategy eminently sound.

We must recognise, however, that such a bold and possibly novel approach involves a philosophical and strategic paradigm shift that demands intellectual, perceptual and systemic adjustment on the part of all stakeholders with respect to the way we are used to seeing and doing things.

HIV/AIDS Research and Development

The imperative for Lesotho to take ownership of the challenge of the HIV/AIDS pandemic is not an isolated one confined to this crisis. Rather, it is an imperative for Lesotho and for all of Africa to take ownership of the full spectrum of their development challenge and to seize the special demands for solution as a unique opportunity for innovation, at all levels. In a global environment in which intellectual property has become the main asset for global competitiveness, and given the fact that in most cases, intellectual property derives from problem-solving, this imperative would suggest the strategic wisdom of Lesotho engaging in high-level research and development efforts on critical aspects of HIV/AIDS. Whether basic research, or applied research, such an engagement will not only result in greater local knowledge and understanding of the disease, but also serve as the platform for finding some solutions locally.[2]

The idea of research and development activities in Lesotho towards a search for a vaccine or a cure, or some aspect of the treatment of HIV-infection or the full-blown AIDS disease, does not only make sense, but would seem to be of strategic importance.[3] How such research is carried out, in collaboration with whom, and in what specific aspect of the challenge, are all matters of detail that can be worked out if the disposition to undertake such a bold step is in place. Such an innovative approach will not only help stimulate medical and pharmacological research in Lesotho, thus creating a new industry in the country with its obvious development benefit, but would also upgrade the level of academic research in tertiary instructions such as the National University, which could be brought into the process.

At the end of the day, even above the human factor which, by itself, is compelling enough, the economic realities of the long-term response to HIV/AIDS in Africa is simply that if Africa, in a joint effort and with the support of partners, invests the money and time to engage in the search for a vaccine or cure, it stands not only to accelerate the process of overcoming this pandemic, but also to create an opportunity to establish a new high-level revenue stream from the export of such vaccines or medicines. If, on the other hand, Africa, Lesotho included, does not undertake such a strategic effort, it will have to find billions of dollars to import the vaccines and cure from outside. The choice should be obvious. Needless to say, it is not very easy to just undertake high-level research and development. But given the critical level of the challenge, and also given the extensive African scientific capacity at home and diffused globally, such a bold undertaking is not impossible. Besides, that is what everyone else in the world does, anyway. Why not Africans? What such an initiative will require is vision, resourcefulness, and a belief in Africa's globally competitive intellectual and scientific capacity.

Towards A Permanent Phase of Safe Sexuality

One has dubbed the time period involved in the plan of action detailed in this document as "the aggressive phase of this national response" to the HIV/AIDS pandemic, because at the end of this journey, there will be need for a residual permanent phase of vigilance and enlightened sexuality in order to consolidate the gains promised in return for the sacrifices that lie ahead. Unless the core of the HIV/AIDS competency becomes entrenched as a permanent part of the new social culture, all gains will be in jeopardy as it will take only a short period of relapse and complacency for the prevalence rate to shoot right back up, unless a vaccine is discovered in the interim. And even in the event of so desirable an outcome, safe sexuality will always be required in order to preserve the life and value of society.

Success One Step at a Time

The Response outlined in this undertaking is simultaneously broad-based and yet specific in its programmatic details. Each little gain will go a long way. What constitutes success is progress, cumulative progress, whereby each achievement builds on the preceding one, together building up the critical mass of momentum sufficient to provide internal propulsion for the process. Recognising each progressive achievement, analysing the basis for that achievement, identifying the challenges and the flaws and how to correct them, and reintroducing such lessons learned into the process in order to stimulate exponential impact, would be the necessary strategy for sustainable success.

Documenting the Process and Progress

In order to manage the progress of achievement, we must have in place a structure for systematically recording and analysing the implementation of each component of this response, relating each to the other, and comparing the results against the challenge and the original strategy in a comprehensive programme of analysis. The results from this process will become very useful data and information both to further the success of the programme, as well as to form the basis for best practices, which can then be shared with other countries in the sub-region, on the continent, and globally.

The Nature of the Undertaking–The Fear of the Unknown

In crafting and promoting the programmes in this strategy for scaling up the national (and indeed the global) response to the HIV/AIDS pandemic in Lesotho, none of us can claim to know what lies ahead, or to know it all—not the Government of Lesotho, not the international community, and not the other individuals and institutions that have decided to look on their own resources to join forces in what one might call this major "Enterprise for Sustainable Humanity".

There is much we do not know, and that naturally bothers us. There is so much that can happen, for better or for worse, and that too bothers us. If we admit to a small measure of anxiety and fear of this unknown, it is not an act of cowardice. Rather, it is an admission of humility and faith in the face of a daunting challenge; an assertion of commitment to the struggle, however long and whatever it takes; an affirmation of our human spirit and our belief in the indomitable nature of man to rise to any occasion of self-preservation, especially when our humanity itself is under siege.

There are specific anxieties we have. And we admit them upfront as a way of spotlighting the path ahead. We know, for example, that in seeking to promote a national universal voluntary HIV/AIDS testing programme, there will be a good number of people finding out that they are HIV-positive who probably never knew or suspected they were infected. A lot of complex emotions will be unleashed when they find out. We cannot pretend that this will not matter as long as we undertake the testing. To do so will not only be disingenuous, but it will also betray the legacy of our traditional way of managing delicacy in the face of pain, anguish and tragedy. What we say, instead, is that we know that at the end of the day, knowing the existence of the infection is the only way that it can be managed. And that in managing the pandemic, we have a chance of prolonging the life of those infected, with the proven promise of a longer and more productive life, as well as influencing those not yet infected to remain negative. This promise makes the risk eminently worthwhile.

Phrased differently, we know that in putting out the clarion call of the scaled up response, we are essentially asking a people who are standing on a window ledge of a house on fire with flames blazing wildly behind them to "jump and we will catch you". When we do so, we have to make sure that when they do jump, we will be there ready and properly equipped to catch them. Because what will be happening in this scaling up process will involve asking people to jump—to undertake leaps of faith into the unknown. Hence, in building up the courage of the people to face up to the reality of the pandemic, we will also be unleashing new fears and anxieties. How to manage these is perhaps the greatest challenge to Government and its partners. It will also require substantial resources, new ones as well as those freed-up by greater and more innovative management and fiscal efficiency.

But the first priority in this response is to be there for everyone, to be there resolutely, fully committed. It is that which will also give the people the courage to jump, as they must, because the fire is definitely burning relentless, behind them, and the flames are fierce and furious. For our part, those of us who, by virtue of the response detailed in this document, are asking others to jump, we are prepared to be there to catch them—if for no other reason than simply because we are one with them—Government, organs of civil society, the international community, private individuals or institutions and all.

A Human Response to a Human Crisis

Above all, the context of the HIV/AIDS pandemic and the response to it is a human situation, replete with all our hopes and fears, and calling up all our talent. There will be failures, lapses, intangible challenges emanating from angles we least expect. This is only natural. But there will be successes too, and each success will serve to reinforce our will and strengthen our hope and resolve.

In the final analysis, on the basic human level, what we are seeking to fight for here is the survival and revitalisation of Basotho brothers and sisters, husbands and wives, children, elders, neighbours and friends, and, in all of this, family, culture and society, and, therefore, all Basotho.

Standing up to the challenge of the HIV/AIDS pandemic, what is called for, and what all can offer, is knowledge, old and modern (and including especially traditional knowledge), strength, courage and diligence, for whatever coherent value can be derived from them. Therefore, what we need most of all is love and affection, for others, for each other and for ourselves. We also need that measure of humour and levity necessary in tackling a serious challenge so as not to lose perspective. Given all of this, and given the wisdom and blessings of our ancestors, we cannot but win the battle against this pandemic. In seeking to turn this Crisis into an Opportunity, we must win in our efforts at Scaling Up the National Response to the HIV/AIDS Pandemic in Lesotho, because victory is our only option. As the Prime Minister said in the *Foreword* to this document, it can be done! All we have to do is for each of us to play his or her part.

Khotso! *Pula! Nala!*

NOTES *for Chapter 16*

1. See *Ownership of Problems, Intellectual Property and the Digital Divide--The Enabling Challenge of Solutions,* by Joseph O. Okpaku, Sr., World Intellectual Property Organisation Second International Conference on Electronic Commerce and Intellectual Property, Geneva, September 19, 2001.

2. An example of indigenous initiative in Lesotho is the Holi-life Project, a holistic and integrated community-based HIV/AIDS project organised by Dr. Molotsi Monyamane. The , and whose focus of this project is to enhance the effectiveness of medical care and treatment, through the establishment of self- help initiatives in order to improve the competence of communities to deal with HIV/AIDS. Holi-life is a project of the Healthy Lifestyles Clinic and Diabetic Centre (HLCDC) HIV/AIDS Program, a health Service service Centre centre specializing in the management of chronic diseases and HIV/AIDS. More information on this project is available aton www.healthylifestylesclinic.co.ls.

3. See Joseph O. Okpaku, Sr., *Towards an Innovative Approach to South-South Cooperation in Science and Technology for Development: Challenges, Opportunities and Strategies,* A Presentation to the Forum on South-South Cooperation in Science and Technology, sponsored by the Government of the Republic of Korea and the United Nations Unit for Technical Cooperation amongst Developing Countries (TCDC), Seoul, Republic of Korea, February 14-17, 2000.

REFERENCES

Barnett, T., and A. Whiteside, *AIDS in the Twenty-First Century: Disease and Globalisation*, New York: Palgrave Macmillan, 2002.

Baylies, C. *Perspectives on Gender and AIDS in Africa* in AIDS, Sexuality and Gender in Africa: Collective Strategies and Struggles in Tanzania and Zambia, (eds) C. Baylies and J. Bujra. London: Routledge, 2000.

Chapman, J., and D. Harding. *Capacity Building*. Not published, 1999.

Commonwealth Secretariat. *Gender Mainstreaming in HIV/AIDS: Taking a Multisectoral Approach*. London: Commonwealth Secretariat, 2002.

Community Development Resource Association (CDRA). *Capacity Building: Myth or Reality?* Community Development Resource Association (CDRA), 1995.

Covey, Stephen R. *The Seven Habits of Highly Effective People: Powerful Lessons in Personal Change*, New York: Free Press, 1989.

De Waal, A. *New Variant Famine in Southern Africa*. Presentation for SADC VAC Meeting. Victoria Falls, 2002.

Ewen, Judith. *Developing Indicators for Monitoring Children's Rights: Manual for Training Trainers*. Draft Report, 1996.

Freeman, David H. Harvard Management Update, March 2002, Vol. 7, no. 3.

Gill, Stephen. *A Short History of Lesotho*, 1993.

Government of Lesotho. *Policy Document on HIV/AIDS in the Workplace*. Government of Lesotho, Maseru, 1999.

————. *National AIDS Strategic Plan 2000/2001-2003/2004.* Government of Lesotho, Maseru, 2000.

————. Ministry of Health and Social Welfare. *The Problems of Orphans in Lesotho.* Final Report. Government of Lesotho, Maseru, 2001.

Government of Lesotho/UNDP. *The War Against AIDS. Draft Progress Report: Millennium Development Goals, Lesotho.* Unpublished Report, Government of Lesotho and UNDP, Maseru, 2003.

Hogle, Janice A. (ed.). *What happened in Uganda? Declining HIV Prevalence, Behaviour Change and the National Response.* Contributors: Edward Green, Virand Nantulya, Rand Stoneburner, John Stover and Daniel Lowbeer. Uganda USAID Synergy Project, September 2002.

Humana People to People. *Total Control of the Epidemic.* Powerpoint presentation to the UN Theme Group, Lesotho, 25 February 2003.

ILO/UNIFEM. *The Care Economy, HIV/AIDS and the World of Work.* Geneva: ILO/UNIFEM, 2002.

LAPCA *Towards a More Effective and Efficient District HIV/AIDS Coordinating Programme,* LAPCA: Government of Lesotho, Maseru, 2003.

Leibowitz (2002).

Lelimo, Martin M. *The Question of Lesotho's Conquered Territory: It's Time for an Answer,* 1998.

Makara, A. Mosibolli oa Basotho. Mazenod: The Catholic Centre, 1960.

Maputo Declaration on Malaria, HIV/AIDS, Tuberculosis, and Other Infectious Diseases. Maputo, Mozambique, 10-12 July, 2003.

Matšela, F.Z.A. Bochaba ba Basotho. Mazenod, 1990.

Matšela, F.Z.A. and R.I.M. Moletsane. 'Mantilatilane. Morija: Sesotho Book Depot, 1993.

McKee, Neil. *Social Mobilisation and Social Marketing in Developing Communities: Lessons for Communicators,* 1992.

Meeting of the Government of Lesotho/United Nations Task Force on HIV/AIDS at UN House. Chaired by Mrs. Scholastica Kimaryo, Resident Coordinator of the UN System in Lesotho and co-chaired by the Principal Secretary, Cabinet (Economic Affairs), 30 October 2003.

Meeting of the United Nations Country Team with Consultants from the UN Secretary General's Task Force on Women, Girls and HIV/AIDS, 16 October 2003.

Mturi A. J. *HIV/AIDS and the World of Work in Lesotho*. Report prepared for the ILO Area Office, Lesotho, 2002.

O'Connor, Joseph, and Ian McDermott. *The Art of Systems Thinking*. New York: Thorsons Publishers, 1997.

Okpaku, Joseph O., Sr., *Developing Knowledge Societies: Challenges and Opportunities*, Kuala Lumpur, Malaysia, ASEAN Preparatory Conference for Global Knowledge Conference II, January 2000.

————. *E-Culture, Human Culture and In-between: Meeting the Challenges of the 21st Century Digital World*, Coventry, UK , ITU Conference on Creating New Leaders for e-Culture, August 2001.

————. "Information and Communications Technologies as Tools for African Development," in *Information and Communications Technologies as Tools for African Development: An Assessment of Progress and Challenges Ahead*. New York: UN/ICT Task Force, Series 2, 2003.

————. *Ownership of Problems, Intellectual Property and the Digital Divide— The Enabling Challenge of Solutions*, Geneva, WIPO Second International Conference on Electronic Commerce and Intellectual Property, September 2001.

————. *The Role of Information and Communications Technologies in the African Development Agenda*. A keynote address to the CAFRAD Regional Workshop on Building e-Governance Capacity in African Countries sponsored by the African Training and Research Centre in Administration for Development (CAFRAD), the United Nations Department of Economic and Social Affairs—Division for Public Economics and Public Administration (UNDESA/DPEPA), and the Government of South Africa, Ministry for Public Service and Administration, under the auspices of NEPAD, Johannesburg, October 2002.

————. *SMART e-GOVERNMENT—Adopting Information and Communications Technologies to Enhance Strategic Development Without Undermining Fundamental Human Priorities*, A Keynote Address to the e-Government Africa 2003 Conference, September 2003, Johannesburg, Republic of South Africa.

————. *Towards an Innovative Approach to South-South Cooperation in Science and Technology for Development: Challenges, Opportunities and Strategies*, A Presentation to the Forum on South-South Cooperation in Science and Technology, sponsored by the Government of the Republic of Korea and the United Nations Unit for Technical Cooperation amongst Developing Countries (TCDC), Seoul, Republic of Korea, February 14-17, 2000.

Sechaba Consultants. *Poverty and Livelihoods in Lesotho 2000: More Than a Mapping Exercise*, Sechaba Consultants, 2000.

Sen, Amartya. Winner of the Nobel Prize for Economics. *Development as Freedom*. Oxford: Oxford University Press, 1999.

Senge, Peter. *A Fifth Discipline Resource: The Dance of Change: The Challenges of Sustaining Momentum in Learning Organisations*, New York: Doubleday/ Currency Publishers, 2002.

————. *The Fifth Discipline: The Art and Practice of Learning Organisations*. New York: Doubleday/Currency Publishers, 1990.

————. Harvard Management Update, May 2002.

Sheddick V.G.J. The Southern Sotho. London: International African Institute, 1953.

Taylor, Viviene. *Social Mobilisation: Lessons from the Mass Democratic Movement*. SADEP, 1997.

Thompson, L. *Survival in Two Worlds: Moshoeshoe of Lesotho*, 1975.

UNAIDS. *Policy on Criminal Law, Public Health and HIV Transmission*. Report on HIV/AIDS and Human Rights. Mission to Lesotho, Miriam Maluwa, UNAIDS Law and Human Rights Advisor, UNAIDS, Switzerland: Geneva.

————. *Report on the Global HIV/AIDS Epidemic 2002*, UNAIDS, Switzerland: Geneva, 2002.

UNAIDS and Pennsylvania State University. *Communications Framework for HIV/ AIDS: A New Direction*. UNAIDS and Pennsylvania State University, 1999.

UNDP Lesotho. Internal Report by Jonathan Love, UNDP Consultant on Leadership Training for Results. UNDP Lesotho, November 2003.

UNDP Regional Project on HIV and Development in Sub-Saharan Africa. Concept Paper. *Conceptual Shifts for Sound Planning: Towards an Integrated Approach to HIV/AIDS and Poverty*. UNDP Regional Project on HIV and Development in Sub-Saharan Africa, South Africa: Pretoria, 2002.

———. Concept Paper 2. *Development Planning and HIV/AIDS in Sub-Saharan Africa.* UNDP Regional Project on HIV and Development in Sub-Saharan Africa, South Africa: Johannesburg, 2002.

———. Concept Paper. *Development Planning and HIV/AIDS in Sub-Saharan Africa.* UNDP Regional Project on HIV and Development in Sub-Saharan Africa, South Africa: Pretoria, 2003.

UN ICT Task Force. UN Secretary-General, Mr. Kofi Annan's address at the opening of the Third Meeting of the United Nations Information and Communications Technologies Task Force. New York: UN ICT Task Force, September 30, 2002.

United Nations General Assembly Special Session (UNGASS) on HIV/AIDS Declaration of Commitment. Goals set to be achieved by 2003-2005. New York: UNGASS, June 2001.

United Nations Report of the January Mission to Lesotho, Malawi, Zimbabwe, and Zambia. UN, Switzerland: Geneva, 31 January 2003. [www.undp.org.ls/New_Events/index.htm]

Whiteside, Alan, Nkosinathi Ngcobo, Jane Tomlinson, and Alison Hickey (eds.). *What is Driving the HIV/AIDS Epidemic in Swaziland? And What More Can We do About It?* For National Emergency Response Committee on HIV/AIDS in Swaziland (ERCHA) and UNAIDS. Not published, 2002.

WHO/UNAIDS. *Statement on Global AIDS Emergency Treatment: Emergency and 3X5 Strategy.* WHO/UNAIDS, 2003.

World Bank. *Social Protection of Africa's Orphans and Vulnerable Children: Issues and Good Proactive and Practice Program Options.* World Bank: African Human Development Paper Series, 2002.

Inventory of HIV/AIDS Activities by Government Sectors

Table 11.	Inventory of HIV/AIDS Activities by Government Sectors	
Institutional responsibility	**Current activities**	**Planned activities/weaknesses as identified by the sector**
Ministry of Agriculture, Cooperatives and Land Reclamation		
HIV/AIDS unit	Training of trainers to integrate HIV/AIDS into agricultural extension services Facilitation of progress area groups to enable citizens to access medical care, support community-based care and basic counselling Impact Mitigation Programme to provide support to affected households, particularly child-headed families.	
Ministry of Communications, Science and Technology		
Information Education Communication (IEC) Unit	Information dissemination through a variety of media.	Would like to communicate community-level HIV/AIDS activities.
Ministry of Defence and National Security		
HIV/AIDS unit in military hospital	Awareness workshops for staff Home-based care for army staff Follow-up visits to bases/patrol stations. Assessments of the scale of orphanhood.	Outposts receive less support due to transport and time implications.

Table 11.	Inventory of HIV/AIDS Activities by Government Sectors	
Institutional responsibility	**Current activities**	**Planned activities/weaknesses as identified by the sector**
Ministry of Education and Training		
HIV/AIDS unit	Draft Action Plan integrating HIV/AIDS activities into the Ministry's core programme developed, including (i) awareness campaigns among teachers, pupils and the public at large, (ii) awareness workshops for senior officials, (iii) HIV/AIDS campaigns in high schools and secondary schools, (iv) incorporation of HIV/AIDS awareness programme into curriculum. Provision of scholarships to orphans, including AIDS orphans HIV/AIDS management committees in schools.	No strategic plan on how to implement its vision on HIV/AIDS. Plans to conduct an impact assessment on the impact of HIV/AIDS on the demand and supply of teachers. Is exploring the possibility of providing ARVs to teachers.
Ministry of Finance and Development Planning		
Ministry as a whole responsible for enforcing 2% budget allocation for HIV/AIDS.	Condom distribution to staff members.	Intends to allocate its 2% to awareness-raising activities, condom distribution and counselling for staff.
Ministry of Foreign Affairs		
HIV/AIDS focal person within the Directorate of Economic and International Organisations, serving on the AIDS Task Force.	Sensitisation workshops for staff at all levels.	Intends to encourage voluntary testing for staff Establish a fund for employees' orphans and dependents Collaborate with foreign missions on resource mobilisation and negotiating on behalf of Basotho living with HIV/AIDS outside Lesotho.
Ministry of Health and Social Welfare		
National AIDS Control Programme	HIV prevention and control programmes Home-based care programmes, coupled with nutrition programmes; IEC materials Youth programmes Income-generating projects Foster care training for foster parents Materials development (training manuals and protocol documents).	No coherent plan that provides the vision and direction of a comprehensive health sector response. No nationwide coverage of activities due to financial constraints (and lack of resource mobilisation strategy).

Table 11.	Inventory of HIV/AIDS Activities by Government Sectors	
Institutional responsibility	**Current activities**	**Planned activities/weaknesses as identified by the sector**
Ministry of Justice, Human Rights and Rehabilitation		
	Awareness-raising activities among prisoners (men, women, youth).	HIV/AIDS workshops for the judiciary. Intends to pass heavy judgment on rapists who know they are HIV-positive. Provide counselling and care for victims of rape and incest. Collaborate with churches to advocate abstinence, instead of condom use. Need to sensitise court personnel towards PLWHA.
Ministry of Labour and Employment		
Four staff members	Awareness campaigns Draft code of conduct on HIV and employment developed with trade unions and business sector, which awaits parliamentary approval.	Hopes to increase the number of private companies with HIV/AIDS policies. Conduct a workshop on Training of Trainers.
Ministry of Local Government		
HIV/AIDS unit	HIV/AIDS strategic framework developed.	No HIV/AIDS activities implemented yet. Income-generating activities planned. Training of Ministry staff and local authorities planned. Networking with other sectors.
Ministry of Natural Resources		
HIV/AIDS focal points in all six technical departments.	HIV/AIDS awareness-raising activities at district and/or community level. Condom provision for ministry staff.	No vision on HIV/AIDS. Lack of coordination of HIV/AIDS activities within the Ministry.
Ministry of Planning and Economic Development		
HIV/AIDS focal person in the Department of Population Planning.	Condom distribution among staff Integration of HIV/AIDS activities in existing plans, such as the Population and Development Strategies Programme and the Population and Family Life Education Programme.	

Table 11.	Inventory of HIV/AIDS Activities by Government Sectors	
Institutional responsibility	**Current activities**	**Planned activities/weaknesses as identified by the sector**
Ministry of Public Services		
Two HIV/AIDS focal points in the Directorate of Organisational Development, representing the Ministry on the AIDS Task Force.	Awareness and sensitisation campaigns for staff members Condom distribution, including procurement and distribution of female condoms.	No planned HIV/AIDS programme.
Ministry of Tourism, Culture and Environment		
No HIV/AIDS unit/focal point	No activities recorded.	No stated HIV/AIDS projects yet, nor is there a focal point within the Ministry.
Ministry of Trade and Industry, Cooperatives and Marketing		
No HIV/AIDS unit/focal point	No activities yet.	Intends to develop a HIV/AIDS policy and adopt a support structure for employees who are infected and affected. Considers hiring an information officer for HIV/AIDS programmes.
Ministry of Public Works and Transport		
	HIV/AIDS awareness campaigns through workshops, presentations, etc., for staff Materials-development for taxi drivers in progress.	No HIV/AIDS strategic plan or comprehensive programme.
Ministry of Gender, Youth, Sports and Recreation		
	Awareness-raising in rural communities on gender-based violence, poverty and HIV/AIDS by the Dept. of Gender Prevention and control programme targeting youth (Dept. of Youth).	*Lipitsos*[1], training workshops and coordinator activities with stakeholders are planned. Also plans to disseminate the National Youth Policy programme, provide vocational skills training to youth, conduct a survey on youth needs and establish youth councils throughout the country.

Drawn from LAPCA (2002), Review of HIV and AIDS-Related Initiatives and Activities in Lesotho, Draft Report, LAPCA and the findings of a UN Interdisciplinary Diagnostic Mission to Lesotho in 2002.

NOTES *for Appendix 1*

1. Sesotho word (plural for Pitso) for general public gatherings called for the purpose of creating awareness of HIV/AIDS.

2

List of Participants at the Meeting to the Presentation by the UN Resident Coordinator and Chairperson of the Expanded Theme Group on HIV/AIDS

to the Right Honourable Prime Minister, the Cabinet and Principal Secretaries on Strategies for Scaling up the National Response to the HIV/AIDS Pandemic in Lesotho

NAME	DESIGNATION	ORGANISATION
Hon. Pakalitha B. Mosisili	Rt. Honourable Prime Minister	Prime Minister's Office
Hon. Lesao Lehohla	Minister of Education and Training	Ministry of Education and Training
Hon. Monyane Moleleki	Minister of Natural Resources	Ministry of Natural Resources
Hon. Thomas Thabane	Minister of Home Affairs and Public Safety	Ministry of Home Affairs and Public Safety
Hon. Mpho Malie	Minister of Trade and Industry, Cooperatives and Marketing	Ministry of Trade and Industry, Cooperatives and Marketing
Hon. Mofelehetsi Moerane	Minister of Public Works and Transport	Ministry of Public Works and Transport
Hon. 'Mathabiso Lepono	Minister of Gender, Youth, Sports and Recreation	Ministry of Gender, Youth, Sports and Recreation
Hon. Mohlabi Tsekoa	Minister of Foreign Affairs	Ministry of Foreign Affairs
Hon. Pont o Sekatle	Minister of Local Government	Ministry of Local Government
Hon. Clement Machakela	Minister of Labour and Employment	Ministry of Labour and Employment
Hon. Motloheloa Phooko	Minister of Health and Social Welfare	Ministry of Health and Social Welfare

NAME	DESIGNATION	ORGANISATION
Hon. Refiloe Masemene	Minister of Justice, Human Rights and Rehabilitation, & of Law and Constitutional Affairs	Ministry of Justice, Human Rights and Rehabilitation, & of Law and Constitutional Affairs
Hon. Lebohang Ntšinyi	Minister of Tourism, Culture and Environment	Ministry of Tourism, Culture and Environment
Hon. Ralechate 'Mokose	Minister of Forestry and Land Reclamation	Ministry of Forestry and Land Reclamation
Hon. Rakoro Phororo	Minister of Agriculture and Food Security	Ministry of Agriculture and Food Security
Hon. Popane Lebesa	Assistant Minister of Finance and Development Planning	Ministry of Finance and Development Planning
Hon. Molise Tšoele	Assistant Minister of Agriculture and Food Security	Ministry of Agriculture and Food Security
Hon. Ntlejoa Metsing	Assistant Minister of Trade and Industry, Cooperatives and Marketing	Ministry of Trade and Industry, Cooperatives and Marketing
Hon. Hlompho Ntšekhe	Assistant Minister of Gender, Youth, Sports and Recreation	Ministry of Gender, Youth, Sports and Recreation
Mr. Tlohang Sekhamane	Government Secretary	Prime Minister's Office
Mr. Lefu Lehloba	P.S. Home Affairs	Ministry of Home Affairs and Public Safety
Mr. Monyane Mathibeli	P.S. Public Works and Transport	Ministry of Public Works and Transport
Mr. Limpho Mandoro	P.S. Labour and Employment	Ministry of Labour and Employment
Ms. Mahali S. Lebesa	P.S. Cabinet (Economic Affairs)	Cabinet Office
Mr. Kubutu Makhakhe	P.S. Cabinet (Administration)	Cabinet Office
Ms. Lebohang S. Bosiu	P.S. Defence and National Security a.i.	Ministry of Defence and National Security
Mr. P.K. Motholo	P.S. Justice, Human Rights and Rehabilitation	Ministry of Justice, Human Rights and Rehabilitation
Mr. Makalo Theko	P.S. Local Government	Ministry of Local Government
Ms. 'Mamoruti A. Malie	P.S. Agriculture	Ministry of Agriculture and Food Security
Ms. Mahlompho 'Mota	P.S. Forestry and Land Reclamation	Ministry of Forestry and Land Reclamation
Mr. Tšeliso Mokela	P.S. Communications	Ministry of Communications, Science and Technology
Mr. Teleko Ramotšoari	P.S. Health and Social Welfare	Ministry of Health and Social Welfare
Mr. Motlatsi Ramafole	P.S. Foreign Affairs	Ministry of Foreign Affairs
Mr. Semano Sekatle	P.S. Public Services	Ministry of Public Services
Mr. Tau	P.S. Natural Resources a.i.	Ministry of Natural Resources
Dr. L.M. Mophethe	P.S. Gender, Youth, Sports and Recreation a.i.	Ministry of Gender, Youth, Sports and Recreation
Ms. Mamoruti Seitlheko	Senior Private Secretary to the Prime Minister	Prime Minister's Office
Mrs. M. Malise-Ramakoae	Chief of Protocol	Ministry of Foreign Affairs

NAME	DESIGNATION	ORGANISATION
Mr. Matlamukele Matete	Clerk to the National Assembly	Parliament
Ms. Mahlape Qoane	DPS Trade and Industry	Ministry of Trade and Industry, Cooperatives and Marketing
Ms. M. Makhakhe	Director of Health Planning and Statistics Unit	Ministry of Health and Social Welfare
Dr. T. Ramatlapeng	Medical Doctor	Ministry of Health and Social Welfare
Mr. L. Ndumo	Human Resource Officer a.i.	Ministry of Industry
Mr. M. Molelle	Counsellor, Protocol	Ministry of Foreign Affairs
Dr. Pearl Ntšekhe	Director Disease Control	Ministry of Health and Social Welfare
Ms. P. Ramaqele	Director Public Services	Ministry of Public Services
Mr. J.E. Molapo	DPS Tourism, Culture and Environment a.i.	Ministry of Tourism, Culture and Environment
Dr. N. Letsie	Medical Doctor	Ministry of Health and Social Welfare
Ms. M. Tiheli	Director	Ministry of Health and Social Welfare
Mr. Ernest Fausther	Deputy Resident Representative	UNDP
Dr. Miguel Kiasekoka	Representative	WHO
Dr. Betrand Desmoulins	Representative	UNICEF
Mr. T. Zergaber	Representative	WFP
Dr. C. Camarada	Representative	FAO

Members of the Expanded UN Theme Group on HIV/AIDS in Lesotho

Mrs. Scholastica Kimaryo
UNDP Resident Representative,
UN Resident Coordinator and Co-Chairperson,
Expanded Theme Group on HIV/AIDS

H.E. Mr. Robert G. Loftis
USA Ambassador to Lesotho and Co-Chairperson,
Expanded Theme Group on HIV/AIDS

Members
Donors/Bilateral Partners

H.E. Mr. Frank Martin
British High Commissioner,
British High Commission

H.E. Mr. Robert Collingwood
Delegate, European Commission

H.E. Mr. Zahang Xianyi
Chinese Ambassador,
Chinese Embassy

Mr. Pinkerton Mjikeliso
Acting South African High Commissioner,
South African High Commission

Mr. Bill Nolan
Irish Consul-General,
Irish Consulate

Mr. Heinz Fiebig
German Honorary Consul,
German Consulate

Mr. Jean-Michele Freville
Honorary Consul,
French Consulate

Ms. Barbara Nkoala
Honorary Consul,
Canadian Consulate

Mr. L. Jabbie
Honorary Consul,
Guinea Consulate

Members

UN Agencies/UNAIDS Co-Sponsors

Dr. Admir Bay
FAO Representative

Dr. Castro P. Camarada
FAO Representative

Ms. Kimberly Gamble-Payne
UNICEF Representative

Dr. Bertrand Desmoulins
UNICEF Representative

Mr. Techeste Zergaber
WFP Representative

Dr. Miguel Kiasekoka
WHO Representative

Mr. George Nsiah
UNFPA Country Director

Mr. Kenneth Andoh
ILO Representative to South Africa and Lesotho

Mr. Johny McClain
UNESCO's Regional Office, Windhoek

Mr. Omar Fayez
World Bank Representative for Southern Africa

Mr. Ernest Fausther
UNDP Deputy Resident Representative

Mr. John Wayem
UN Resident Economic Advisor, UNDP

Mr. Joe Feeney
UN Resident Coordinator System Focal Point

Mr. Tim Rwabuhemba
UNAIDS Country Programme Advisor

Dr. Givans Ateka
UN Physician and Chairperson, HIV/AIDS Technical Working Group

Observers

H.E. Mrs. 'M'athato Mosisili
First Lady of Lesotho

Dr. M. Moteetee
Director General,
LAPCA

Ms. Christine Djondo
Executive Director,
United States Peace Corps

Mr. D. Sinnathamzy
CARE International

Mr. K. Byrne
SCF (Save the Children Fund)—UK

Mr. Seifert Ingo
Positive Action, Maseru

4

List of Participants at the Lesotho National Consultative Stakeholders Workshop on HIV/AIDS

Convention Centre, Maseru, 25 July, 2002

NAME	TITLE	ORGANISATION
Chief Seeiso B. Seeiso	Principal Chief	The Senate
Chief L.J. Mathealira	Chief	The Senate
Mr. M. Metsing	MP	National Assembly
Mrs. Scholastica Kimaryo	UN Resident Coordinator	UNDP Lesotho
Ms. Matau Futho-Letsatsi	Director	Ministry of Gender
Dr. Mpolai Moteetee	Chief Executive Officer	LAPCA
Ms. Nkhala Sefako	Chief Planner	LAPCA
Ms. Malebajoa Sesoane	Education Officer	LAPCA
Ms. Mathoriso Monaheng	Director of Administration	LAPCA
Mr. Tony Djondo	Project Coordinator	U.S. Embassy
Ms. Matseliso Schares-Mosene	Special Projects Assistant Coordinator	U.S. Embassy
Ms. Anne Githuku-Shongwe	Advisor	UNDP Regional Project on HIV/AIDS
Mr. Gabriel Rugalema	Advisor	UNDP Regional Project on HIV/AIDS
Ms. Barbara Barungi	Advisor	UNDP/BDP SADC SURF
Mr. Elesani Njobvu	ICT Programme Advisor	UNAIDS ESA
Mr. Owen Kaluwa	Advisor	WHO/AFRO
Ms. Gift Malunga	HIV/AIDS Specialist	UNIFEM

NAME	TITLE	ORGANISATION
Mr. Dan Odallo	ICT Programme Advisor	UNAIDS
Ms. Mandisa Mashologu	Poverty Monitoring Advisor	UNDP
Ms. Lineo Mdee	Sustainable Development Advisor	UNDP
Mr. Tim Rhwabuhemba	Programme Advisor	UNAIDS
Mr. Sebastian Levine	Economist	UNDP
Ms. Rose Wambura	Project Coordinator	UNFIP
Mr. M. Mathaha	Social Policy Planner	UNDP
Ms. L. Moholi	Programme Officer	UNFPA
Ms. M. Mokose	Programme Officer	UNDP
Mr. T. Peshoane	Project Coordinator	Africa 2000 Network
Ms. A. Kalaka	Programme Officer	UNICEF
Ms. Malineo Motsephe	Programme Communication Officer	UNICEF
Ms. Neo Mokoena	Medical Sociologist	LHDA
Ms Matlokotsi Makoa	Senior Statistician	Bureau of Statistics
Ms. Ntoetse Kabi	Producer	Lesotho News Agency
Ms. Makhauta Diaho	Camera Operator	Lesotho News Agency
Mr. Lekoai Phakoe	Student Teacher	Ministry of Education
Mr. Koali E. Jobo	President	Ha o Mong HIV/AIDS Group
Ms. Nonkululeko Zaly	Member	Lesotho Youth and Environment
Ms. L. Letsoela	Inspector	Lesotho Mounted Police Service
Ms. Matsotang Tsietsi	Chief Statistician	Bureau of Statistics
Ms. Kharebe Mota	Member	Leribe Task Force
Mr. Pontso Lebotsa	Chief Legal Officer	Ministry of Justice
Thabo Kamolane	General Secretary	Lesotho Youth Federation
Mr. Mosala Raboko	Board Member	Thusanang Life Line
Ms. Rosemary Matsie	Treasurer	Thusanang Life Line
Mr. K. Lekoane	Member	Leribe Task Force
Mr. Matete Motlojoa	Coordinator	Lesotho Blood Transfusion Service
Ms. Leratang Mohapeloa	Assistant Producer	Mejametalana Media House
Mr. T. Magaga	Reporter	Lesotho Mounted Police Service
Mr. P. Kotela	Chief Information Officer	Ministry of Home Affairs
Mr. Macheli Macheli	Youth Worker	Ministry of Gender, Youth, Sports & Recreation
Ms. Matseliso Pheko	Nurse	Ministry of Health
Ms. M. Lebuso	Statistician	Bureau of Statistics
Ms. M. Makojoa	Assistant Statistician	Bureau of Statistics

NAME	TITLE	ORGANISATION
Ms. P.W. Moerane	Assistant Statistician	Bureau of Statistics
Ms. Q. Lesenya	Senior Economic Planner	Ministry of Agriculture
Ms. K. Ntoampe	Chief Health Educator	Ministry of Health
Mr. N. Sello	Economic Planner	Ministry of Communications
Ms. L. Moketa	Member	Hand of Grace Association
Mr. P. Ramokoanyane	Research Officer	Berea Scouts Association
Ms. Libuseng Mile	Project Officer	UNFPA
Mr. Lehlohonolo Ndumo	H. Resource Officer a.i.	Ministry of Industry
Mr. Lekhetho Phakisi	Animator	Lesotho Council of NGOs
Ms. Ntilo Matela	Coordinator	People Living with HIV/AIDS
Mr. Thabiso Motsusi	Chairperson	Positive Action
Ms. Paballo Lineo Mahomo	Counsellor	Leribe Task Force
Mr. Thabiso Mohapeloa	Religious Minister	Lesotho Evangelical Church
Prof. Allan Femi Lana	Director	NUL Consultants
Mr. Letebele Molefi	Human Resource Manager	Nedbank
Mr. L. Ntsekhe	Head of Marketing	Nedbank
Ms. Keneuoe Fobo	Senior Nursing Officer	Ministry of Health
Ms. Tsepiso Mncina	Reporter	Lesotho News Agency
Ms. Mpho Morojele	Statistician	Bureau of Statistics
Mr. K.B. R Kalosi	Producer	Lesotho Television
Ms. Mamokhantso Phoofolo	Chief Nutrition Officer	Ministry of Agriculture
Mr. Thabang Mpeka	Chief Statistician	Bureau of Statistics
Ms. Tebello Makama	Officer	Ministry of Home Affairs
Ms. Mantoetse Molapo	Youth Development Officer	Ministry of Gender
Ms. M. Mphana	Programme Director	Lesotho Planned Parenthood Association (LPPA)
Mr. T. Thaanyane	Journalist	Police Headquarters
Mr. P. Luka	Journalist	Police Headquarters
Ms. M. Chabane	Lady-in-Waiting	Office of the First Lady
Ms. Masoro Pakisi	Safety Officer	Lesotho Electricity Corporation
Mr. Mokuoane Ramakhula	Coordinator	HIV/AIDS Task Force
Mr. Lethola Mafisa	National Coordinator	Scripture Union
Ms. Tiny Sefuthi	Freelance Photo Journalist	
Mr. Tsoele Mpopo	District Secretary	Ministry of Local Government
Ms. Ntharetso Lieta	Secretary-General	Lesotho Red Cross
Ms. Elizabeth Tlalajoe	Agricultural Officer	Ministry of Agriculture

NAME	TITLE	ORGANISATION
Ms. Thato Masiloane	DPS	Cabinet Office, Government of Lesotho
Ms. Mathato Pule	Senior Counsellor	Ministry of Health
Ms. A. Mongoako	Chief Rehabilitation Officer	LAPCA
Ms. Jeanet Kori-Khalala	Social Worker, AIDS Prog.	Lesotho Catholic Bishops Conference
Mr. R.L. Ntokoane	Project Manager	Ministry of Environment
Mr. P. Martel	Consultant	UNICEF
Mr. P. Phori	National Programme Officer	WHO
Ms. Mamosebi Pholo	Vice President	Federation of Women Lawyers
Mr. S. Maloleka	Assistant Secretary-General	Lesotho Consumer Organisation
Mr. P. Khohlokoane	Journalist	Moeletsi of Basotho
Mr. Jacob M. Lenka	Community Trainer	Transformation Resource Centre
Mr. Kenneth Molapo	Student Teacher	
Mr. Pule Mothibi	HIV/AIDS Educator	
Mr. Manketsi Makara	Economic Planner	Ministry of Development Planning
Ms. Malefu Khanyapa	Monitoring and Evaluation Officer	UNICEF
Ms. Mathato Makwate	Administration Manager	Office of the First Lady
Mr. Napo Ntlou	National Programme Officer	WFP
Mr. M. Mabolloane	Member	Leribe Task Force
Ms. M. Motselebane	Director	Ministry of Agriculture
Ms. L. Maqalika-Lerotholi	Chief Inspector	Ministry of Education
Ms. Lati Letsela	Principal Gender Officer	Ministry of Gender, Youth, Sports & Recreation
Mr. Motsamai Phakoe	Chairperson	Khathang Tema Baitsokoli Association
Ms. Matseko E. Thulo	Member	Centre for Empowerment and Social Analysis
Mr. Thabo Motlamelle	Freelance Journalist	
Mr. Posholi Jonathan	Labour Commissioner	Department of Labour
Ms. Limpho Letsela	Director	Ntlafalang Consultants
Ms. Mampho Molaoa	Director	Ntlafalang Consultants
Ms, Mamasupha Bereng	Office Assistant	Selibeng
Mr. Hoolo Nyane	Member	LCN
Mr. Paul Phuroe	Member	Lesotho Amateur Athletics Association, Maseru
Mr. Lebohang Makara	Coordinator	Student Christian Movement
Mr. Tsolo Lebitsa	Chairman	Khathang Tema Baitsokoli
Mr. Tholoana Emmanuel Matsoso	Project Manager	Lesotho Young Christian Students

NAME	TITLE	ORGANISATION
Ms. Pascalina Mokhothu	Youth Development Officer	Youth Development Office, Thaba Tseka
Ms. S. Sefako	Peer Educator	Lesotho Youth Anti-AIDS Movement
Mr. M. Sekese Rakotsoane	Youth Development Officer	Youth Development Office, Butha-Buthe
Ms. Mamaoa M. Makhunoane	Member	Butha-Buthe Task Force
Mr. Matsela Mphafi	District Secretary	Thaba Tseka
Mr. Mpheng Ramaili	District Secretary	Butha-Buthe Task Force
Mr. Thabang Leaba	Journalist	
Ms. Tsepang Mncina	Journalist	The Mirror
Ms. Nthatisi Nkhabu	Member	Positive Action
Mr. Molapo Moshoeshoe	Member	Lesotho Youth Anti-AIDS Movement
Ms. Likeleli Mokhethi	Peer Educator	Lesotho Youth Anti-AIDS Movement
Mr. Tlali Nyareli	Member	Tsiu Tsenola Youth Support Group
Mr. Manare J. Thuso	Secretary	Tsiu Tsenola Youth Support Group
Mr. Isaac Tlamane	NEC Member	Congress of Lesotho Trade Union(COLETU)
Mr. Monaheng Mokoena	NEC Member	COLETU
Mr. Tsepo Tshabala	Counsellor	Positive Action
Ms. Lirontso Moaki	Peer Counsellor	Lesotho Girls Guide Association
Ms. Marethabile Mokhele	Counsellor	Makoanyane Military Hospital
Mr. Thaba Tsoeu Mohale	Member	AIDS Task Force/Lesotho Mounted Police Service (LMPS)
Ms. Kambule Deliwe	Principal Gender Officer	Ministry of Gender
Ms. F.N. Rathabaneng	Coordinator	SWAALES (Society of Women and AIDS in Africa)
Ms. V. Sekhibane	Administrative Assistant	UNDP
Ms. L. Banda	Human Resources Assistant	UNDP
Ms. J.M. Tiheli	Information Technology Assistant	UNDP
Ms. Likeleli Qhobela	Finance Clerk	UNDP
Mr. Selatela Ramakatane	Asset Management Assistant	UNDP
Mr. Lebohang Maketa	Driver	UNDP
Mr. Benjamin Mojakisane	Driver	UNDP
Ms. M. Khabisi	Administrative Assistant	UNDP
Ms. N. Tlahali	Receptionist	UNDP
Ms. G. Poka	Programme Clerk	UNDP
Ms. M. Mosuoe	Programme Assistant	UNDP
Ms. N. Matsoso	Senior Secretary	UNDP

NAME	TITLE	ORGANISATION
Mr. Maama Jasong	Driver	UNDP
Ms. Litsoanelo Morai	Cleaner	UNDP
Ms. P. Henson	Programme Assistant	UNDP

Members of the UN Inter-Agency, Multi-Disciplinary Mission on HIV/AIDS to Lesotho
July 2002

Anne Githuku-Shongwe	Team Leader, UNDP Regional Project on HIV/AIDS
Gabriel Rugalema	UNDP Regional Project on HIV/AIDS
Barbara Barungi	Macroeconomic Advisor, UNDP/BDP
Elesani Njobvu	ICT Programme Advisor, UNAIDS
Owen Kaluwa	Regional Programme Advisor, World Health Organisation (WHO)
Gift Malunga	UNIFEM HIV/AIDS Specialist
Sisonke Msimang	Youth AIDS Network/UNIFEM
Dan Odallo	Programme Advisor, UNAIDS

INDEX

T

Scholastica Sylvan Kimaryo is the Resident Representative of UNDP and Resident Coordinator of the UN System in Lesotho, as well as the Chairperson of the Expanded Theme Group on HIV/AIDS in Lesotho. An expert in strategic planning, social policy as well as development communication, Mrs. Kimaryo holds an MSc in Social Policy, Planning & Participation in Developing Countries from the London School of Economics and Political Science; a BSc in Home Economics with Education from the Victoria Manchester University and a Post-Graduate Diploma in Development Journalism from the Mwananchi Publishing Ltd in Dar-es-Salaam. Prior to her current assignment, Mrs. Kimaryo served with UNICEF for twenty three years, including as head of office in Botswana (1984–1990), South Africa (1992–1998) and Liberia (1998–2001).

Joseph O. Okpaku, Sr. is the President and Chief Executive Officer of the Telecom Africa Corporation and Head of the African Self-Development Institute. A renowned scholar and expert in strategic planning and development, Dr. Okpaku Sr. is a leading authority on Information and Communications Technologies and their strategic deployment for development. In this regard, he has done extensive work on strategies for deploying these technologies in support of the response to the HIV/AIDS epidemic. An adviser to the United Nations ICT Task Force, Dr. Okpaku holds a Bachelor of Science Degree in Civil Engineering from Northwestern University, a Master of Science Degree in Structural Engineering and a Doctorate Degree in Theatre History and Dramatic Literature, both from Stanford University.

Anne Githuku Shongwe is the Regional Policy Advisor for HIV/AIDS and Development for the UNDP Africa based in Pretoria. Anne has worked for the UNDP as a Policy Advisor for the past six years coordinating national human development reports on HIV/AIDS and development, on Poverty and Inequality and gender issues. She joined the UNDP Regional Project in 2001 as a Policy Advisor for Southern Africa on HIV/AIDS and it is in this capacity that she provided support to this process with UNDP Lesotho.

Joseph Feeney is a graduate of Trinity College, Dublin and University College Dublin. He is the Policy Team Leader with UNDP Lesotho. Prior to joining UNDP, he worked with Ireland Aid, the Development Cooperation agency of the Irish Government after working with the NGO sector for some ten years. He has worked on Community Development, Governance and HIV/AIDS programmes for over twenty years.